Virtual Reality The

CW00740906

Practical, down to earth, clearly written, and easy for therapists to understand and apply, *Virtual Reality Therapy for Anxiety* is a useful guide for any clinician treating anxiety, regardless of setting (in-office or via telehealth), theoretical orientation, or level of training. Written by an experienced psychologist who has used multiple VR systems since 2010, it's the only up to date, clinically informed, evidence-based training manual available.

Easy-to-understand concepts and diagrams explain anxiety and its treatment, and the book incorporates research findings and clinical expertise. VRT is described step by step with multiple case examples, and an extended case-vignette chapter presents a session-by-session treatment protocol of a complex case with transcript excerpts. Key findings and quotations from research are also presented.

After completing the guide, therapists and other mental health professionals will understand the unique clinical benefits of VR, be prepared to use VR in therapy comfortably and effectively either in the office or remotely, and will have expertise in a new, needed, and empirically validated treatment for a common clinical problem.

Elizabeth McMahon, PhD, is a licensed psychologist in private practice, consultant, author of *Overcoming Anxiety and Panic Interactive Guide*, and an acknowledged expert in virtual reality therapy for anxiety who has used VR in clinical practice since 2010.

Debra Boeldt, PhD, is the deputy director of the National Mental Health Innovation Center and senior instructor in the Departments of Family Medicine and Public Health at the University of Colorado Anschutz Medical Campus.

Virtual Reality Therapy for Anxiety

A Guide for Therapists

Elizabeth McMahon with Debra Boeldt

 Routledge
Taylor & Francis Group

NEW YORK AND LONDON

First published 2022
by Routledge
605 Third Avenue, New York, NY 10158

and by Routledge
2 Park Square, Milton Park, Abingdon, Oxon OX14 4RN

Routledge is an imprint of the Taylor & Francis Group, an informa business

Library of Congress Cataloging-in-Publication Data
Names: McMahon, Elizabeth, author. | Boeldt, Debra, author.
Title: Virtual reality therapy for anxiety : a guide for therapists /
Elizabeth McMahon, PhD, Debra Boeldt, PhD.
Description: New York, NY : Routledge, 2022. |
Includes bibliographical references and index. |
Identifiers: LCCN 2021023113 (print) | LCCN 2021023114 (ebook) |
ISBN 9780367699529 (hardback) | ISBN 9780367699512 (paperback) |
ISBN 9781003154068 (ebook)
Subjects: LCSH: Anxiety--Treatment. | Virtual reality therapy.
Classification: LCC RC531 .M366 2021 (print) |
LCC RC531 (ebook) | DDC 616.85/2200285--dc23
LC record available at https://lccn.loc.gov/2021023113
LC ebook record available at https://lccn.loc.gov/2021023114

ISBN: 978-0-367-69952-9 (hbk)
ISBN: 978-0-367-69951-2 (pbk)
ISBN: 978-1-003-15406-8 (ebk)

DOI: 10.4324/9781003154068

Typeset in Bembo
by Taylor & Francis Books

Contents

Figures

Acknowledgments

Many thanks to my collaborator, Debra Boeldt, PhD. I am sincerely grateful to Walter Greenleaf, PhD, Mimi McFaul, PsyD, Matt Vogl, and the entire National Mental Health Innovation Center team for their support for this project from its inception. Thanks go to Kim Bullock, MD, Jessica Lake, PhD, and Albert "Skip" Rizzo, PhD for reviewing the book proposal and offering encouragement. In addition, thanks are due to Debra Boeldt, PhD, Kim Bullock, MD, Chris Gilbert, PhD, and DeLee Lantz, PhD for assistance with references and to Kim Bullock, MD, Tamara McClintock Greenberg, PsyD, and Harry Nozicka, LCSW for feedback on the manuscript.

Thank you to the following companies, listed in alphabetical order, who graciously gave permission to use images of their VR software to illustrate a range of virtual environments: BehaVR, Inc. (Figures 7.1, 8.1, 14.1, and Appendix A.2), C2Care (Figures 9.1, 10.1, and 11.1), Psious (Figures 3.1, 13.1, 17.1, and Appendix A.1), and Virtually Better, Inc. (Figures 12.1, 14.2, and 16.1). Thanks also to Hands-On-Guide for permission to use diagrams of the Anxiety Cycle (Figure 2.1) and Breaking the Anxiety Cycle (Figure 2.2).

Finally, and always, thanks to my husband for his editorial assistance and steadfast loving support.

About the Authors

Elizabeth McMahon, PhD, is a clinical psychologist and recognized expert in virtual reality therapy (VRT) for anxiety. She has specialized in treating anxiety disorders for 40 years and has been using virtual reality (VR) technology with clients since 2010.

She received her PhD in clinical psychology from Case Western Reserve University and completed a predoctoral fellowship at the University of Virginia Medical Center in Charlottesville, Virginia and a postdoctoral residency at Sheppard-Pratt Psychiatric Hospital in Towson, Maryland.

Before entering private practice, Dr. McMahon worked for Kaiser Permanente Medical Group in Fremont, California, for over 30 years. At Kaiser she specialized in anxiety disorders, helping create best practice guidelines, teaching, and supervising postdoctoral psychology residents.

Currently she trains therapists on anxiety treatment and using VR in continuing education courses organized by ADAA, APA, CPA, PESI, VR technology providers, and other organizations. For more information see her website: www.elizabeth-mcmahon.com.

Her client workbook *Overcoming Anxiety and Panic Interactive Guide* (2019) helps explain anxiety and its treatment and prepares clients to benefit from VR therapy.

Special offer for therapists who treat anxiety: e-mail elizabeth@elizabeth-mcmahon.com to receive a complimentary review copy of *Overcoming Anxiety and Panic Interactive Guide*.

Debra Boeldt, PhD, is deputy director of the National Mental Health Innovation Center at the University of Colorado Anschutz Medical Campus. She received her PhD in clinical psychology from the University of Colorado Boulder and completed an internship at the University of California San Diego/Veterans Administration and a postdoctoral fellowship at the Scripps Research Translational Institute.

Dr. Boeldt is an advocate of the adoption of VR to improve mental health and behavioral health services. She has co-authored several peer-reviewed publications, is a frequent presenter at conferences, and supports the Tech Innovation Network, a network of diverse clinical and community partners that functions as a test bed through which new technological solutions can be rapidly developed, iterated, tested, and validated.

1 Introduction

Christina sat in my office shaking and crying as she talked about wanting to fly to her best friend's wedding. "I've known her all my life. I promised I would be there for her, but it means I have to fly, and I just can't!" The wedding was only three months away and Christina was frantic. She desperately wanted to overcome her fear of flying but wasn't sure it was even possible.

Normally poised and professional, when faced with the prospect of getting on a plane she began hyperventilating, crying, and feeling nauseous. Sometimes she vomited. She had refused promotions if they required business travel, but she wasn't willing to miss the most important day of her friend's life.

Luckily, I had an answer.

For years, I had treated anxiety using cognitive-behavioral therapy (CBT) combined with mindfulness, acceptance, relaxation, guided imagery, and other interventions. Treatment results were generally good, but I had recently read about a technological breakthrough: virtual reality therapy (VRT). Christina's face lit up when I told her about it.

First, Christina learned about the cycle of anxiety and how to break it. She practiced diaphragmatic breathing, identified and explored her fears, and gathered the information she needed to combat them. She learned that flying was safe, even when turbulent. "I know the plane's not really going to fall out of the sky and I'm not going crazy, but I'm still really nervous every time I think about getting on a long flight, especially if it's rainy, or bumpy, or dark and I can't see outside."

We discussed that you may know something intellectually, but it's hard to really "know it" on a gut level until you have experienced it and that virtual reality (VR) could give her that experience. She was nervous, but excited and ready to try.

Because Christine got scared "before I even get to the airport", I had her start by riding to the airport in a virtual taxi. She practiced voicing her fears and talking back to them while using her relaxation skills. I coached her and monitored her anxiety level, which went from 6 on a scale of 0–10, down to 1. At this point she announced, "I'm ready to go into the airport."

DOI: 10.4324/9781003154068-1

Waiting at the gate was easier than she expected. Next, she moved down the virtual jetway to her window seat. After only two repetitions, she felt ready to fly.

Her first virtual flights were in daylight with clear skies. As her comfort increased, I had her "flying" at night, and finally through bumpy nighttime storms. After three sessions of virtual flights, her anxiety stayed between 0 and 2 regardless of the weather. "I feel ready."

Her exuberant email arrived two weeks later: "I did it! There were even some bumps, but they didn't really bother me. I couldn't have done it without the virtual reality. Thank you, thank you, thank you!"

Why This Book Was Written

> *"This is life changing. Thank you!"*

Helping Christine and similar clients has made me a passionate advocate for VR therapy. I am not alone; many other therapists have similar examples of using VR in creative ways to help clients.

VR is a technological breakthrough for therapy—especially for anxiety. This guide is written *by* clinicians *for* clinicians so that you—and your clients—can experience the benefits of VRT based on clinical experience, research findings, and case examples.

Although I have specialized in treating anxiety disorders for 40 years, I would have never predicted that I might become an expert in using VR. In 2008, I read an article that changed my life: Parsons and Rizzo (2008) said that exposure in VR was as effective as in vivo exposure—the gold standard for anxiety treatment. That got my attention and a literature review in 2009 cemented my interest. I started using VR with clients in 2010 and seeing great success. In the intervening years, I have taught continuing education workshops, spoken at conferences, consulted with therapists about adding VR to their practices, and written about VR.

My collaborator, Debra Boeldt, PhD, is a licensed psychologist, Deputy Director of the National Mental Health Innovation Center, and another advocate for VR. She has peer-reviewed publications to her name, speaks at conferences nationwide about VR, and supports the Tech Innovation Network.

Practical

This book provides a practical guide to integrating VR for anxiety into your practice in ways that are easy to understand and apply. It explains VR's benefits and uses, reviews key research, answers common questions, and addresses common concerns. It covers using VR in person, for teletherapy, and for client homework.

Recommendations are informed by clinical experience as well as research. Case examples and quotations illustrate ways to use VR in clinical settings.

Names and identifying details have been changed to protect client privacy and confidentiality, but all are based on actual people who sought help for anxiety.

Chapter 2 presents a general model of anxiety and its treatment. Chapters 3 and 4 describe therapeutic uses of VR followed by a VR anxiety treatment protocol and case example in Chapter 5. Chapter 6 provides an overview of VRT for specific phobias. VRT for blood-injection-injury phobia, claustrophobia, driving phobia, flying phobia, height phobia, and insect and animal phobias is discussed in Chapters 7 through 12. VRT for panic disorder and agoraphobia is covered in Chapter 13, social anxiety disorder in Chapter 14, stress, tension, and insomnia in Chapter 15, posttraumatic stress disorder (PTSD) in Chapter 16, and for generalized anxiety disorder, obsessive-compulsive disorder, and illness anxiety disorder in Chapter 17. Chapters 18 through 20 discuss how VR can be used with non-CBT therapies, provide answers to frequently asked questions, and discuss likely future developments. Appendix A explains types of VR equipment and content and Appendix B is a Virtual Reality Therapy Checklist.

Anxiety Focus

Anxiety is used as an umbrella term embracing all its clinical and subclinical manifestations ranging from tension, insomnia, or stress through panic attacks, phobias, intrusive worries, obsessions and/or compulsions, and post-trauma symptoms. VR can also be used for issues outside the scope of this book such as eating disorders, body image, social skills, increasing empathy, etc.

VR can be used for multiple purposes at different stages of anxiety treatment. Client responses to virtual stimuli can help confirm a diagnosis or evaluate treatment effectiveness. VR can facilitate relaxation, skills training, and skills practice, as well as be used for exposure, reinforcement, relapse prevention, and homework.

Integrative Approach

I use an integrative approach to treatment grounded in a comprehensive model of anxiety (Chapter 2). My background includes training in (listed alphabetically) assertiveness training, behavior therapy, client-centered therapy, cognitive therapy, cognitive-behavioral therapy, dialectical behavior therapy, ego state therapy, existential therapy, exposure therapy, eye movement desensitization and reprocessing, family systems therapy, gestalt therapy, guided imagery, hypnosis (directive and Ericksonian nondirective), mindfulness, motivational interviewing, positive psychology, psychodynamic therapy, rational-emotive therapy, relaxation techniques, solution-focused brief therapy, stress management, stress inoculation training, and other approaches.

I believe in treating the whole person. I have seen skilled professionals get good clinical results using many different techniques. In my experience, the most successful therapists use a combination of approaches flexibly adapted to each individual client.

Research Support

I also believe in research-informed practice. Quality research advances our knowledge. Incorporating new knowledge into practice increases efficacy. Human beings are complex, and it helps to be able to view clients through different theoretical lenses and to have as many tools in your toolkit as possible. VR is a flexible, research-tested tool deserving a place in your clinical armamentarium.

Interested readers can learn more about the relevant research by exploring the studies cited in the "Evidence Base" section of most chapters.

What Is Virtual Reality?

"After a few minutes, it began to feel real."

Virtual reality (VR) creates a three-dimensional world. When a client dons a VR headset, they enter a virtual environment (VE) that surrounds them. As they turn around or move, the images they see change appropriately, as if they were in a real place. Views of the *actual* environment are blocked; clients are immersed in a *virtual* environment. This sense of immersion is part of what makes virtual experiences convincing.

Figure 1.1 VR Headset Example

Clients may have a virtual body (avatar) within the VE. Have clients physically mirror their avatar's body position and movements. This deepens clients' sense of presence or feeling as if they are truly present in the VE.

Sounds appropriate to the VE are played through the headset (or a phone held in the headset). Some VEs allow clients to move (or be transported) to different places within the virtual world.

Therapy-specific products allow the therapist to control and monitor the client's virtual experience using a therapist workstation computer or tablet device. You have a 2-D view of the VE and can see what clients are doing and where they are looking.

Additional equipment can be used to make clients' VR experience more convincing. Some examples include:

- Hand-held controllers that enable clients to interact with virtual objects or move within the VE. Some controllers provide haptic (tactile) feedback.
- Specialized devices such as a steering wheel and pedals for driving simulations or simulated weapons for treating war-related PTSD.
- Vibrating platforms that add kinesthetic stimuli by mimicking the vibrations on an airplane or a bomb exploding.
- Scents such as alcohol (for substance abuse treatment) or gunpowder (for war-related PTSD).

Figure 1.2 VR Therapist Workstation Example

When selecting VR products, look at the specific contents of each VE included in the product. Consider which VEs you might use most often in your clinical practice. Consider VE content and potential applications, not just the VE title or its intended purpose. This is discussed in more detail in "VR Product Questions" in Chapter 19. For more information about VR equipment and content types, see Appendix A.

Do Clients Respond to VR?

You might expect that clients would not respond to VR. After all, they know they are sitting in your office. They know they just put on a headset. Research says that most clients do respond (Cardoş et al., 2017; Carl et al., 2019; Diemer et al., 2016; Garcia-Palacios et al., 2007; Maples-Keller et al., 2017; Wechsler et al., 2019).

What do clients say? The most common response to entering VR is "Wow!" And the most common response afterward is "I didn't expect it to be so real."

Here are samples of frequent client comments:

- "This is cool!"
- "I didn't think I would react to it so strongly."
- "That's AMAZING!"
- "It's really working. I feel much less scared than I did at first."
- "I'm a lot farther than I thought I would be at this point in therapy."
- "Things that used to be hair-raising are perfunctory."
- "I think VR is really fun. It's a good way to get over things."

Do Clients Accept VR?

Client interest and acceptance of VRT is extremely high. At least half my clients come specifically requesting VR therapy. Would-be clients from around the country call asking how to find clinicians offering VRT.

Can VR Be Used in Teletherapy?

Yes, certain VR systems (not all) are compatible with teletherapy and allow you to control and monitor your client's virtual experience from a distance. I have found that teletherapy works very well and has some advantages, although there can be technical challenges.

Clients need a VR headset (or smartphone and headset/holder combination) that is compatible with your VR system and a reliable internet connection. The company that produces your VR system will have detailed instructions about what equipment a client needs and how to use it.

I strongly recommend having a video connection during VR teletherapy sessions so you can observe how your client responds and what they do.

Clients tend to move when standing in VR. You want to observe and minimize any chance of clients tripping or bumping into things.

If you are considering using VR during teletherapy, follow the standard ethical and risk management teletherapy guidelines such as getting teletherapy informed consent and knowing where clients are, how to contact them, and what the local crisis services are.

Agree ahead of time on what to do if there are technical issues. Consider whether any negative reaction to VR or VR exposure can be safely and appropriately handled remotely.

Virtual Reality "Therapy"?

VR is a powerful tool with numerous clinical applications, including but not limited to exposure or virtual reality exposure therapy (VRET) (Gonçalves et al., 2012; Parsons & Rizzo, 2008; Powers & Emmelkamp, 2008). Virtual reality therapy (VRT) includes all therapeutic uses of VR.

Despite what the term *virtual reality therapy* seems to imply, *VR is a tool—not a treatment*. VR experiences are not inherently therapeutic. Therapist skills and knowledge remain the key ingredients, but VR can increase the impact of those skills.

Goals

The purpose of this guide is to help you:

- Understand anxiety and guide treatment using an anxiety model that is easy to explain to clients and helps prepare them for therapy.
- Incorporate VR into anxiety treatment for relaxation, skills training and practice, reinforcement, and exposure therapy.
- Learn how VRT works in practice based on a VR treatment protocol and multiple case examples.
- Use VR to treat a range of anxiety disorders.
- Integrate VR with therapies other than CBT.
- Answer clinical and practical questions.

References

Cardoş, R. A. I., David, O. A., & David, D. O. (2017). Virtual reality exposure therapy in flight anxiety: A quantitative meta-analysis. *Computers in Human Behavior*, 72, 371–380. doi:10.1016/j.chb.2017.03.007.

Carl, E., Stein, A. T., Levihn-Coon, A., Pogue, J. R., Rothbaum, B., Emmelkamp, P., Asmundson, G. J. G., Carlbring, P., & Powers, M. B. (2019). Virtual reality exposure therapy for anxiety and related disorders: A meta-analysis of randomized controlled trials. *Journal of Anxiety Disorders*, 61, 27–36. doi:10.1016/j.janxdis.2018.08.003.

Diemer, J., Lohkamp, N., Mühlberger, A., & Zwanzger, P. (2016). Fear and physiological arousal during a virtual height challenge—effects in patients with acrophobia and healthy controls. *Journal of Anxiety Disorders*, 37, 30–39. doi:10.1016/j.janxdis.2015.10.007.

Garcia-Palacios, A., Botella, C., Hoffman, H., & Fabregat, S. (2007). Comparing acceptance and refusal rates of virtual reality exposure vs. in vivo exposure by patients with specific phobias. *CyberPsychology & Behavior*, 10(5), 722–724. doi:10.1089/cpb.2007.9962.

Gonçalves, R., Pedrozo, A. L., Coutinho, E. S. F., Figueira, I., & Ventura, P. (2012). Efficacy of virtual reality exposure therapy in the treatment of PTSD: A systematic review. *PLoS ONE*, 7(12). doi:10.1371/journal.pone.0048469.

Maples-Keller, J. L., Yasinski, C., Manjin, N., & Rothbaum, B. O. (2017). Virtual reality-enhanced extinction of phobias and post-traumatic stress. *Neurotherapeutics*, 14(3), 554–563. doi:10.1007/s13311-017-0534-y.

Parsons, T. D. & Rizzo, A. A. (2008). Affective outcomes of virtual reality exposure therapy for anxiety and specific phobias: A meta-analysis. *Journal of Behavior Therapy and Experimental Psychiatry*, 39(3), 250–261. doi:10.1016/j.jbtep.2007.07.007.

Powers, M. B. & Emmelkamp, P. M. G. (2008). Virtual reality exposure therapy for anxiety disorders: A meta-analysis. *Journal of Anxiety Disorders*, 22(3), 561–569. doi:10.1016/j.janxdis.2007.04.006.

Wechsler, T. F., Kümpers, F., & Mühlberger, A. (2019). Inferiority or even superiority of virtual reality exposure therapy in phobias?—A systematic review and quantitative meta-analysis on randomized controlled trials specifically comparing the efficacy of virtual reality exposure to gold standard in vivo exposure in agoraphobia, specific phobia, and social phobia. *Frontiers in Psychology*, 10. doi:10.3389/fpsyg.2019.01758.

Part I

Anxiety Treatment Overview

This section explains the principles of virtual reality therapy (VRT) for anxiety including:

- Anxiety cycle model explaining the causes of anxiety and how treatment breaks this cycle. This anxiety model is not VR-specific and can be used with a variety of diagnoses and approaches.
- Uses of virtual reality (VR) in anxiety treatment *other* than for exposure therapy.
- Using VR for exposure therapy.
- An extended case example of a VR treatment protocol. See also the Virtual Reality Therapy Checklist in Appendix B.

DOI: 10.4324/9781003154068-2

2 Anxiety Cycle Model

"This makes sense! Now I understand what's been going on."

This chapter presents a model for the pathological cycle of anxiety and how treatment interrupts this cycle. Chapters 3 and 4 explain how virtual reality (VR) is used within this model.

I use this simple, yet comprehensive and flexible, anxiety model to explain symptoms and structure treatment. The model makes sense to clients. As a therapist, you can use these diagrams to explain, normalize, and validate clients' experiences, explain the rationale for treatment interventions, monitor progress, and troubleshoot problems.

The model provides a framework for organizing information about clients' specific issues. You can emphasize different parts of the diagram to match different clients' situations. Identifying the client's anxiety triggers, physical sensations, fears, and resulting fear-based actions helps you understand, validate, and explain your client's experience using the anxiety cycle diagram. It also highlights where and how to intervene and suggests uses for VR.

You can use the treatment cycle diagram to structure treatment and explain interventions in a way that makes sense to clients. This shared understanding creates hope and motivation. These, in turn, help create a positive therapeutic alliance and increase treatment adherence.

The client workbook, *Overcoming Anxiety and Panic Interactive Guide* (McMahon, 2019), includes more detailed explanations of this model along with supporting information, instructions for interoceptive exposure exercises, forms for identifying client-specific issues, and progress tracking records. Clients can read it and complete the forms between sessions to support treatment and can refer back to it help prevent relapse.

DOI: 10.4324/9781003154068-3

A Model for Understanding and Explaining Anxiety

"I like the way this breaks things down. It explains things."

Mapping clients' experiences onto the anxiety cycle helps them understand why they have anxiety and why what they are doing in response to their anxiety is not helping. The diagram of breaking the anxiety cycle helps clients understand what they need to change. You and your client can refer to these diagrams frequently to reinforce key concepts.

Down-to-earth language like "Reacting Brain" and "Thinking Brain" makes concepts easy to grasp. Talking about the Reacting Brain as devoted but dumb, well-intentioned but misinformed, helps make fearful thoughts and actions ego dystonic.

Four factors interact to create and maintain a vicious cycle of anxiety, fear, worry, and/or panic:

1   Anxiety triggers
2   Anxiety sensations (bodily response)
3   Thoughts of fear or danger (cognitive response)
4   Fear-based actions (behavioral response)

Uncovering and exploring the specific factors involved in your client's anxiety disorder allows you to target treatment and incorporate VR in ways that will be most helpful in interrupting the cycle of anxiety.

Anxiety Triggers

The five anxiety triggers below make anxiety more likely. Acting singly or together, they can activate the fear response *in the absence of real danger.*

1   Genetic predisposition
2   Chemical factors
3   External stresses
4   Negative self-talk and/or unrealistic self-demands
5   Unhelpful lessons from the past

Each trigger is explained below with a case example. Clients typically have multiple triggers that interact. Listen for them during your history-taking and diagnostic evaluation and think how virtual experiences might help clients reduce or cope with their triggers.

Genetic Predisposition

Genetics can make someone more vulnerable to developing anxiety (Hettema et al., 2001; Leonardo & Hen, 2006). Genetic traits and temperament help explain why anxiety disorders often run in families and why certain clients seem predisposed to anxiety. Ask about blood relatives with anxiety, substance abuse, or other psychological issues.

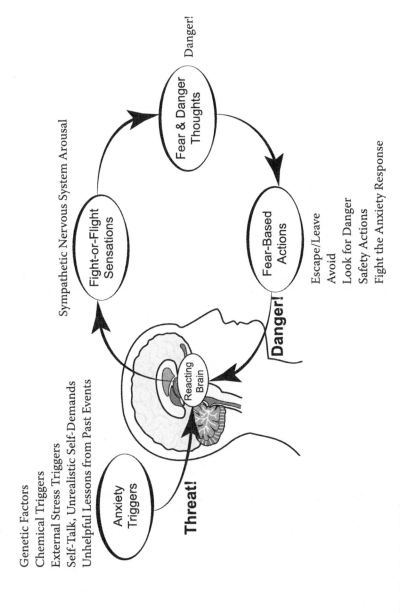

Figure 2.1 The Anxiety Cycle

Case Example

Juan reported, "I've always been anxious. I was an anxious kid." He worries a lot and startles easily. Several relatives including both parents and two of his four siblings have panic attacks or phobias; other relatives struggle with worry, depression, or substance abuse.

Chemical Factors

Chemical and biochemical factors can cause somatic sensations of anxiety (Broderick & Benjamin, 2004; Warrington & Bostwick, 2006; Zender & Olshansky, 2009). Chemical triggers can include medication side effects (e.g., corticosteroids, asthma medicines), substance use or withdrawal (e.g., alcohol, marijuana, ephedra, caffeine, tobacco), female hormonal changes (e.g., PMS, perimenopause). Medical conditions such as thyroid problems, asthma, or mitral valve prolapse can cause anxiety symptoms, especially if undiagnosed.

Case Examples

John had his first panic attack after eating a marijuana edible.

Amida gets more anxious during the premenstrual phase of her cycle and her panic attacks began soon after her child's birth.

Joe had not realized that he felt more anxious after drinking heavily the night before.

External Stress

Life can be filled with stresses: financial, physical, interpersonal, occupational, etc. Stressors may be acute or chronic, mild or severe, single or many. External stress *of any kind* makes anxiety more likely. Ask about stresses and listen for correlations with symptom onset or severity.

Case Examples

Mark's worry, tension, insomnia, and palpitations occur when he's working 12–18 hours a day to meet work deadlines.

Maria is a single mom whose panic attacks began when a new manager criticized her and began talking about downsizing.

Negative Self-Talk or Unrealistic Self-Demands

The impact of stress is filtered through what clients tell themselves and expect of themselves. Negative self-talk like labeling ("stupid"), catastrophizing ("awful"), and so on makes stresses more stressful and threatening.

Unrealistic self-demands, like expecting to be perfect, never make mistakes, never feel anxious or embarrassed, create tension, fear, and anxiety. Explore what clients think and expect of themselves, especially when stressed or anxious.

Case Examples

Lee finds anxiety "horrible", sees himself as generally incapable, and has problems with distress tolerance.

Shanice is harshly self-critical. Work tasks trigger panic because she expects perfection of herself and assumes others are equally critical and demanding of her.

Unhelpful Lessons from Past Events

Lessons about oneself, other people, and the world are learned from past experiences. Such lessons may be conscious or unconscious, circumscribed ("bumpy flights are dangerous") or broad ("I'm vulnerable", "others are untrustworthy", "the world is dangerous"), currently applicable or outmoded, true or false, helpful or unhelpful.

Past experiences can create phobias, worries, panic, or posttraumatic stress disorder (PTSD). Listen for relevant past events and lessons clients may have learned.

Always ask clients to tell you about any experiences of trauma, violence, molestation, or abuse. In the initial session, I explain that I always ask a few questions of everyone the first time we meet. One of those questions is, "Tell me about any experience you have had with any violence, trauma, molestation, or abuse." I am astonished at how many clients say they never mentioned past traumas because prior therapists never asked. Even when processing past traumatic experiences is not the focus of treatment, it is valuable to understand their contribution.

Case Examples

Seventeen-year-old Danielle was afraid to shower alone for months after seeing the horror movie *Psycho*, although she had no prior anxiety and reports no other symptoms.

Darryl's PTSD symptoms began after two tours of military duty overseas with repeated trauma exposure.

Karen suffered childhood abuse and neglect, which left her believing that she is weak and vulnerable, that others are untrustworthy or malevolent, and that the world is full of unpredictable dangers.

A Message of "Threat!"

When anxiety triggers are activated, a message of "Threat!" is sent to the brain (primarily the amygdala and hypothalamus) (Schaefer et al., 2014). In response, these primitive brain areas (which I call the Reacting Brain) cause stress hormones to be released triggering sympathetic nervous system (SNS) arousal, better known as the fight-or-flight response.

The end result is an *automatic* triggering of the types of physical sensations, emotional responses, and patterns of thinking associated with anxiety disorders. What clients **do in response** to this automatic reaction determines whether or not a vicious cycle of anxiety is created. In other words, anxiety is not the problem; the problem is the client's *response* to anxiety. Let's examine this in more detail.

Somatic Response: Anxiety Sensations

Physical Response: Fight or Flight

SNS arousal is a very physical experience causing multiple bodily sensations ranging from slight tension to full-blown panic. Clients often report physical symptoms such as a fast, strong heartbeat, tensed muscles, dizziness, chest tightness or pressure, feeling short of breath, tingling or numbness, feeling hot or cold, visual changes, a sense of being not quite present (depersonalization), or things around them feeling not quite real (derealization).

Fight, Flight, or Freeze?

The threat response is sometimes called the "Fight, Flight, or Freeze" response (Schauer & Elbert, 2010). Although there is justification for this description, there are clinical disadvantages to using it with clients, especially those with panic or phobias. These clients often fear they will be physically paralyzed by panic and unable to move or take appropriate action. They fear panic will render them physically incapacitated and unable to function, for example, unable to speak or control a car. Describing the anxiety response as including "freeze" seems to give credibility to such fears.

When clients worry about "freezing", I usually explain that freezing can be a temporary response intended to allow the person to decide whether to run, fight, or hide but that the body remains prepared for vigorously fighting or fleeing. The person is not frozen. Humans can be temporarily overwhelmed, frightened, and indecisive, but they do not become temporarily paralyzed.

Cognitive Response: Thoughts of Fear and Danger

In response to a message of "Threat!", the mind is automatically flooded with thoughts of fear and danger. Attention and concentration are instinctively focused on identifying possible threats. Anxious thinking can range from recurrent mild worry to a terrifying belief that one's life is in danger.

It is important to emphasize that all of these reactions are normal and hard-wired into our nervous systems. You might explain:

> When your triggers get hit, your Reacting Brain gets a message of threat. It reacts automatically by sending adrenaline to prepare your body to run or fight and by sending messages of fear and danger to your Thinking Brain to find the danger. This is how our bodies are built. It is hard-wired. We are designed to have this reaction.

Behavioral Response: Fear-Based Actions

The emotional response to anxiety sensations and thoughts can range from mild uneasiness to intense terror. When the body, mind, and emotions are all saying there is danger, clients naturally respond with the types of fear-based actions that are life-saving and appropriate *when real danger exists*, but that create and maintain a vicious cycle of anxiety by reinforcing the message that danger existed and was only escaped by taking these actions.

Fear-based actions are:

* Leave/escape
* Avoid
* Be hypervigilant; look for danger
* Take "safety" actions
* Fearfully fight the anxiety

Leave or Escape

Clients may physically leave feared situations. If they don't or can't leave physically, they may try to "escape mentally" through distraction, counting, imagery, listening to music, or other means *because they fear being present in the situation,* or *because they fear the experience of anxiety itself.* Message: "Something bad is going to happen. Get out!"

Avoid

After an aversive experience of fear, worry, or panic, clients frequently physically or mentally avoid situations, actions, thoughts, and sensations associated with anxiety. Message: "Don't go back!"

Be Hypervigilant/Stay Hyperalert/Look for Danger

Hypervigilance is a common response. Clients stay on the lookout for signs of danger which makes them hyperalert, aroused, tense or worried. They *notice* details or sensations that would otherwise go ignored, *misinterpret* things as dangerous that are not, and *ignore* important information that might disconfirm fears because their attention is focused on finding the source of the presumed threat. Naturally, hypervigilance maintains or increases sympathetic nervous system arousal. Message: "Don't relax. Don't let your guard down. Look out!"

Take Safety Actions

Clients take unneeded actions to protect themselves against activities, situations, experiences, and thoughts they think are dangerous. Message: "These actions keep you safe!"

Safety actions can take many forms. Some common examples include:

- Taking anti-anxiety medication to suppress feared sensations
- Only driving on certain roads or in certain lanes perceived to be "safe"
- Staying close to home, loved ones, or medical care; not going beyond a "safe" distance
- Engaging only in safe activities or interacting only with safe people
- Making frequent, unneeded medical visits "just to be sure"
- Repeatedly reassuring themselves or seeking reassurance
- Carrying out compulsive behaviors to prevent feared dangers
- Over-planning and over-preparing

Fearfully Fighting Anxiety

Clients who have deliberately confronted feared situations—and are still afraid—may be discouraged, frustrated, and puzzled ("I *faced* my fear, and it didn't work"). They may have fallen into the common trap of *fighting* to stop or control the anxiety response because they *fear* it. Message: "Relax! Stop it! Control anxiety NOW or else!"

This understandable, but unhelpful, fear-based action generally takes two forms:

1   Clients complain that anxiety management skills (diaphragmatic breathing, relaxation, mindfulness, etc.) "don't work". These clients are often using skills in a frightened attempt to make anxiety *go away*, reinforcing the idea that anxiety is intolerable or dangerous.
2   Clients "white-knuckle" through the experience. They stay in the situation, but fear and hate the panic, as opposed to accepting and tolerating it. It is as if they mentally clench their fists, close their eyes, and repeat a mantra along the lines of, "OMG, OMG, OMG. When will this be over? I can't stand it. Just let me get through this." Obviously, this doesn't do much to teach the Reacting Brain that the experience is safe!

Summary

Anxiety triggers result in anxiety sensations and thoughts of fear and danger causing clients to feel tense, worried, panicky, or endangered. It is natural to then take actions to escape, avoid, prepare to survive, or fight off the perceived danger.

Explain why—even when they give transient relief—these actions maintain or worsen the cycle of anxiety.

Responding with fear-motivated actions closes the loop, creating a vicious cycle. Internal stimuli (thoughts, emotions, or sensations) and external stimuli—like people, places, activities, or situations—can become additional anxiety triggers, while fearful actions strengthen unhelpful narratives, beliefs, and behavior patterns.

Once the client's anxiety cycle is understood, their actions always "make sense", even when those actions are objectively unjustified and unhelpful.

Understanding and explaining the anxiety cycle normalizes the client's experience. It reduces the shame and hopelessness many clients feel about having an anxiety disorder. This shared understanding offers hope and a path for treatment. It clarifies how and where VR can assist in effective intervention.

Breaking the Anxiety Cycle

"By doing what scares me, I find out it's not as bad as I thought it was."

The first step in treating anxiety is understanding what triggers and maintains it. Clients who understand how anxiety works have hope, are motivated, and see the reason for treatment interventions.

Merely identifying relevant anxiety triggers can, in and of itself, reduce client fears. When clients can attribute anxiety to known triggers, their fear response makes more sense. Fear seems less inexplicable and therefore less frightening.

All four parts of the cycle are addressed in virtual reality therapy (VRT) for anxiety:

1   Reducing anxiety triggers.
2   Learning and practicing skills to tolerate anxiety when it occurs.
3   Identifying and exploring clients' fears and effectively countering them with facts, evidence, and logic.
4   Having clients use new knowledge and skills to deliberately face fears without taking fear-based actions.

Let's walk through each of these steps.

Reducing Anxiety Triggers

Multiple therapeutic interventions may be appropriate and helpful for reducing triggers.

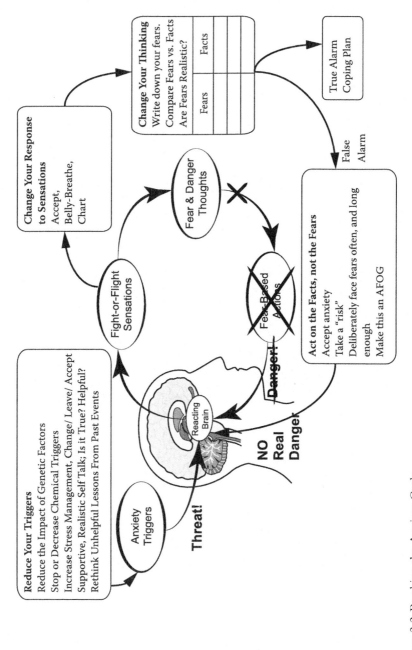

Figure 2.2 Breaking the Anxiety Cycle

Genetics

Clients with a strong family history of anxiety may always be at higher risk of anxiety symptoms. Learning how to accept and cope with anxiety is vital. Some clients may benefit from medication.

When you and the client identify a genetic tendency to anxiety, emphasize how important it is for the client to understand how anxiety works and diligently apply what they will learn in treatment.

CASE EXAMPLE

In the case of Juan, mentioned earlier, he needs anxiety tolerance skills because he may always have an inherited heightened tendency to be anxious. VR can help him learn and practice such skills.

Chemicals

Whenever possible, encourage clients to reduce or discontinue chemicals that trigger anxiety, such as excessive alcohol and drugs. Marijuana, especially edibles, can trigger panic attacks.

Clients whose symptoms are triggered by hormonal fluctuations or necessary medications may find it helpful to identify the cause and track cause and effect, so the sensations are no longer inexplicable. Interventions like motivational interviewing, mindfulness, reframing, distress tolerance, and others may be helpful.

When substance use is identified as an anxiety trigger, saying no to alcohol or drugs in virtual reality can help clients decrease actual drinking and substance use.

CASE EXAMPLE

In Joe's case, once he realized that his drinking contributed to his anxiety, he was able to practice refusing offers of alcohol in virtual bars and social settings, which helped him do so in reality.

External Stress

I tell my clients there are only four responses to stress and only the first three are any good:

1   Change whatever is under your control to reduce the stress.
2   Leave the situation.
3   If you can't change the situation and cannot or choose not to leave, accept the situation as it is, understanding the reasons you are staying.
4   Stay upset.

Assertiveness training, limit-setting, stress management, stress inoculation training, mindfulness, healthy self-care (exercise, healthy diet, yoga, etc.), social support, and other interventions may be appropriate.

CASE EXAMPLE

Mark was very stressed by work demands. By taking Mark away from his stressful reality and putting him into calm virtual environments (VEs), VR helped Mark relax initially and improve his ability to relax at night.

CASE EXAMPLE

Maria benefited not only from learning relaxation skills in VR but also from practicing responding to criticism from virtual avatars who voiced the kind of remarks her manager was making and by virtually interviewing for other jobs, so she felt like she had more options.

Negative Self-Talk/Unrealistic Self-Demands

Interventions to reduce negative self-talk and/or unrealistic self-demands may include cognitive therapy, cognitive-behavioral therapy (CBT), narrative therapy, dialectical behavior therapy (DBT), acceptance and commitment therapy (ACT), self-compassion, and insight-oriented therapies. Identifying and changing core beliefs may help with self-talk, self-demands, and unhelpful lessons from the past.

CASE EXAMPLE

Lee experienced VR as a place where it felt safer and easier to take the risk of failing and try new things. Gradually, virtual successes supported a changed view of himself as more capable than he previously thought.

CASE EXAMPLE

After learning how to be more self-compassionate and less perfectionistic, Shanice can practice applying new self-talk and expectations in virtual situations that normally elicit self-criticism. She can also gain confidence in responding to increasingly unrealistic demands and criticism from virtual others.

Unhelpful Lessons from Past Events

Any of several standard psychotherapy approaches can help clients make connections between past events and present difficulties, change unhelpful beliefs and behaviors, or change the past's lingering emotional impact. Working to articulate and replace unhelpful (conscious or unconscious) lessons stemming from past experiences paves the way for clients to accept anxiety, question fearful assumptions, and respond successfully to exposure.

You may use varying interventions depending on the specific client, the overall treatment goal, and your own training and theoretical orientation. Many of the interventions mentioned previously can help. Additional interventions may include schema therapy, prolonged exposure (PE), cognitive processing therapy (CPT), trauma-informed therapy, and corrective emotional experiences.

CASE EXAMPLE

VR helped Danielle respond differently to anxiety. Staying alone in an increasingly dark virtual house might also provide gradual virtual exposure.

CASE EXAMPLES

Treating simple and complex PTSD requires specialized knowledge and expertise. Darryl and Karen saw therapists with special training: in treating war-related PTSD for Darryl and in treating complex PTSD for Karen. As part of treatment, VR helped them both with self-soothing, symptom management, and exposure therapy.

Summary of Reducing Triggers

How much time and effort you spend reducing the client's anxiety *triggers* varies from client to client. You may spend *more* time on the triggers if you identify past events and resulting lessons that have an enduring, negative impact on the client. These might include events that have left the client with:

- Impaired object relations.
- The belief that he or she is vulnerable, weak, unable to cope, unable to tolerate distress, etc.
- Beliefs that the world in general is an inherently unsafe place.
- Beliefs that other people cannot be trusted or relied upon.

Techniques from a wide variety of therapeutic approaches can be incorporated. Depending on your background and training, the specific trigger, and the client's preference, you may use techniques drawn from acceptance commitment therapy (ACT), cognitive challenging or reframing, dialectical behavior therapy (DBT), existential therapy, eye movement desensitization and reprocessing therapy (EMDR), mindfulness, narrative therapy, psychodynamic therapy, schema therapy, writing interventions such as those researched by James Pennebaker (Pennebaker, 2004; Pennebaker & Evans, 2014; Pennebaker & Smyth, 2016) or other approaches.

VRT is compatible with all the above interventions. VR can help clients learn and practice mindfulness. Some VR products can provide visual cues for EMDR. Clients can apply new skills, lessons, and insights from therapy in virtual situations as preparation for applying them in real-life situations.

You may also choose to spend more time reducing anxiety triggers if you have the option of providing longer-term therapy and/or if the client sees this as a priority.

Tolerating Anxiety Sensations

When anxiety triggers are hit, the anxiety response fires. This is hard-wired into our nervous system, automatic, and outside our control. The Reacting Brain reacts.

If humans controlled the anxiety reaction, treatment would take five seconds. You would say, "Don't be anxious." The client would say, "Gee, I never thought of that," leave your office, and never again be anxious.

Acknowledge that fear, worry, anxiety, and panic can occur involuntarily. Emphasize the importance of acceptance.

The goal of anxiety management skills like breathing, relaxation, and mindfulness is to tolerate and minimize sensations, not necessarily stop or prevent them. Clients who use the skills in a desperate, frightened attempt to make anxiety stop are taking fear-based actions. They are trying to escape, using the skills as safety actions, and fighting anxiety because they fear it—which explains why these skills rarely work if used alone.

Use the anxiety and treatment diagrams to help clients see the importance of accepting anxiety. Trying to avoid or actively suppress the feared experience of anxiety maintains unhelpful beliefs that anxiety is to be feared and is itself somehow dangerous. It weakens client self-efficacy and strengthens the cycle of anxiety. *Accepting*, rather than fighting or avoiding, is *paradoxically* helpful.

Countering Thoughts of Fear and Danger

Identify and Articulate

Help clients to identify their fears as specifically as possible. Articulate in detail what the fear is assuming or predicting. What threat(s) is the Reacting Brain protecting them from? What are the underlying assumptions (i.e., panic is dangerous; fear is proof of danger)?

A client's fear is not always obvious to them or to you. One client who called about "fear of flying" believed flying was inherently dangerous and routine noises meant the airplane is breaking apart; another feared that any turbulence meant the plane was about to fall from the sky. On the other hand, other clients who called about their "flying phobia" were actually not afraid of flying itself, but avoided flying due to other fears, such as:

- Being trapped in an enclosed space
- Suffocating due to heat and lack of air
- Having a panic attack which they believed would cause heart attack, fainting, or death
- Embarrassing themselves
- Being exposed to germs (without a medical basis for the concern)
- Not being in control, having to trust the pilots
- Being on a plane with other passengers who could be terrorists

Different clients have different fears. You need to know the relevant fears in order to give the relevant facts. Providing facts about aircraft safety doesn't help clients who fear having a panic attack and being unable to get out.

It is essential to uncover what each client fears. Only then can you and the client determine whether those terrifying assumptions and predictions are accurate—or not. You cannot use facts or logic to counter a fear you don't know about.

Question and Explore

Questioning helps you and the client put fears into words so they can be logically examined and challenged. Ask questions such as:

- "If the situation (or sensation, or activity, or thought) was dangerous, what might the danger be?"
- "And if *that* were true, then what would happen next or what might that mean?"

Continue questioning and exploring:

- "And if *that* happened, *then* what?"
- "And what would happen next?"
- "What would be the worst thing about that?"
- "What would make that so frightening or awful?"
- "What are the worst possible outcomes?"
- "How long would that last?"
- "How would you cope?"

Clients may have never thought about what happens after the feared event or sensation. Or they may have quickly sought to reassure themselves without actually exploring their fears. This doesn't work because underlying fears or beliefs that haven't been put into words can't be evaluated and believably refuted.

Counter Anxiogenic Thoughts

Some fears can be disproved using facts, evidence, or logic. Here the emphasis is on how likely or realistic are the fearful predictions and the assumptions supporting these fears.

Other fears are best countered by viewing them within a larger perspective. Explore with the client "How bad would that be really?", "How long would it last?", and/or "How would you cope?"

Self-soothing, distress tolerance, and acceptance may be needed. Additional interventions can include changing distorted automatic thoughts, challenging negative core beliefs or schemas, creating a more helpful narrative, gaining insight into how the client is unconsciously repeating dysfunctional patterns from childhood, or mindful nonjudgmental awareness of thoughts.

Fear of death may be addressed using an existential approach and/or radical acceptance: first acknowledging and accepting that inevitably we all die, then emphasizing the choice of how to live one's life. Do they want to die having lived a life of fear?

Acting on the Facts, Not the Fear

Normalize Fear-Based Actions

Explaining the anxiety cycle helps normalize and validate clients' actions, even those that maintain the cycle. Fear-based actions are understandable, although unhelpful.

You may say something like:

> Your body, your emotions, and your mind are all telling you that you are in danger. It is natural to take the kinds of actions that are protective and life-saving if you are really threatened: leave the dangerous situation and avoid it in the future; if you have to enter a dangerous situation, be hypervigilant and take actions to keep yourself safe; and if you *have* to fight, fight with all your might.

Reason to Act on Facts, Not Fears

You then explain why these instinctive actions are unhelpful.

> The trouble is that when your anxiety triggers are hit and your primitive Reacting Brain sends a false alarm, if you do any of these fear-based actions, it sends a message *back* to your bodyguard Reacting Brain that there really IS danger. Otherwise, you wouldn't be acting like this and taking these actions. As a result, your Reacting Brain remembers everything about where you were, how you felt, what you were doing and thinking, and all those things

can now become signs of danger, triggering more false alarms in the future and strengthening the cycle of anxiety.

Explain and Reframe Exposure as an AFOG

Clients need a credible, strongly convincing, motivating rationale for exposure because really, who wants to face something that scares them? Here is an example of such an explanation:

> You can't get over a fear that you never face. When you avoid or leave situations that make you afraid, anxiety stays or spreads and gets worse. So, you have to face what you fear, but if you white-knuckle through the experience being scared the whole time, you just learn to be more afraid. Does that make sense?
>
> Getting the facts that your fears are unrealistic gives you and your Thinking Brain the courage to act on the facts, not the fears. This means you take what your Reacting Brain thinks is a "risk" by acting on the facts despite your fear, accepting anxiety, and turning each experience of anxiety into an AFOG: Another Fabulous? Fantastic? Flipping? F★★★ing? Opportunity for Growth. This is the only way the Reacting Brain learns that what it fears does not happen.

Every episode of anxiety can become an AFOG, an opportunity for learning and growth.

Treatment Overview

You can use the anxiety cycle diagrams to give clients an overview of treatment along the following lines:

> You want to work on reducing your anxiety triggers. And while you are doing that, you want to break out of the anxiety cycle. Since there are three parts to the anxiety cycle, we will target all three parts.
>
> First, you need a way to manage the unpleasantness of unnecessary anxiety, fear, or panic, and to understand what is happening in your mind and body when you experience anxiety [or panic, or fear, or re-experience trauma].
>
> Then you need to put your fears into words, so you can evaluate whether those fears are realistic. This gives you and your Thinking Brain the courage to act on the facts, not the fears.
>
> Acting on the facts and facing your fears even when you are anxious shows your Reacting Brain that there is no danger and that you can cope.
>
> Fear-based actions strengthen anxiety. Fact-based actions *weaken* anxiety and *strengthen* you.

Think about a few of your anxious clients. How do their histories and symptoms map onto these diagrams? How can your treatment apply the concepts and address *all components* of their anxiety cycle? Keep these questions in mind as you read Chapters 3 and 4, which discuss specific applications of VR in therapy.

References

Broderick, P. & Benjamin, A. B. (2004). Caffeine and psychiatric symptoms: A review. *The Journal of the Oklahoma State Medical Association*, 97(12), 538–542. doi:15732884.

Hettema, J. M., Neale, M. C., & Kendler, K. S. (2001). A review and meta-analysis of the genetic epidemiology of anxiety disorders. *American Journal of Psychiatry*, 158(10), 1568–1578. doi:10.1176/appi.ajp.158.10.1568.

Leonardo, E. D. & Hen, R. (2006). Genetics of affective and anxiety disorders. *Annual Review of Psychology*, 57(1), 117–137. doi:10.1146/annurev. psych.57.102904.190118.

McMahon, E. (2019). *Overcoming Anxiety and Panic Interactive Guide*. Hands-on-Guide.

Pennebaker, J. W. (2004). *Writing to Heal: A Guided Journal for Recovering from Trauma and Emotional Upheaval*. New Harbinger Publisher.

Pennebaker, James W., & Evans, J. F. (2014). *Expressive Writing: Words that Heal*. Idyll Arbor, Inc.

Pennebaker, James W., & Smyth, J. M. (2016). *Opening Up by Writing it Down* (3rd ed.). The Guilford Press.

Schaefer, H. S., Larson, C. L., Davidson, R. J., & Coan, J. A. (2014). Brain, body, and cognition: Neural, physiological and self-report correlates of phobic and normative fear. *Biological Psychology*, 98(1), 59–69. doi:10.1016/j.biopsycho.2013.12.011.

Schauer, M. & Elbert, T. (2010). Dissociation following traumatic stress etiology and treatment. *Journal of Psychology*, 218(2), 109–127. doi:10.1027/0044-3409/a000018.

Warrington, T. P. & Bostwick, J. M. (2006). Psychiatric adverse effects of corticosteroids. *Mayo Clinic Proceedings*, 81(10), 1361–1367. doi:10.4065/81.10.1361.

Zender, R. & Olshansky, E. (2009). Women's mental health: depression and anxiety. *Nursing Clinics of North America*, 44(3), 355–364. doi:10.1016/j.cnur.2009.06.002.

3 Uses of VR in Anxiety Treatment

"The different visual experience made me feel better. It changed my breathing, changed my thinking. Really pulled me into the moment. It was really powerful."

Now that you are familiar with the anxiety cycle, let's explore how virtual reality (VR) is used to treat anxiety.

This chapter covers these uses of VR:

- Facilitating relaxation and calm
- Teaching anxiety management skills
- Uncovering fears
- Practicing other skills
- Confirming treatment efficacy
- Providing pleasurable reinforcing experiences
- Preventing relapse
- Homework including home practice

VR exposure therapy (VRET) is explained in Chapter 4 and an anxiety treatment protocol/case example is provided in Chapter 5. When reading this case transcript, notice how various uses of VR are intermingled to address issues as they arise and optimize the client's experience.

If you are unfamiliar with exposure therapy, consider reading the case transcript first. If you have concerns about using VR for exposure, read "Therapist Concerns About VRET" in Chapter 4.

Facilitating Relaxation and Calm

Because VR is immersive, clients are removed from the stressful real world, which can facilitate or deepen relaxation (Anderson et al., 2017). Simply entering a safe, peaceful environment in VR can lead to clients achieving deeper levels of mental and physical calm, giving them a respite from fear and tension.

Pleasant virtual experiences create a sense of peace, safety, or distance from distress. Clients may find it easier to relax when in a calming virtual environment. They can better focus on breathing, relaxing, mindfulness, or

DOI: 10.4324/9781003154068-4

imagery in a soothing virtual environment (VE) and may learn and practice such skills more easily when immersed in relaxing virtual settings. Who wouldn't relax more completely in a peaceful setting like a beach, meadow, forest setting, or meditation room?

VR provides richer sensory experiences. Some clients may respond more to auditory stimuli while others prefer visual stimuli. Richer experiences may have more impact, both during the experience and when recalled. VR offers vivid experiences with a minimal time cost.

Teaching Anxiety Management Skills

Before a client can benefit from exposure therapy, they must be willing to face whatever triggers their anxiety, fear, or panic. This may mean facing long-avoided activities, situations, emotions, memories, and/or physical sensations that trigger fear.

You want clients to overcome their *fear* of fear. Anxiety management skills help clients accept, minimize, and tolerate the unpleasant experience of unnecessary sympathetic nervous system (SNS) arousal because being able and willing to tolerate anxiety enables them to confront feared experiences, which provides opportunities for changing their thinking, actions, and emotional reactions.

Learning anxiety coping skills can be easier, more vividly engaging, and memorable in VR. The immersive quality of VR helps engage and sustain clients' attention to keep their minds from wandering.

Figure 3.1 Relaxing Nature VE Example

Some VR experiences reinforce instructions with visual prompts. For example, clients may see an avatar performing the progressive muscle relaxation (PMR) exercises or practicing diaphragmatic breathing following the instructions.

Many VR products have pre-recorded instructions for teaching diaphragmatic breathing, PMR, or mindfulness that you can also use during exposure to prompt clients to recall and use these skills and to help clients internalize them.

If the instructions are played aloud and clients respond well to them, clients can record them on a smartphone to listen to during home practice. Or clients can record your personalized instructions during VR and use that recording for home practice.

More clients now have VR headsets at home—or their children do—and may be interested in using VR to practice at home. Depending on the VR product you use, you may be able to record a VR training session and have the client re-experience it at home. Alternatively, you may find a consumer VR app you are comfortable recommending.

Think about your caseload and client population. What skills would you like to see clients practice and reinforce in a virtually real environment during or between sessions?

Four Common Anxiety Management Skills

Diaphragmatic Breathing

Diaphragmatic breathing activates the parasympathetic branch of the nervous system, which counters SNS arousal. Variations of diaphragmatic breathing are taught and can be easy for clients to learn and practice. Clients can do it anywhere, any time, and without anyone noticing.

Teaching diaphragmatic breathing takes very little session time. You can easily monitor client skill and correct as needed when clients are learning or when they are in VR. By having clients put a hand on their chest and a hand on their abdomen, you can see whether they are breathing using their diaphragm.

Progressive Muscle Relaxation

Although teaching and practicing PMR takes more time initially, this skill has decades of research supporting its effectiveness with a variety of anxiety disorders. Some clients prefer it or respond best to it.

Once learned, clients can use PMR to achieve overall relaxation or to relax specific body parts. Muscle relaxation may be especially useful for muscle tension, pain, and/or insomnia.

Driving phobics often tense their arms and shoulders when driving and benefit from being guided in PMR while driving a virtual car and applying this skill during real driving.

Mindfulness

Mindfulness can help quiet the mind, increase distress tolerance, and has been shown to help with anxiety, pain, depression, ADHD, and other issues (Goyal et al., 2014; Ioannou et al., 2020). Many clients tell me that a brief morning meditation helps them set their priorities for the day.

Mindfulness skills and concepts are easily incorporated into anxiety treatment. The diagram of Breaking the Anxiety Cycle (Figure 2.2) stresses the importance of acceptance and of observing feared somatic sensations and thoughts without acting on them, fighting them, believing them, or focusing on them in a frightened way. Mindful awareness can help clients ally with their Thinking Brain to reassure, refute, defy, or ignore their Reacting Brain.

EEG data shows that nature-based mindfulness VR creates a greater physiological anxiety reduction than a quiet resting control condition (Tarrant et al., 2018).

Imagery

Some clients prefer to use imagery to manage anxiety. Imagery may reinforce suggestions of safety and calm coping. You may have VE scenes that are compatible with this guided imagery. Clients are "present" in VR, which increases the impact.

Visual VEs mean clients don't have to imagine; the visual stimuli are vividly present everywhere they look. Clients are transported into another world. The visual VR experience is more vivid and immersive than guided imagery alone.

Of course, you encourage clients to use imagery—or any anxiety management skill—to tolerate anxiety rather than mentally avoiding or fighting it.

Choosing Skills for Your Client to Use in VR

Each skill has its benefits. I usually start with diaphragmatic breathing but use different skills or skill combinations for different clients. Some clients learn or respond to one approach more than another, so you want to be flexible.

During my pre-intake screening call and intake, I ask what previous therapy and skills the client has tried. Then I ask what worked and didn't work, so I get a sense early on of which skills may best suit each client.

Ask yourself these questions when choosing among the skills:

- Which skills are *you* most comfortable with, trained in, and successful using?
- Which skills is *your client* most comfortable and successful using?
- Do you have VEs compatible with these skills?

- Does your VR system have recorded instructions for learning and using these skills? If so, do you like them and feel they are appropriate for this client or would you prefer to give your own instructions while the client is in VR?
- Does the client prefer your voice over the pre-recorded instructions?

Uncovering Fears

You cannot reassure a client, counter a client's fears, or plan VR experiences or exposures if you do not *know* what the client fears. VR can provide a soothing, calming, safe space where clients may be more relaxed, open, and willing to speak about their fears. However, some clients have trouble articulating or even identifying their fears and say things like "I just know it scares me".

You can use VR to uncover fears and confirm diagnoses. Because immersive VR is experienced as real, it can bring fears to conscious awareness. Clients are more in touch with what they fear when they are immersed *in* a feared situation—even virtually.

Asking about thoughts and reactions while clients are in VEs may bring previously unrecognized fears to the surface or provide additional information about fears, making effective treatment possible. Clients' reactions in VR can also uncover skill deficits, such as a need for distress tolerance skills.

VR may also be a way to engage adolescents in treatment. They may be intrigued by the technology and may be more open to "doing" than talking.

Case Example

Seventeen-year-old David was more willing to talk about upsetting issues while he was in VR and didn't have to make eye contact. He was more in touch with his experience while at the same time VR made therapy feel safer.

Practicing Other Skills

The whole point of learning skills is for clients to be able use and benefit from these skills in anxiety-provoking or stressful situations. In addition to anxiety management skills, clients can practice a multitude of other treatment skills in VR during sessions.

Clients may interact with virtual others to practice eye contact and communication, engage in social interactions, speak up at work, be assertive with others, interview for jobs, and so on. You can speak for the virtual others and role play with the client in VR.

They may virtually return to the real-world sites of past difficulties or traumas as an opportunity to practice distress tolerance and apply new insights to change thoughts, reactions, and behaviors.

They may visit virtual situations that would activate old schemas and take the opportunity to challenge negative core beliefs, strengthen new positive core beliefs, and use cognitive skills such as restructuring, reframing, challenging thought distortions, changing self-talk, applying a new narrative, and so on.

Confirming Treatment Efficacy

Measure the client's response to treatment by monitoring client anxiety levels during various VR scenarios. VR allows you to observe the client's ability to successfully apply new skills or learnings.

With VR, you can gauge the client's ability to effectively apply treatment skills and insights. VR gives you the unique opportunity to actually see how your client copes, thinks, and reacts in the virtually real world.

You can confirm that treatment is working and identify problem areas to be addressed without relying on client report alone.

Providing a Pleasurable, Reinforcing Experience

People tend to evaluate experiences based on the moment of the highest emotional intensity and the end of the experience (the peak-end rule) (Kahneman, 2019). Ending a session on a positive note helps color the client's recollection of the whole session as being more positive.

VEs designed to promote relaxation or anxiety management are pleasurable for most clients. Having clients spend a few minutes in an enjoyable VR at the end of a session rewards clients for attending and doing the work of therapy. Positive VR experiences may also increase emotional engagement in therapy.

CAVEAT: Always describe a VE to each client before having them enter it. Just because a VE is *intended* to be relaxing does not mean your client will find it relaxing or pleasurable. For example, claustrophobic clients may find floating under the sea quite anxiety-provoking. Agoraphobic clients often find deserted beach or forest scenes frightening.

Case Examples

For Barbara, being in a virtual forest with birdsong and gentle sounds of running water triggered an immediate increase in anxiety. She felt alone, abandoned, and far from help. Carol, on the other hand, found the forest soothing: "It brings a feeling of joy and calmness."

Preventing Relapse

VR can reduce relapse risk and support clients' ability to maintain treatment gains even when stressed. Encourage clients to plan and imagine how they could cope successfully with situations that might trigger a recurrence of anxiety symptoms—then test those plans in VR.

VR permits repeated practice of important skills, which strengthens new skills and increases self-efficacy.

Having clients practice skills in a *variety* of settings strengthens new skills, supports generalization and transfer, and minimizes risk of relapse.

Incorporating VR exposure overcomes the limitations of just talking about or imagining future situations. In VR, the client can virtually confront difficult situations in advance including the presence of anxiety cues.

As clients cope successfully with challenges in VR, you can have them confront more challenging virtual situations while you lessen your support—allowing them to become more independent. You and the client can test their readiness to terminate.

Homework

Homework speeds treatment by supplementing the education and training provided in session. I frequently ask clients to complete specific tasks between sessions. Homework may include readings, forms, or exercises from my client workbook (McMahon, 2019), other readings, or using apps. Clients with VR equipment can be assigned VR-based homework.

Some VR products offer an app for clients to download and use to practice anxiety managements skills on their own. Another option is to recommend a VR app designed for psychoeducation or self-help or even VR content not designed specifically for self-help or therapy.

Your VR product may let you record a client's VR session and give the client access to re-experience it at home.

CAVEATS: Keep in mind that when clients enter VR at home, you have no control over the pace, intensity, or duration of their VR experience. They are not being monitored or receiving personal guidance or coaching. Even when an app has an avatar coach or "therapist" the avatar's responses are pre-programmed, not specific to the individual client.

For these reasons, I tend to be cautious when recommending home VR. Generally, I only assign VEs or VR apps we have used in session and to which the client had a positive response, or VR content I have reviewed and decided is appropriate.

Some clients want to do at-home VR exposure using content found on games or via an internet search of websites such as YouTube. Warn them that most content is not designed to be therapeutic and, indeed, is often designed to elicit extreme emotional reactions. You want clients to avoid frightening VR experiences.

References

Anderson, A. P., Mayer, M. D., Fellows, A. M., Cowan, D. R., Hegel, M. T., & Buckey, J. C. (2017). Relaxation with immersive natural scenes presented using virtual reality. *Aerospace Medicine and Human Performance*, 88(6), 520–526. doi:10.3357/AMHP.4747.2017.

Goyal, M., Singh, S., Sibinga, E. M. S., Gould, N. F., Rowland-Seymour, A., Sharma, R., Berger, Z., Sleicher, D., Maron, D. D., Shihab, H. M., Ranasinghe, P. D., Linn, S., Saha, S., Bass, E. B., & Haythornthwaite, J. A. (2014). Meditation programs for psychological stress and well-being: A systematic review and meta-analysis. *JAMA Internal Medicine*, 174(3), 357–368. doi:10.1001/jamainternmed.2013.13018.

Ioannou, A., Papastavrou, E., Avraamides, M. N., & Charalambous, A. (2020). Virtual reality and symptoms management of anxiety, depression, fatigue, and pain: a systematic review. *SAGE Open Nursing*, 6. doi:10.1177/2377960820936163.

Kahneman, D. (2019). Evaluation by moments: Past and future. In *Choices, Values, and Frames*, 693–708. doi:10.1017/CBO9780511803475.039.

McMahon, E. (2019). *Overcoming Anxiety and Panic Interactive Guide*. Hands-on-Guide.

Tarrant, J., Viczko, J., & Cope, H. (2018). Virtual reality for anxiety reduction demonstrated by quantitative EEG: A pilot study. *Frontiers in Psychology*, 9, 1–15. doi:10.3389/fpsyg.2018.01280.

4 VR Exposure Therapy

"I had therapy before, but I never had a breakthrough like this."

Virtual reality exposure therapy (VRET) can result in therapeutic break-throughs. Virtual reality (VR) can support anxiety treatment in many ways but the most well-known, and arguably most important, is by providing controlled virtual exposure, sometimes called in virtuo exposure (Carl et al., 2019a; Meyerbröker & Emmelkamp, 2010; Parsons & Rizzo, 2008). Therapist concerns about exposure therapy and VRET are addressed later in this chapter.

What Is Exposure and Why Is It Important?

Exposure, or facing one's fears, is essential. You cannot overcome a fear if you run away from and avoid it. Every evidence-based anxiety treatment involves exposure whether it is facing and coping with anxiogenic thoughts, sensations, situations, or actions. Traditional forms of exposure include imaginal (using imagination, visual imagery, and clinical discourse to address anxiety) and in vivo (facing feared situations or stimuli in real life). VR adds a highly effective additional form of exposure that helps counter or circumvent the limitations of other exposure options.

All therapists share a common goal without regard to theoretical orientation or therapeutic approach: empowering our clients so they can freely choose their actions and live their lives without being restricted by fear. VR helps achieve these goals.

Two historic approaches to therapeutic exposure are implosion therapy and systematic desensitization:

1 Implosion therapy (also known as flooding or implosive therapy) involves prolonged exposure at high fear intensity with the goal of speedy extinction of the fear response (Stampfl & Levis, 1967). While effective and quick, this approach can cause intense client distress and may be difficult for clients to accept and tolerate.

DOI: 10.4324/9781003154068-5

2   Graduated exposure or systematic desensitization (Wolpe, 1990). Clients initially face stimuli which trigger no more than mild to moderate distress and are not exposed to more intense fear-triggering stimuli until the current fear response is reduced or extinguished.

Personally, I have a strong preference for gradual exposure done collaboratively with therapist support and monitoring and only *after* giving the client tools for handling exposure successfully. I encourage you to embed exposure, including VRET, within the comprehensive model of anxiety treatment.

Let's start by reviewing the strengths and weaknesses of imaginal and in vivo exposure followed by the advantages of VR exposure.

Imaginal Exposure

With imaginal exposure, clients face or relive a feared situation, thought, memory, or emotion using their imagination. Clients may talk about the situation in session, write about it, or use guided imagery techniques such as prolonged exposure (PE).

Imaginal exposure has two primary advantages: it does not require any equipment and it can be used in session or by clients at home. On the other hand, it also has several limitations, which VR exposure circumvents.

One limitation of imaginal exposure is that clients vary in their willingness to talk or write about what makes them anxious. Some clients are unwilling because of the intensity of the emotional response that is triggered. With these clients, VR can prompt the client to use their anxiety management skills or provide a soothing, calming safe space where clients may feel safer discussing their fears.

Other clients may write or talk at length but experience no emotional response or involvement. With such clients, VR can make their experience a more vivid, present, lived experience.

A second limitation is that clients vary in their ability to imagine. Not every client imagines well and the ability to create vivid mental images declines with age. What the client imagines may not be vivid enough to be evocative and therapeutically useful. VR provides a vivid visual experience.

Alternatively, what the client envisions may be *too vivid* and frightening. You may not know—or control—details of what is being visualized and consequently have less control over the level of exposure. With VR exposure, you see what the client sees, and you may control aspects of virtual experiences.

In Vivo Exposure

Facing fears in real life situations is called in vivo exposure. It is considered the gold standard for exposure therapy and is often the bar against which VR exposure is compared in research studies.

The major advantage of in vivo exposure is its proven efficacy. Indeed, the goal of treatment is for clients to be able to confront—and cope with—what they previously feared, avoided, or tolerated with great distress. You want them to overcome their fears in real life.

In vivo exposure, however, also has limitations that VR can avoid or counter.

Arranging in vivo exposure may be difficult or expensive. In contrast, taking virtual flights, for example, is easy and cheap. Virtual audiences, job interviews, or social interactions can be convened at any time.

Experiences that are *impossible* to arrange in real life may be available in VR. Commercial flights can repeatedly take off until your client is comfortable. Weather, traffic conditions, room size, etc. can be controlled or altered at will.

It can be easy for clients to procrastinate and find excuses to avoid in vivo exposure homework. VR exposure is done in session with your support and encouragement.

In vivo exposure can be uncontrolled and have unpredictable results. Experiences may be too mild—or too intense—to be helpful. In the worst case, in vivo exposure can be a frightening experience that seems to validate the client's fears and makes them reluctant to continue treatment. VR generally can avoid either of these extremes. You have more control over the client's experience and the virtual environment (VE). You are more likely to achieve an optimal level of exposure: not too mild; not too intense.

Accompanying clients during in vivo exposure can create risks to confidentiality and privacy. In VR, clients virtually leave the office, yet you are available to support, guide, monitor, and intervene as needed.

Changes in VR generalize and transfer, which means that successfully facing fears in VR prepares clients to cope successfully with fears in real life.

Uses and Benefits of VR Exposure

To summarize, using VR:

- Offers vivid visual, immersive "real" experiences.
- Increases therapist knowledge of and control over the client experience.
- Makes exposure easier and makes impossible experiences possible.
- Removes the barriers and excuses that can interfere with completing in vivo exposure homework.
- Maximizes therapist ability to create optimally therapeutic experiences.
- Protects confidentiality while permitting therapist support.

Clients who have read about virtual reality therapy (VRT) may be more hopeful and willing to engage in treatment. Clients are often more willing to face fears in VR because they know VR isn't "real". Despite that knowledge, research and clinical experience confirm that most clients respond emotionally and physiologically, making VR exposure therapeutically valuable.

For clients with limited ability to imagine or visualize, VR can create more vivid, therapeutically useful experiences. For clients with strong fear reactions, having control over anxiety-triggering variables helps avoid sensitizing (rather than desensitizing) experiences. Virtual exposure can be stopped or started at any time and repeated as often as needed.

Interoceptive exposure (exposure to somatic anxiety sensations) can be added before or during virtual exposure. Some VR products have built-in interoceptive features, including audio that simulates a rapid heart rate or breathing, and visual manipulations that virtually mimic blurred or tunnel vision.

VR facilitates effective therapist guidance and support by allowing you to see and hear what your client sees and hears. You can control and tailor VR exposure to client needs and create individualized experiences, allowing clients to prepare before facing fears in the unpredictable real world. Clients can habituate and change their cognitive, emotional, and physical responses.

My clinical experience based on more than a decade of using VR in therapy is that it truly is a breakthrough in anxiety treatment. Successful VR exposure increases client optimism and self-efficacy and strengthens the therapeutic alliance. Changes in VR generalize to real life. The majority of clients who begin by confronting fears in VR go on to successfully confront those fears in real life. Success stories include becoming able to fly, take a ski lift, drive on the highway, have an MRI, or enjoy giving presentations, among other activities. And clients attribute at least part of their improvement specifically to VRT.

Research support for these statements is reviewed in the "Evidence Base" section of this chapter.

Preparing for VRET

As you have learned, exposure is necessary and VR exposure has unique advantages, but exposure alone is not necessarily curative. Repeatedly doing something that scares a client may leave the client *more afraid* rather than less.

You want your client's response to change during VRET. You want to plan and carry out exposures that leave clients feeling strengthened—not overwhelmed. You can do that by preparing clients for VR exposure and incorporating exposure into a comprehensive treatment plan.

I follow these steps to prepare for VRET:

- Creating a shared understanding of anxiety treatment.
- Monitoring the client's anxiety tolerance skills.
- Identifying and countering client fears.
- Explaining the rationale for VRET and obtaining client permission.

Create a Shared Understanding of Anxiety and Treatment

Chapter 2, "Anxiety Cycle Model", outlined the benefits of developing a shared understanding of anxiety and its treatment. Mapping clients' histories and symptoms onto the anxiety cycle normalizes and validates their experiences. Accurate empathy and nonjudgmental acceptance help create a strong treatment alliance.

I use the anxiety cycle diagram (Figure 2.1) to explain key concepts and point out how the client's past and present life experiences, somatic sensations, intrusive fears or worries, and resultant fear-motivated actions created a vicious cycle of anxiety.

Having completed the "bad news" part of the explanation (why their anxiety problem exists and continues), I turn to the diagram of breaking the anxiety cycle (Figure 2.2) to highlight key treatment principles and explain how interventions at each point in the diagram help break this vicious cycle.

At this point, clients are ideally feeling understood, hopeful, and motivated to start treatment despite some understandable ambivalence and anxiety. If needed, motivational interviewing can increase treatment engagement and adherence (Rollnick & Miller, 1995).

Monitor Anxiety Tolerance Skills

VRET's goal is to change clients' responses to feared stimuli. Clients should have at least one effective anxiety tolerance skill (as described in Chapter 3) prior to exposure.

During exposure, monitor clients' skill use:

- Ask what anxiety tolerances skill(s) they are using.
- Observe if they are doing diaphragmatic breathing correctly.
- As needed, prompt them to use their skill(s).
- Provide more skills training and practice if necessary.

Identify and Counter Fears

Address every fear your client can verbalize. Explore each one deeply and in detail. Help uncover unrecognized fears or assumptions that play a role in fears. Exposure will activate fears, so you want your client prepared to convincingly refute them.

Are there fears your clients might voice that you would find difficult to counter? What scares *you*? What do *you* worry about? Identify and think through those fears. Plan ahead.

How will you respond if a client says, "I'm afraid I'll have a panic attack," "I'm afraid I'll lose control and crash the car," "What if the plane crashes?" "What if I have a flashback?" or "What if having these awful thoughts means I will act on them?"

Get facts to credibly refute common, inaccurate fears. Think about how to help clients accept what cannot be changed (like having anxiety or eventually dying) and talk back to distressing, fearful thoughts.

Consider preparing handouts with facts about fears frequently presented by your clients. Find or create handouts with reassuring facts about the safety of panic attacks, air travel even during turbulence, elevators, enclosed spaces, physical sensations, and other topics that frighten your clients.

Explain the Rationale

VRET allows clients—in session with your support and encouragement—to gradually face their fears rather than avoiding or escaping. They learn to accept the discomfort of an unneeded anxiety response rather than fearing and fighting it. They can practice letting go of unnecessary hypervigilance and safety actions. VRET helps clients break free of the anxiety cycle.

Since VRET is likely to trigger anxiety, you want clients to understand why it is necessary and helpful and to be reassured that you will not simply throw them into a terrifying situation. VR exposure needs to be tolerable. The diagrams of the anxiety cycle and treatment (Figures 2.1 and 2.2) explain the rationale for exposure and reinforce the key role it plays in overcoming anxiety.

Obtain Client Permission

Collaborate with your client to choose the specifics of VR exposure. Describe each VE or variable beforehand. Get client permission to enter the VE and ask before changing aspects of the virtual experience.

Implementing Successful VRET

Track Anxiety

Before beginning VRET, determine how you will measure client response to exposure. Two commonly used methods are client self-report of anxiety using the Subjective Units of Distress Scale (SUDS) and biofeedback measures of physiological response.

Subjective Units of Distress Scale (SUDS)

The SUDS is a numbered scale used for clients to self-report their level of distress or anxiety (Wolpe, 1967). I use a scale from 0 to 10 where 0 is "none" or "not at all" and 10 is "extremely high".

I use the 0–10 scale rather than the standard 1–100 SUDS for four reasons (Benjamin et al., 2010):

- I find a 0–10 scale more intuitive.
- 0–10 is easier for me to track.
- A 0–10 scale seems easier for clients to use.

- Using 0–10 makes tracking anxiety consistent with other questions I ask using a 0–10 scale, making for a more cohesive treatment experience.

For example, I may ask clients to report their treatment readiness and confidence using a 0 to 10 scale. Or I may ask how doable a homework assignment feels, or how helpful or effective the client expects the homework to be, from 0 to 10.

Similarly, I often track treatment alliance by asking three questions near the end of a session:

- On a 0 to 10 scale, where 0 is not at all and 10 is absolutely, to what degree did you feel heard and understood?
- On a 0 to 10 scale, where 0 is not at all and 10 is absolutely, to what degree did we talk about what was most important to you?
- On a 0 to 10 scale, where 0 is not at all and 10 is absolutely, to what degree does this approach make sense to you?

Example SUDS are reported using a 0–10 scale; if you use 1–100 SUDS, translate the numbers given throughout the book.

Biofeedback

Biofeedback can track clients' physical responses during exposure (Wiederhold & Wiederhold, 2003; Wood et al., 2008). Depending on your training and equipment, you may measure breathing, galvanic skin response (GSR), heart rate, or heart rate variability (Weerdmeester et al., 2020). Such measures give you direct information about the client's physiological response, although I have noticed that client hand movements affect GSR readings.

Biofeedback results can be used for your own information or shared with clients during exposure to reinforce successful change.

Even if I use biofeedback, I also ask for SUDS to check the client's emotional response to the VE, especially since a key treatment goal is for clients to no longer panic in response to sympathetic nervous system (SNS) physiological arousal.

Validity of Self-Report

A study by Côté and Bouchard (2005) is of particular interest, because it not only supports the efficacy of VRET, it also provides strong evidence that client self-report of anxiety (SUDS) is a valid measure that correlates with objective measures of anxious physiological arousal and client behavioral approach or avoidance.

Create a VR Exposure Hierarchy

By now, you should have a clear understanding of which specific stimuli trigger more or less fear for your client. Together, you will create an VR exposure hierarchy: a plan for facing these fear stimuli in VR. The exposure hierarchy is a list of specific situations or activities, sensations, and/or thoughts the client finds progressively more frightening and variables that increase or decrease their fear.

For example, a client may generally fear flying, but be less frightened of day flights, more frightened of night flights, and be particularly fearful of flying through a thunderstorm at night.

The exposure hierarchy for this client may be:

- Riding in a virtual taxi to the airport.
- Waiting at the virtual gate.
- Walking down the virtual jetway.
- Having the virtual plane taxi down the runway.
- Taking off.
- Flying in clear weather and daylight.
- Flying at night.
- Flying in a storm during the day.
- Flying in a storm at night.

More hierarchy items may be created by adding interoceptive exposure at each step or creating increasing amounts of turbulence.

The goal of VRET is to reduce the client's fear response by providing *therapeutic, tolerable* exposure. As mentioned earlier, I strongly advocate starting with VEs likely to trigger only mild to moderate fear, gradually progressing to VEs higher on the hierarchy as client anxiety drops but clients may surprise you with their willingness to face feared situations.

Coordinate with your client. Get permission before starting or changing VR exposure variables. Collaboration emphasizes the respectful nature of therapy and enhances client feelings of control and self-efficacy.

Clients may have multiple fears, i.e., fear of flying and of public speaking, so you may design exposure hierarchies for each fear. Hierarchies may be formal or informal, as you will see.

Formal VR Exposure Hierarchy

To create a formal hierarchy, have the client rate the degree of anxiety they think each virtual experience would cause, using the 0–10 SUDS. Using these ratings, you and the client agree on a list of ten or more VEs beginning with low pre-dicted SUDS ratings and ending with VEs predicted to cause high anxiety. Avoid large jumps in SUDS from one item on the hierarchy to the next. If there is a large jump in SUDS between two items, add exposures with intermediate ratings.

Informal VR Exposure Hierarchy

Rather than a formal rated hierarchy, you may create an informal exposure hierarchy using your knowledge of the client's fear stimuli and the available VEs and variables. Choose two or more virtual experiences you feel would be a reasonable next exposure step for the client: not too frightening, not too easy. Describe them to the client and let the client choose.

Change VEs or aspects of a VE to create virtual situations that fall lower or higher on the client's fear hierarchy. Move gradually or more quickly through the client's exposure hierarchy based on the client's anxiety (SUDS) levels and the client's ability to convincingly challenge and replace their fearful thinking.

Be prepared to flexibly move or skip hierarchy items based on client response. With VRET, my clients often surprise me with how quickly they move through their hierarchy.

For More Information

Examples of hierarchies are found in the case examples throughout this book. More information and examples can also be found in therapist and client workbooks that incorporate exposure therapy, e.g., Craske, Antony, & Barlow (2006) or McMahon (2019).

Monitor Progress and Prompt to Use Skills

I remain actively engaged with clients during VRET. I get frequent SUDS ratings, asking, "What's your anxiety level from 0 to 10, where 0 is not at all and 10 is very high?" or "What's your anxiety from 0 to 10?"

Although some VR products have an option to visually superimpose a rating scale inside the VE, I prefer to get spoken ratings rather than disrupt the client's visual experience and risk lessening their immersion and presence.

Anxiety ratings let you monitor client response and give you information about the client's ability to recall and effectively use what has been learned in therapy. They help you evaluate client progress and treatment effectiveness.

During VR exposure, I actively encourage clients to use the new information and skills. I may prompt clients to use a specific skill or remind clients of relevant information or important ideas. If clients are struggling, I model the new responses and see if that helps. And I always enthusiastically point out and reinforce each sign of effort and success.

Remember, VR hardware and software are not the therapy. They are tools. *You* provide the therapy.

If SUDS Ratings Increase

The client's SUDS numbers should decrease during virtual exposure. If SUDS ratings increase or remain the same, re-evaluate what is happening:

- Does the client simply need a more time to habituate and the anxiety to decline?
- Would the client benefit more from a different VR experience? Did you or the client underestimate how anxiety-provoking this virtual experience would be?
- Is the client using their anxiety management skills appropriately? It is not uncommon for clients to be chest breathing when they think they are belly breathing or for muscles to be more tensed than they realize.
- Is the client not immersed (not allowing VR to feel real)?
- Is the client employing safety actions or unable to convincingly counter their fearful thoughts?
- Is the increased anxiety a clue that there are unaddressed or undiscovered fears, negative core beliefs, distress intolerance, or other factors that need to be addressed?

If SUDS Ratings Drop

When SUDS decrease, have the client tell you what they did that decreased their fear. This not only helps *you* identify what works for them, it helps *your client* be more aware of what works for them.

It is powerful to have clients say out loud what they did or learned. I often have clients write down important insights, information, or skills and read back what they have written.

Having clients tell you what they did to reduce anxiety also lets you catch and correct unhelpful fear-based actions that reduce anxiety short-term but maintain it in the long run. These may include mentally escaping, white knuckling through, or using mental safety actions.

The goal is for clients to reduce or tolerate anxiety symptoms and to change anxiety-maintaining thinking and behaviors.

Case Example

I was surprised by Tony's uniformly low SUDS ratings during VRET to overcome his claustrophobia. As we talked, I discovered he was doing a mix of mental safety actions and mental escape to avoid feeling anxious. He reported that he had kept telling himself, "I can always take the headset off if I get scared" (safety action) and "This isn't real" (escape).

We reviewed the anxiety model and treatment diagrams and he agreed to let himself imagine that the situation was real. We also explored his fears about what might happen if it was real, and he could not leave.

Upon re-entering the VE, his anxiety level rose at first. He was able to tolerate the anxiety, remain in the situation, and reduce his fear, by using his new skills.

Homework

Homework can include imaginal, in vivo, or VR exposure if clinically appropriate. VR exposure is an option for clients who have access to the necessary equipment. These questions may be helpful in deciding whether to assign VR exposure homework:

- Are there suitable VR content options that the client can access from home?
- Does the client have the knowledge and skills to use VR at home and to control the pace, intensity, and duration of the VR experience without your guidance?
- Is there a trauma history that increases the chance of VR triggering significant symptomatology? Is the client at heightened risk of an intense emotional and physiological reaction?

When assigning VR homework that includes an app or VE that has not previously been used in session, I generally review the content with the client before the end of the session to ensure that the content is appropriate and acceptable, and the client understands its use and purpose.

Relapse Prevention

VRET reduces the risk of relapse by giving the client opportunities to face fears repeatedly and successfully in a variety of realistic settings. Shiban, Pauli, and Mühlberger (2013) confirmed that VRET using different virtual settings or contexts (i.e., different VEs) supports generalization to real world behavior (Shiban et al., 2013).

As you approach termination, explore with your client whether there are any remaining fears or issues. Sometimes clients will show progress but report a lingering fear of body sensations in certain situations.

My height phobic clients sometimes say, "I don't worry about trembling in my legs except when I am standing at a height." In these cases, I explore their fears about trembling legs when standing at a height and then ask the client to perform exercises that create trembling legs (holding a plank position or crouching position) either immediately before or while standing at a virtual height so the fears can be disconfirmed.

After the client has completed their exposure hierarchy and can face their highest-rated VEs without significant anxiety or distress, I implement additional relapse prevention. In fact, I don't wait until the entire hierarchy has been completed; I start the process at various points in the hierarchy as the client achieves success.

Once the client's SUDS ratings are low, I often ask clients in VR to deliberately focus on feared thoughts, sensations, and/or aspects of the situation and try to scare themselves. For example, I may say, "Deliberately bring on your anxiety. What do your fears say? How anxious can you make yourself by focusing on your fears (or previously feared sensations or variables of the situation)?" I may assist by speaking their fears aloud.

Then I get a SUDS rating: "How anxious are you from 0 to 10, where 0 is not at all and 10 is extremely anxious?" The SUDS rating should be much lower than earlier ratings and at a level the client feels is tolerable.

I highlight this evidence of progress and encourage the client to now actively reduce their anxiety: "Great. Now use your tools to bring down the anxiety and talk back to the fear."

This is a wonderful way to test the effects of treatment. When clients succeed, it solidifies skills and increases confidence. If clients are unable to handle fear, it alerts you that something is missing.

As part of termination and relapse prevention, you can measure treatment progress using the 0 to 10 scale. While clients are in VR, you can ask how much they *now* believe their fears are accurate from 0 to 10, where 0 is not at all and 10 is absolutely. Conversely, you can ask how much they now believe the counter statements to their original fears, from 0 to 10. You can also ask how confident they *now* are about their ability to successfully confront the phobic object or situation.

Rating of their belief in fears should have plummeted, ideally to 2 or less. Ratings of belief in their new thoughts, and confidence in their ability to successfully cope with the phobia, should be at least 7, preferably higher. If this is not the case, explore for any lingering fears or other issues.

Insufficient response to treatment may signify a need for more exposure or more relevant exposure. You can try lengthening the exposure time in VR, changing variables, or exploring fears more thoroughly while clients are in VR. You can also remind clients to allow themselves to become immersed and to act and think "as if this is really happening".

Therapist Concerns About VRET

Some therapists have reservations about exposure therapy or feel unprepared to provide it. You may:

- Be interested in VRET but have no experience doing exposure therapy.
- Fear that exposure therapy is cruel and painful for clients and could make clients worse.
- Have been told that removing a symptom will result in symptom substitution.
- Have been taught that anxiety or panic attacks are dangerous or so distressing that they should be suppressed and avoided.
- Worry that you won't know what to do if exposure triggers anxiety.

The above concerns are important and deserve consideration. Let us consider them one at a time.

No Prior Training in Exposure Therapy

You may find it deeply reassuring that exposure therapy for anxiety disorders has decades of strong research support (CDC, n.d.; Sars & van Minnen, 2015; Wolitzky-Taylor et al., 2008). You are applying an evidence-based treatment used worldwide.

The goal of this manual is to provide guidance and training in VRT, including VRET, to therapists (or clinicians in training) with a background in diagnosis and empirically supported treatments. Multiple case examples illustrate the practical and clinical specifics of incorporating VR into treatment with the hope that the information and examples provide enough guidance that you feel ready to offer effective VRET.

I encourage you to read the research articles referenced throughout the book and as needed, attend training in exposure and VRET or obtain consultation or supervision.

Exposure Is a Cruel, Painful Treatment and May Make Clients Worse

Some therapists equate exposure with implosion therapy, where anxious clients are thrust immediately into high-anxiety scenarios with the goal of speedy desensitization. Although this approach has some research support, I neither use it nor recommend it. In my opinion, it increases the risks of client refusal, dropout, or traumatization, may damage the therapeutic alliance, and can leave clients reluctant to enter treatment in future.

I strongly recommend preparing clients with tools before starting exposure so they can tolerate the emotional and physical experience of anxiety and successfully counter the fears that create, worsen, or maintain anxiety. Decisions about exposure scenarios and variables are made with the client and client response guides the process.

As presented here, VRET involves providing optimal therapeutic exposures that are individualized, graduated, and controlled. VR is a treatment breakthrough because it gives you far more control over clients' experiences than other types of exposure.

Always obtain a thorough history, including asking the client about any past experiences of trauma, violence, molestation, or abuse.

CAVEAT: If you plan to do VRET with clients who dissociate or decompensate in response to stress, who are actively suicidal or in crisis, or who have PTSD, make sure you are trained in standard treatments and can evaluate and intervene appropriately. This manual alone is not sufficient training to address these issues.

If you are still afraid that VRET will be traumatizing, do a Fears vs Facts dialogue table yourself. Do you have the training to treat the diagnosis? Is there a positive alliance? Does the client have anxiety management skills? Have client fears been explored and addressed? Can you monitor and guide clients throughout exposure?

Will There Be Symptom Substitution?

Concern about symptom substitution is a holdover from psychological theories developed well over a century ago. In the more than 120 years since then, dramatic advances have occurred in neuroscience, knowledge of the brain, and psychotherapy research. Psychodynamic and psychoanalytic theories have been updated to reflect the increased knowledge.

The original theory underpinning concern about symptom substitution posited that every symptom had an underlying meaning or purpose. For example, a phobia might be the manifestation of an unresolved intrapsychic conflict. This theory further assumed that clients must first gain insight into the symptom's symbolic meaning or function. The fear was that, if the presenting problem were removed prior to insight and resolution of the unconscious conflict, another symptom (perhaps worse than the phobia) would result.

Luckily this prediction has been tested. The overwhelming conclusion from case studies and clinical research is that, far from causing another or worse symptom, removing a phobia increases client happiness and self-efficacy. In fact, successfully curing a phobia may result in spontaneous improvement of other untreated comorbidities (Botella et al., 1999).

This is consistent with my clinical experience. Overcoming an anxiety disorder can improve client functioning and happiness in multiple areas of life.

This is not to say that there may not be changes in the client's relationships. If a client's friends, partner, or family members are used to caring for an avoidant, anxious client, their relationship dynamics and expectations will change.

Such changes may be welcomed—or resisted—by people in the client's life. These other people may rejoice and be relieved at the client's new-found confidence, independence, and self-efficacy, or they may resent it and be frightened by it. The client may now feel empowered to make changes that are unwelcome to others, such as leaving an emotionally abusive relationship or no longer continuing to be codependent.

I have seen both outcomes. But I have never seen a new symptom replace the phobia that was successfully treated. And I have *never* had a client say they were better off with their phobia!

Worry About Fear and Panic

You may have been taught—explicitly or implicitly—that acute episodes of anxiety or panic are dangerous and need to be avoided or suppressed. Breathing, relaxation, mindfulness, imagery, self-hypnosis, distraction, and so forth are useful tools, but the problem is that many training programs teach them as ways to *suppress or avoid* anxiety, rather than as tools to *tolerate* anxiety.

The anxiety and treatment cycle diagrams in Chapter 2 highlight the importance of accepting, countering, and coping, even while anxious.

There are several reasons why avoiding anxiety is a poor long-term strategy:

- SNS arousal is not under voluntary control.
- Using anxiety management techniques to *avoid or prevent* anxiety leaves clients with few options when the tools don't work.
- Even when clients succeed, they are left in the vulnerable position of *hoping* panic will not recur but *fearing and dreading* that it might. They are using the tools to escape or fight anxiety symptoms (fear-based actions) and are vulnerable to relapse because their *fear* of anxiety, worry, or panic remains.

Many clients have come to me saying that past treatment focused on not having anxiety and "it worked for a while but then it stopped working."

You need to be comfortable with anxiety. The first time a client had a panic attack in my therapy group, we *both* panicked. But that experience helped me see and believe what I had read:

- Panic is temporary.
- Panic is not dangerous.
- Panic is not an emergency.

Obviously, if *you* are worried about panic, you can't reassure your client that panic is harmless—unpleasant, but harmless. You don't want to join your client in catastrophizing their experience.

Get a medical consultation if your client has a medical condition that you worry may be worsened by anxiety, exposure, or VRT.

Review the research on anxiety and its treatment and share the findings with clients. Get the facts about clients' fears.

Facts help your *clients* feel reassured and empowered; they allow *you* to be calm, encouraging, and optimistic.

I Won't Know What to Do!

What if your client panics, starts crying, or has trouble calming down? What if you don't know what to say?

The beauty of preparing your client before *any* kind of exposure—imaginal, written, verbal retelling, in vivo, or virtual—is that you and your client understand in advance the sensations and fears that may be triggered. Together, you will have uncovered, explored, evaluated, and countered those fears. You will have also taught the client skills to manage and tolerate panic, to surf the wave of adrenaline.

If your client does become distressed, you can:

- Encourage the client to use their anxiety management skills.
- Urge the client to talk back to the fears, either vigorously disputing them or using calming self-talk and loving compassion.

- Model for the client talking back to the fears, emphasizing the facts about the situation, activity, panic response, and/or the client's ability to cope.
- Model using supportive, calming self-talk such as a nurturing parent uses with a frightened child.
- Alter VE variables or move to a different VE to lessen distress.
- Stop VRET and switch to a VE you know the client finds relaxing.
- Stop the VR entirely, process what happened, and do further preparation before the next exposure.

Remember—and believe—that every experience of anxiety, fear, or panic truly is an AFOG. Another F*** (Flipping? F***ing? Fabulous? Fantastic?) Opportunity for Growth.

Think ahead and prepare. Ask yourself in advance:

- What problematic client reactions are likely and how could you avoid or handle them?
- What would be the most positive lessons clients can take away from an exposure experience, even a difficult experience?
- What will you do or say to help clients derive helpful lessons from VRET?

Remember that clients often take their cue from you. If you continue to be encouraging and optimistic, they are more likely to trust themselves and the treatment. Expecting eventual success is often a self-fulfilling prophecy.

Evidence Base

The consensus of several meta-analyses and literature reviews is that VRT exposure is effective and well accepted by clients. A meta-analysis covering 20 randomized control trials totaling 1,057 participants with anxiety related disorders found VRET was an effective and equal medium for exposure therapy (Carl et al., 2019b).

Maples-Keller et al. (2017) stated, "Virtual reality has emerged as a viable tool to help in a number of different disorders, with the most strength of evidence for use in exposure therapy for patients with anxiety disorders" (Maples-Keller et al., 2017). Several other researchers concur (Baños Rivera et al., 2015; Mishkind et al., 2017; Opriş et al., 2012; Parsons & Rizzo, 2008; Wechsler et al., 2019).

After studying 265 exposure sessions, Robillard and colleagues concluded that exposure in VR is less burdensome and more adaptable to client needs than exposure in vivo (Robillard et al., 2011) and a meta-analysis of studies using behavioral assessments by Morina and colleagues found that gains from VRET generalize to real life (Morina et al., 2015).

References

Baños Rivera, R. M., Arbona, C. B., García-Palacios, A., Castellano, S. Q., & López, J. B. (2015). Treating emotional problems with virtual and augmented reality. In S. S. Sundar (Ed.), *The Handbook of the Psychology of Communication Technology* (pp. 548–566). John Wiley and Sons Inc.

Benjamin, C. L., O'Neil, K. A., Crawley, S. A., Beidas, R. S., Coles, M., & Kendall, P. C. (2010). Patterns and predictors of subjective units of distress in anxious youth. *Behavioural and Cognitive Psychotherapy*, 38(4), 497–504. doi:10.1017/S1352465810000287.

Botella, C., Villa, H., Baños, R., Perpiñá, C., & García-Palacios, A. (1999). The treatment of claustrophobia with virtual reality: Changes in other phobic behaviors not specifically treated. *CyberPsychology & Behavior*, 2(2), 135–141. doi:10.1089/cpb.1999.2.135.

Carl, E., Stein, A. T., Levihn-Coon, A., Pogue, J. R., Rothbaum, B., Emmelkamp, P., Asmundson, G. J. G., Carlbring, P., & Powers, M. B. (2019a). Virtual reality exposure therapy for anxiety and related disorders: A meta-analysis of randomized controlled trials. *Journal of Anxiety Disorders*, 61, 27–36. doi:10.1016/j.janxdis.2018.08.003.

Carl, E., Stein, A. T., Levihn-Coon, A., Pogue, J. R., Rothbaum, B., Emmelkamp, P., Asmundson, G. J. G., Carlbring, P., & Powers, M. B. (2019b). Virtual reality exposure therapy for anxiety and related disorders: A meta-analysis of randomized controlled trials. *Journal of Anxiety Disorders*, 61, 27–36. doi:10.1016/j.janxdis.2018.08.003.

CDC. (n.d.). *Exposure Therapies for Specific Phobias*. Society of Clinical Psychology Division 12, American Psychological Association. Retrieved September 3, 2021, from https://div12.org/treatment/exposure-therapies-for-specific-phobias.

Côté, S. & Bouchard, S. (2005). Documenting the efficacy of virtual reality exposure with psychophysiological and information processing measures. *Applied Psychophysiology and Biofeedback*, 30(3), 217–232. doi:10.1007/s10484-005-6379-x.

Craske, M. G., Antony, M. M., & Barlow, D. H. (2006). *Mastering Your Fears and Phobias* (2nd ed.). Oxford University Press.

Maples-Keller, J. L., Bunnell, B. E., Kim, S.-J., & Rothbaum, B. O. (2017). The use of virtual reality technology in the treatment of anxiety and other psychiatric disorders. *Harvard Review of Psychiatry*, 25(3), 103–113. doi:10.1097/HRP.0000000000000138.

McMahon, E. (2019). *Overcoming Anxiety and Panic Interactive Guide*. Hands-on-Guide.

Meyerbröker, K. & Emmelkamp, P. M. G. (2010). Virtual reality exposure therapy in anxiety disorders: A systematic review of process-and-outcome studies. *Depression and Anxiety*, 27(10), 933–944. doi:10.1002/da.20734.

Mishkind, M. C., Norr, A. M., Katz, A. C., & Reger, G. M. (2017). Review of virtual reality treatment in psychiatry: Evidence versus current diffusion and use. *Current Psychiatry Reports*, 19(11), 80. doi:10.1007/s11920-017-0836-0.

Morina, N., Ijntema, H., Meyerbröker, K., & Emmelkamp, P. M. G. (2015). Can virtual reality exposure therapy gains be generalized to real-life? A meta-analysis of studies applying behavioral assessments. *Behaviour Research and Therapy*, 74 (November), 18–24. doi:10.1016/j.brat.2015.08.010.

Opriş, D., Pintea, S., García-Palacios, A., Botella, C., Szamosközi, Ş., & David, D. (2012). Virtual reality exposure therapy in anxiety disorders: A quantitative meta-analysis. *Depression and Anxiety*, 29(2), 85–93. doi:10.1002/da.20910.

Parsons, T. D. & Rizzo, A. A. (2008). Affective outcomes of virtual reality exposure therapy for anxiety and specific phobias: A meta-analysis. *Journal of Behavior Therapy and Experimental Psychiatry*, 39(3), 250–261. doi:10.1016/j.jbtep.2007.07.007.

Robillard, G., Bouchard, S., Dumoulin, S., & Guitard, T. (2011). The development of the SWEAT questionnaire: a scale measuring costs and efforts inherent to conducting exposure sessions. *Studies in Health Technology and Informatics*, 167, 105–110.

Rollnick, S. & Miller, W. R. (1995). What is Motivational Interviewing? *Behavioural and Cognitive Psychotherapy*, 23(4), 325–334. doi:10.1017/S135246580001643X.

Sars, D. & van Minnen, A. (2015). On the use of exposure therapy in the treatment of anxiety disorders: A survey among cognitive behavioural therapists in the Netherlands. *BMC Psychology*, 3(1). doi:10.1186/S40359-015-0083-2.

Shiban, Y., Pauli, P., & Mühlberger, A. (2013). Effect of multiple context exposure on renewal in spider phobia. *Behaviour Research and Therapy*, 51(2), 68–74. doi:10.1016/j.brat.2012.10.007.

Stampfl, T. G. & Levis, D. J. (1967). Essentials of implosive therapy: A learning-theory-based psychodynamic behavioral therapy. *Journal of Abnormal Psychology*, 72 (6), 496–503. doi:10.1037/h0025238.

Wechsler, T. F., Kümpers, F., & Mühlberger, A. (2019). Inferiority or even superiority of virtual reality exposure therapy in phobias?—A systematic review and quantitative meta-analysis on randomized controlled trials specifically comparing the efficacy of virtual reality exposure to gold standard in vivo exposure in agoraphobia, specific phobia, and social phobia. *Frontiers in Psychology*, 10. doi:10.3389/fpsyg.2019.01758.

Weerdmeester, J., Van Rooij, M. M. J. M., Engels, R. C. M. E., & Granic, I. (2020). An integrative model for the effectiveness of biofeedback interventions for anxiety regulation: Viewpoint. *Journal of Medical Internet Research*, 22(7). doi:10.2196/14958.

Wiederhold, B. K. & Wiederhold, M. D. (2003). Three-year follow-up for virtual reality exposure for fear of flying. *CyberPsychology & Behavior*, 6(4), 441–445. doi:10.1089/109493103322278844.

Wolitzky-Taylor, K. B., Horowitz, J. D., Powers, M. B., & Telch, M. J. (2008). Psychological approaches in the treatment of specific phobias: A meta-analysis. *Clinical Psychology Review*, 28(6), 1021–1037. doi:10.1016/j.cpr.2008.02.007.

Wolpe, J. (1967). *The Practice of Behavior Therapy: Pergamon General Psychology Series*. Allyn & Bacon.

Wolpe, J. (1990). *The Practice of Behavior Therapy: Pergamon General Psychology Series* (4th ed.). Pergamon Press.

Wood, D. P., Murphy, J. A., Center, K. B., Russ, C., McLay, R. N., Reeves, D., Pyne, J., Shilling, R., Hagan, J., & Wiederhold, B. K. (2008). Combat related post traumatic stress disorder: A multiple case report using virtual reality graded exposure therapy with physiological monitoring. *Studies in Health Technology and Informatics*, 132, 556–561. doi:10.3389/conf.neuro.14.2009.06.028.

5   VR Anxiety Treatment Protocol

This chapter takes you, step by step, through a treatment protocol for virtual reality therapy (VRT) using an in-depth case example. Details have been changed to protect client privacy. For the sake of simplicity, in the transcribed conversations, "T" is used for the therapist and "C" for the client, in this case Sophia. See also the Virtual Reality Therapy Checklist in Appendix B.

Pre-Intake Phone Screening

If possible, I recommend having a pre-intake screening phone call with prospective clients during which you and they get a sense of each other's styles. Diagnostic assessment and treatment planning can begin during this call. You can start to formulate diagnostic hypotheses, ask about any crises, listen for client strengths and weaknesses, and think about possible interventions and uses of virtual reality (VR).

Obviously, clients with trauma history, substance abuse, or symptoms of psychosis or personality disorder require more evaluation. The client in this example was stable, motivated, not in crisis, and had no indication of serious comorbidities.

Sophia had seen on social media that "virtual reality therapy helps people get over fears." An internet search for virtual reality therapy led her to my website. We scheduled a free 15 to 20-minute telephone call.

T: "Hi Sophia, thank you for calling back as scheduled. Is this a good time and place to talk?"
C: "Yes."
T: "Okay. So, tell me a little about the problem you want to work on. How are you hoping I can help?"
C: "Well, I have anxiety attacks that scare me and they're getting worse. They started ten years ago when I was in a really stressful job. I figured they'd go away when I quit, and they did for a while, but then I had one on an airplane and I panicked because I couldn't get off. Now I'm starting to avoid elevators, buses, subways, boats—anywhere I can't leave. I'm even anxious during work meetings. I'm turning down

DOI: 10.4324/9781003154068-6

business trips and missing family events because I don't want to fly. I heard that virtual reality therapy can treat fears. Is that true? Have you treated people like me?"

T: "Absolutely. Virtual reality can really help people overcome fear. Tell me, have you had any therapy for this or any other problem?"

C: "Well, my doctor gave me a tranquilizer. I don't like taking it because it knocks me out, but I always have it with me just in case. I see a massage therapist and drink chamomile tea to relax. It seems like I'm tense all the time now."

T: "Okay. What happens in your body when you get anxious or panicky?"

C: "My throat feels like it's closing up and my voice shakes. I feel like everybody can hear it and thinks something's wrong with me. I've stopped talking in meetings. My hands shake and I feel like there's not enough air, like I can't get a breath. I just want to run, like I've got to get out."

T: "I'm so glad you called. These sound like pretty classic anxiety symptoms and the good news is that there are very effective treatments for anxiety. That's one of the reasons I specialize in it."

C: "So, you think virtual reality could help?"

T: "Yes, indeed. The beauty of VR is that it lets you face your fears during sessions. After you have tools to cope with anxiety, VR lets you practice using those tools to make sure they work. By the time you face situations in the real world, you'll have already conquered them in the virtual world. This is why I love being able to offer VR therapy to my clients."

We scheduled an intake, and I assigned a first treatment task explaining its rationale.

T: "Sophia, I'd like you to write down three things and bring them with you when we meet, okay? Are you ready? Good. First, write down every physical sensation that happens in your body when you get anxious or panicky—like you started to tell me just now: your voice shaking, feeling like your throat's closing up, your hands trembling, and anything else like your heart racing, tightness in your chest, GI symptoms, tingling or numbness, visual changes, whatever."

T: "Second, I want you to write down every fear that comes into your mind, even if you know it's crazy or irrational. Like, are you afraid you're going to pass out, die, suffocate, go crazy, do something uncontrolled, or whatever? Because the part of the brain that triggers anxiety and panic is not a rational part of the brain."

T: "Third, write down all the ways in which panic—or fear of panic—is affecting what you do. What are you doing? What are you avoiding or not doing? What are you doing in some special way to feel safe? How is it affecting your life? For example, you told me that you are avoiding planes, elevators, and other enclosed places and that you are not speaking up in work meetings. You also mentioned getting massages and drinking chamomile tea to try to keep yourself calm and prevent anxiety. Are there other things, like only riding in elevators with other people or with few people, having to have a seat on the plane that's on the aisle and near the exit, and so on?"

C: "Oh my gosh. It sounds like you're describing me."

T: "These are common reactions to panic and fear. These three things are important because what is happening in your body, your mind, and your actions are all interacting. And they are *either* interacting to make things *better*, or they are interacting to make things *worse*. We want to map out what's happening with your anxiety, so we know where to intervene and change it. Okay?"

C: "Okay."

T: "Great. Bring that with you when we meet."

Initial Thoughts and Hypotheses

A screening phone call jumpstarts treatment. It gives you the chance start thinking about likely diagnoses and possible VRT interventions. You can ask prospective clients to bring important information to the intake, offer basic psychoeducation, and start building the therapeutic alliance.

Diagnosis

Sophia's reported symptoms, fears, and actions raise several diagnostic possibilities. Cover the paragraphs below, reread the transcript of the phone call above, and answer these two questions:

1   What possible diagnoses are you considering?
2   What will you ask during the intake to rule each one in or out?

The first diagnosis that came to my mind was panic disorder with agoraphobia. She reports "anxiety attacks" that frighten her, and she is increasingly avoidant.

What about one or more comorbid specific phobias? I wonder if Sophia has claustrophobia. She is avoiding places from which she can't escape. Is she afraid that her panic *reaction* is dangerous if she can't leave (panic disorder), or does she believe the *situation itself* is dangerous (phobia)? Does she think that panic will continue unless she leaves and, if it continues, panic will cause her throat to close so she suffocates? Or does she think the throat sensations are a sign of insufficient air and everyone will suffocate if they don't get out? Does she fear both?

Given Sophia's comment that coworkers will judge her if her voice and hands shake, I will explore the possibility of either social anxiety disorder or a recurrence of adjustment disorder with anxiety. Is her work environment toxic? Are her coworkers or managers critical and judgmental?

Her comment that she's "tense all the time" might be due to fear of panic. It might be an indication of real-life stressors triggering an adjustment disorder. It might even be a sign of generalized anxiety disorder (GAD).

Psychoeducation

By quickly describing the cycle of anxiety, you plant the idea that these components can be observed and changed. Clients are immediately made collaborators in treatment because you encourage them to objectively report the physical experience of anxiety or panic, articulate fears, and reflect on their behavior. These tasks send a powerful message that their fears are not frightening or unusual to you and maybe, therefore, don't need to feel so frightening or weird to them.

Treatment Alliance

Conveying warmth and acceptance over the phone helps potential clients feel safe. Talking about the effectiveness of treatment increases clients' hope, motivation, and willingness to work.

VRT Interventions

Sophia's information suggests several ways VR may help:

- Immersive virtual environments (VEs) may increase treatment engagement by helping her relax and disengage from work stress.
- Immersion in VR may interrupt anxiety-related rumination.
- VR may help her learn and then practice relaxation or mindfulness.
- VR may be used for interoceptive and/or situational exposure.

Session 1

Goals

Goals of Session 1 are to get informed consent to treatment, complete a history, formulate an initial case conceptualization, explain treatment, and assign one or more tasks for the client to carry out before the next session.

History

Sophia denies past or present substance abuse but has begun drinking more at parties "to relax". She only takes benzodiazepines for flights, but always carries them "just in case" she becomes "too anxious".

Other than getting the anxiolytic prescription, she had never sought therapy. She works hard to present herself as a "strong, competent, independent woman" and doesn't want to look "weak or crazy". It becomes clear in this and subsequent sessions that she can be self-critical and demanding of herself.

She has never experienced violence, trauma, molestation, or abuse and reports growing up in a loving, intact family. At the same time, she was the oldest of four children and, from eight years old, was responsible for much of the care for her younger siblings.

As Sophia relates her history (below), notice how you can use the anxiety cycle and terms to tie her past and present together.

C: "My Dad had to travel for work, so he was away except for the weekends. Mom had asthma and food allergies. Before we figured out what she was allergic to, she almost died a couple of times. I remember her throat started to swell closed from anaphylaxis. And she'd get really sick with bronchitis and pneumonia."

T: "It must have been terrifying to see her struggling to breathe. No wonder you are so frightened when you feel like your throat's closing or when you worry that there's not enough air."

C: "Yeah. I know I don't have anaphylactic shock or food allergies, but still..."

T: "It scares you."

(Sophia nods and gets a little teary.)

T: "The other thing I hear is that because you were the oldest, you basically didn't have a lot of freedom. You *had* to take care of everybody. You didn't have a choice."

C: "Yeah. I just felt kind of... trapped... you know? I mean, I love them, and we're close now, but I couldn't wait to get out."

T: "You love them, but you felt trapped and wanted to get out. I think maybe your Reacting Brain learned some lessons when you were growing that aren't helping you now. Like, for example, breathing can stop at any minute and you can die. Or that you don't want to be trapped again, so if you feel trapped, you have to get out right now!"

T: "What about your blood relatives: your parents, siblings, aunts, uncles, cousins, grandparents? Do any of them have trouble with anxiety? Any fears, alcohol or drug abuse, depression, or other emotional issues?"

C: "Not on my dad's side. But my mom always worries about her health. My sister's like me. She won't go on a plane and she doesn't like to drive on freeways. On my mom's side, I think my grandma had panic attacks and one of my cousins does too. And my uncle on that side is always worrying about everything. So, I guess anxiety runs in the family."

T: "What about work? What's happening there?"

C: "I love my job. My supervisor's great. She's really supportive. The only problem is she wants me to take a larger leadership role and I have to be able to travel and do presentations. That's why I called for an appointment. I need to get over this."

Sophia has always worked hard and succeeded in achieving any goal she set for herself. She got good grades throughout school and college. Having panic attacks makes her feel "out of control" and threatens her view of herself.

Socially she has a few close friends, but she describes herself as "naturally shy". Social events are enjoyable but draining.

C: "I worry that I'll say the wrong thing. And I don't really like being the center of attention."

T: "Because if you're the center of attention, then…?"

C: "I don't know. I just feel like everyone's looking at me and expecting something. I'm afraid I'll let them down."

T: "And you don't want to do that."

C: "No."

T: "You know, I have a thought. It may be crazy, but I'll just put it out there and you can tell me if it doesn't make any sense. But it kind of reminds me of how when you were just a child, you had to take on a lot of adult responsibilities at times that you weren't prepared for. You didn't want to let anyone down. I wonder if your Reacting Brain worried about what would happen to your mom or your sisters and brother if you messed up. And so now it keeps worrying about you making mistakes and letting people down."

C: "You mean maybe that's why I get so anxious at the idea of being promoted?"

T: "I don't know. It kind of makes sense to me. What do you think?"

C: "Oh my gosh. I just realized something. My very first anxiety attack happened when I was presenting to the senior VP of Marketing. I had this really demanding micromanaging boss. I could never please her. She yelled at everyone. The day of the presentation, she called in sick and suddenly, with no warning or time to prepare, I had to take over her PowerPoint. I stood up. Everyone was looking at me. My hands and voice started shaking. I was sweating. I remember I stumbled over my words and stammered. My throat was so dry I thought it was going to close up and I couldn't get a good breath. The VP looked bored and all I could think was, 'This is a disaster. Get me out of here!' I started job-hunting the next day."

As you have just seen, obtaining a history can lead to insight. You and the client can both begin to make connections between past experiences and current problems. This understanding helps guide your choice of therapeutic interventions and uses of VR.

Creating a Shared Understanding

Having obtained a general history, I had Sophia show me what she'd written about her anxiety sensations, fears, and ways fear was affecting her life. After reading and asking a few questions, it seemed to me that she had three inter-locking anxiety disorders: panic disorder with agoraphobia, claustrophobia, and social anxiety disorder. Case examples for each of these diagnoses are also found in the chapters on panic disorder and agoraphobia, claustrophobia, and social anxiety disorder. For clarity, her sensations, fears, and actions will be listed here under each diagnosis.

Panic Disorder with Agoraphobia

Symptoms: Sweating / Shaking / Dry throat / Chest tightness / Feeling short of breath.

Fears: Go crazy / Do something uncontrolled like screaming / "Can't think" / Throat will close, and she'll suffocate and die / Panic will continue if she doesn't escape / "Can't stand it".

Actions: Increasingly leave and avoid activities and situations where she feels, or has felt, panicky / Monitor body for any signs of anxiety or impending panic / Try to prevent panic attacks by getting massages, drinking chamomile tea / Tell self frantically to "Relax!" when panicky.

Specific Phobia, Situational (Claustrophobia)

Symptoms: Full or partial panic attack symptoms are now predictably triggered by being in enclosed spaces.

Fears: There is not enough air in an enclosed space, especially if she must be there for a long time or if there are a lot of people / Enclosed spaces like planes, elevators, and subways don't have air flow; they have a limited amount of air / Feeling short of breath is proof that the air is being used up and if she stays, she could suffocate and die / She's trapped and must get out.

Actions: Avoid planes, elevators, subways, and other enclosed or crow-ded places whenever possible / Stay close to exits / Make excuses to open doors or windows or to step out of small rooms / Choose elevator or subway cars with fewer people / Tense and try to hold her breath and breathe as little as possible "so I don't use up the air".

Social Anxiety Disorder (Discrete)

Symptoms: Shaky voice and hands / Dry throat / Sometimes stammers.

Fears: Others notice her voice and hands and judge her / She will "mess up" and "let others down" / She's not ready or prepared / Others have high standards that she will not meet / Others are critical and hard to please.

Actions: Avoid speaking at work meetings / Avoid promotions or leadership roles / Speak as little and as quickly as possible / Hide her hands / Avoid eye contact with audience.

Explain and Plan VRT

It is important within the first one or two sessions to briefly explain the cause and intended protective, helpful purpose of every anxiety sensation clients have experienced. This helps clients be more accepting when anxiety occurs.

The anxiety diagrams can present key concepts and help you explain how clients' anxiety triggers, somatic sensations, intrusive distressing thoughts, and resultant fear-motivated actions have created and maintained a cycle of anxiety. The model helps clients understand key treatment principles. You show how interventions at key points in the diagram interrupt the anxiety cycle.

Sophia and I looked at the anxiety diagram. I tied together what we had learned so that Sophia's anxiety began to make sense to her.

T: "Anxiety runs in your family, which means anxiety or panic may be more easily triggered. You had your first panic attacks in stressful situations. Your self-demand that you never let anyone down heightens the impacts of stressors and past experiences made you sensitive to feeling trapped and made throat- or breathing-related sensations particularly frightening."

T: "These triggers send messages of 'Threat' to your primitive, protective, bodyguard amygdala Reacting Brain, which pumps out adrenaline (creating a lot of physical sensations like shaky hands and voice, dry throat, muscle tension, and so on) and tries to help you by flooding your mind with thoughts of fear and danger ('This is a disaster! I'm letting my team down!'). If you don't understand what is happening, the natural reaction is to believe your fear thoughts and respond with fear-based actions. For instance, you tried to fight the anxiety response ('Stop it!') and you have begun escaping, avoiding, monitoring your body and your situation, and trying to do things to be 'safe'. Can you see how this creates a vicious cycle of anxiety and keeps you tense?"

C: "Yes. That makes a lot of sense. But what do I do and how can VR help?"

T: "Well, let's start with you learning diaphragmatic breathing to activate the parasympathetic branch of the nervous system. Fight-or-flight reactions are sympathetic nervous system arousal. Parasympathetic is the opposite branch of the nervous system, sometimes called the rest-and-digest system. I remember sympathetic nervous system arousal by thinking 'S for Stress or Save Your Life' and parasympathetic by thinking 'P for Peaceful'".

After showing Sophia how to switch to diaphragmatic breathing, I had her spend a few minutes in a relaxing VE of her choice listening to recorded instructions for diaphragmatic breathing. She chose the meadow. I had the instructions play aloud (through the phone's speaker in the headset or through my computer's speaker) so she could record the instructions on her phone for home practice.

Sophia put on the VR headset. I activated the virtual meadow and encouraged her to look around. She responded, "Oh, this is so beautiful. It's so peaceful here." I watched and saw her muscles relax and her breathing slow and switch from chest to diaphragm. Afterward, she said, "That was amazing. I feel so relaxed."

Fostering Progress Between Sessions

Giving homework assignments between sessions consolidates learning and speeds progress. It also reinforces that clients are active partners in treatment. I encourage clients to track relevant variables like symptoms and homework completion and report at each session.

I give clients copies of the two diagrams, as a visual reminder of important treatment information, and recommend reading *Overcoming Anxiety and Panic Interactive Guide* (McMahon, 2019), which includes diaphragmatic breathing instructions, facts about panic, explanations of anxiety sensations, and examples of countering anxiogenic thoughts. Reading reinforces and expands on information covered in session. Basic information is presented and reviewed at home, so sessions can focus on addressing each client's unique needs.

T: "There are three things I'd like you to do between now and when we meet again. Is that okay?"

C: "Absolutely."

T: "Okay, great. First, I'd like you to read the first few chapters that explain the anxiety cycle and how to break free. If you want to read further, go ahead.

T: "Second, start practicing low, slow belly breathing like you did today. You can listen to the recording and go back to the meadow in your mind if you want. As you get familiar with this breathing, start to shift into it before you start your day, before you eat, before you go to sleep, and whenever you feel tense. After that, you can begin to use it before you go into a situation that's likely to make you anxious, and eventually you can use it to get through a panic attack."

T: "The third thing I'd like you to do is sit down with your laptop and make a table with two columns and a lot of rows. In the left column, write every fear, worry, unrealistic self-demand, or unhelpful lesson from the past you can identify—one per row. In the right column, write what you are learning, what you would like to tell your younger self if you could go back in time, or what you would tell someone else who had these thoughts."

A brief example of a Fears vs Facts table appears on the diagram about breaking the anxiety cycle. The workbook gives detailed instructions on how to create a Fears vs Facts table and includes several examples. You can explain that this is a way to start a dialogue between their Reacting Brain (fears) and their Thinking Brain (facts and logic). This is a skill they will use in VR.

Session 2

Check In

At the start of each session, ask about homework, ask about progress, and collaboratively set an agenda. I wanted to check on Sophia's between-session tasks, ask about any changes she had noticed, and ask about her top priorities for today's session.

T: "Hi, Sophia. Come in. Make yourself comfortable. There are couple of things I'd like to do today. First, I want to check in about what you did between the last time we met and today. You were going to start reading the workbook, practicing the breathing, and writing a Fears vs Facts dialogue table. I want to hear about your experience with those. I also wonder what positive changes you've noticed or how things are different."

T: "So that's my list. What do *you* want to make sure we do today? What do you want to have when you walk out of here?"

C: "Well, I really like the VR relaxation and I'd love to do more of that. I'm sleeping better and feeling more relaxed during the day."

C: "Understanding what happens in my body and the actual cause of each of those feelings has been huge. I feel less crazy and out of control, although it's still scary when I feel like I can't get a breath and I'm still embarrassed if I get shaky when I'm talking. There are several fears where I couldn't come up with a good answer."

C: "Oh yeah. I took the first elevator even though there were a lot of people on it and it was slow. I just told my Reacting Brain, 'I'm fine. You don't need to save me. See, everyone is breathing so there's enough air.' And then I practiced my belly breathing. It wasn't comfortable, but I did it."

T: "Wow! That's fantastic. Good for you." [I pulled out the treatment diagram.] "If we take a look at the diagram, you accepted that you had anxiety, got the facts, and acted on the facts. Good work!"

T: "What questions do you have about what we've discussed or what you're learning in the workbook?"

C: "I had trouble coming up with answers to some of the fears."

T: "Okay. We can work on them together. Do you want to do some relaxation in VR before or after working on fears versus facts?"

C: "Let's work on the fears first. I'll feel better if I have more answers. Besides, if I tense up talking about my fears, VR can relax me."

T: "And it'll be a nice reward for your hard work, too."

Anxiety Management Skills

Starting with Session 2, you want to check on your client's ability to tolerate the experience of feeling anxious, fearful, worried, or panicky. Different clients use different skills. The more skills you know how to teach, the better you can arm your clients with skills that work for them.

I had Sophia show me her diaphragmatic breathing to confirm that she was breathing into her belly, not her chest. Diaphragmatic breathing worked well for Sophia, so we moved on to exploring and countering her fear thoughts.

Fears Versus Facts

Reviewing clients' ability to critically evaluate and convincingly counter their fears is essential. Even after learning facts that refute their fears, clients are often still scared, but facts and logic, combined with the ability to tolerate anxiety, allow clients to change their cognitive appraisal of frightening situations or sensations, enabling them to behave differently even when feeling afraid.

What have you learned about Sophia so far? What are her fears about panic? About enclosed spaces? About social criticism, embarrassment, and being observed or judged? How would you help her question, evaluate, and refute or accept her fears?

T: "Sophia, you said you worry about being anywhere you can't immediately leave, you worry about embarrassing yourself and being judged and criticized, and you worry about panicking because anxiety attacks scare you. Do I have that right?"

C: "Yes. Those are the things that scare me."

T: "How about if we start with exploring your fear of having a panic attack? Is that okay?"

C: "Sure."

T: "You wrote that panic could make you go crazy and do something uncontrolled like screaming. You also wrote that the feelings in your throat and chest make you worry that if panic continued or got worse that you could suffocate and die."

C: "That's a really scary thought."

T: "I bet. What have you learned so far about panic attacks? Does panic actually do these things?"

I asked Sophia to tell me about the Reacting Brain and the Thinking Brain, their roles, and how they are different. I had her explain why even though panic reactions feel out of control (they are not consciously or deliberately chosen), panic does not make people go "out of control". I reminded her that the panic response has been passed down from ancestors who survived and that going "crazy" would not have had survival benefit in the wild.

Because having an explanation for symptoms is so important, I spent time explaining the physiological causes and intended protective purpose of each symptom, especially those that scared her the most.

In Sophia's case, the most frightening panic symptoms were shortness of breath, the feeling of a lump in her throat, and that panic occurred without conscious control. I continued to provide corrective information about the panic response and asked her questions (a technique called Socratic questioning). Answering questions like "How many times have you panicked? When panicking, how many times have you started screaming, passed out, suffocated, or died?" helped Sophia realize that none of the things she feared had ever actually happened.

We repeated this process with her fears about enclosed spaces and her fears about being judged and feeling embarrassed.

VRT

Pleasant experiences in virtual reality can end sessions on a positive note. They can also offer an opportunity for clients to practice anxiety management skills and for you to offer suggestions. Clients who are immersed in a relaxed state may be more open to therapeutic suggestions.

I did not use the recorded instructions for diaphragmatic breathing in VR this session because Sophia had learned this skill and was using it. Instead, I offered her a wider choice of virtual experiences that many—but not all—clients find peaceful and calming.

> T: "Sophia, you said you would like to spend some time in VR before we stop. Would you rather keep working on your fears or go into VR?"
> C: "I'd like to go into VR."
> T: "Okay. Here are some options. Tell me what you would prefer."

I explained various VR environments and experiences. Sophia chose to sit on a beach at sunset. While she was in VR, I encouraged her to practice her low, slow breathing to deepen relaxation and strengthen the association between diaphragmatic breathing and feelings of calm and safety. I also quietly offered suggestions that she could begin feeling calmer and more relaxed generally, that she could begin to see things differently and more clearly, and that she could use everything she is learning for her benefit.

Fostering Progress Between Sessions

In the final minutes of the session, we first agreed on her between-session tasks and scheduled the next appointment.

T: "So, between now and when we meet again, I want you to keep reading the workbook. Think about what you are learning—from the book, from our sessions, and from your own reflections."

T: "Keep practicing diaphragmatic breathing a couple times a day. You're doing great. You can start using it whenever you notice that you are tense, before situations that might make you anxious, and when you feel panicky to help you tolerate the unpleasantness of a false alarm."

T: "Continue to write down, explore, question, and objectively evaluate your fears about panic, about enclosed spaces, and about being criticized, feeling embarrassed, or 'letting someone down'".

T: "If you want to—this is optional—you can imagine how you will start using what you are learning. How will you think about what's happening in your body if you panic? What will you tell yourself if you feel trapped or embarrassed?"

The suggestion above combines imaginal rehearsal and imaginal exposure.

C: "So, I should keep reading the book, use the breathing, think about what I'm learning, and start imagining how I could react differently. Is that right?"

T: "Yes. And keep writing what you could say back to your fears. Is your Reacting Brain sending a true alarm or a false alarm? Adding to your Fears vs Facts table is a good way to do that."

C: "Okay. I'll keep working on my fears. I'd like some time to do this. Can we meet in two weeks?"

T: "That would be fine. When you and I agree that you have the knowledge and tools to cope successfully with anxiety, you can start facing your fears in virtual reality."

C: "That sounds good. I'm not ready yet, but I can feel that things are shifting. I'm feeling stronger and more hopeful."

Session 3

Check In

The start of every session after the intake is a chance to quickly check in and agree on the focus for that session. Follow up on between-session tasks. Ask how the client is doing, specifically focusing on what positive changes they have noticed. Ask about their goal for that session and offer suggestions of what the two of you will do.

T: "There were a couple of things we talked about you doing and I'd like to check in on those. I want to ask about what's been helpful from the workbook and whether you have any questions. I want to check in on how the diaphragmatic breathing is going and check in about what sensations still scare you or what fears you feel like you don't have a good answer for."

T: "Did you have a chance to imagine handling panic or anxiety differently? And what positive changes have you noticed?"

C: "The breathing's going great. I used it in the elevator again and in a meeting. I like that the book explains things so clearly. I feel like it's making more sense why I'm so hard on myself and why that first panic attack happened. But I'm still scared of panicking in front of people, especially at work. And the thought of panicking on a plane or an elevator getting stuck still freaks me out."

T: "Okay. So, it sounds as if you'd like to practice being able to talk back to your Reacting Brain more effectively. How about if we work on that today? Would you feel like you got what you came for today if we did that?"

C: "Yes. That would be good."

Preparing for Virtual Reality Exposure Therapy

Virtual reality exposure therapy (VRET) involves clients facing their fears gradually in a virtual world. Clients should be interested in using VR and comfortable with the headset and the experience of entering a VE. Sophia has already experienced immersive VR and enjoyed it. She is comfortable using the headset and has no nausea.

As much as possible, you want to ensure that clients have the skills to successfully enter situations in VR that have caused fear in real life. Clients should be able to tolerate anxiety. Key fears should have been identified and credibly refuted.

Sophia has used her breathing to tolerate anxiety, but the sensation of her throat closing still scares her, so we collaboratively worked on her Fears vs Facts table.

T: "So, what will you say if you feel like your throat is closing up?"

C: "I'm not my mother. I don't have food allergies. This is caused by muscle tightness and a dry throat. I have had this feeling lots of times and always been able to breathe. Just because I am afraid doesn't mean I'm in danger."

Because sensations of chest tightness, shortness of breath, and throat obstruction were her most frightening panic sensations, we spent ten minutes deliberately creating these sensations via interoceptive exposure exercises using the instructions in the *Overcoming Anxiety and Panic Interactive Guide* (McMahon, 2019) and having her rate her anxiety level. She agreed to continue practicing these exercises at home.

VRET

We again spent a few minutes with Sophia in VR. This time, she chose the VE of floating underwater, which was actually an exposure exercise for her because it could raise her fears of not being able to breathe. I double-checked that we felt she was ready for this.

C: "I think this time I'd actually like to float under the sea."

T: "Okay. What are you thinking?"

C: "Well, before I would have thought that there wasn't any air and I couldn't breathe, but now I think I can just do the diaphragmatic breathing and focus on what's around me—not my fears. I feel like I'm better able to reassure my Reacting Brain."

T: "All right. Let's get you set up. (She gets settled in the headset.) I'm about to start you floating in an underwater scene, is that okay?"

C: "Yes. Let's do it. (The VE is activated.) Wow. This is beautiful. I'm a little scared, but I can notice that I'm still breathing. Everything is really okay."

T: "What's your anxiety level on a scale of 0 to 10, where 0 is none at all and 10 is extremely anxious?"

C: "It was about a 6 at first, but it's dropped to a 3. I'm just letting myself enjoy what's around me."

T: "That's terrific. You cut your anxiety in half in less than a minute. What are you doing that's making this possible?"

C: "I'm not getting freaked by being scared. I'm telling my primitive brain, "Look, we're still breathing. You don't have to protect me." It's kind of like I'm reassuring a scared child."

After two more minutes, we stopped. VR had given Sophia the opportunity to practice managing anxiety in a more challenging environment and begin countering her fears without avoiding, escaping, or taking any other fear-based action.

Fostering Progress Between Sessions

After agreeing on her home tasks, I asked when she wanted to check in with me again and we scheduled the next session. She was three-quarters of the way through the workbook and was completing forms in the book that helped track her progress. She now used diaphragmatic breathing routinely at the start and end of the day and whenever she noticed herself feeling tense or anxious.

T: "It sounds like you're almost through the book. Feel free to go back over any parts that are particularly relevant or helpful. Keep reading the workbook, tracking your progress, and using the breathing. Keep reviewing your Fears vs Facts and add anything else that comes to mind, especially when you do the physical [interoceptive] exercises to create the panic-like sensations that have scared you in the past. Start with the least scary exercise and work up to the most scary until none of them scare you."

C: "So, I should practice tensing my muscles and noticing the chest tightness until it doesn't scare me. After chest tightness no longer scares me, I practice breathing through a straw for a minute five times in a row every day until that doesn't scare me. Then I practice pushing against my throat to feel like there's a lump there or like it's closing and do that five times a day until it doesn't scare me."

T: "Exactly. Notice what you learn from these exercises and how you are already using your new knowledge and skills in daily life. If you want, you can write about past events and what you would tell your younger self based on what you now know. Okay?"

C: "Yes. I kind of feel bad for the child I was. It wasn't anyone's fault, but she had a lot on her plate. I'd like to go back and tell her she did an amazing job, that I'm proud of her and it's going to turn out all right. She won't be trapped forever, and she doesn't have to know everything and be perfect. (Sophia tears up as she says these things.)"

C: "It makes me more patient with my Reacting Brain because I can see where it learned stuff. Like you say, it's "devoted, but dumb". (We both laugh.) I'd like to meet in a week or two."

T: "Okay. How do you feel about starting to face your fears in virtual reality next time we meet?"

C: "That sounds good. I feel a lot more ready."

T: "Okay. We'll take it slow."

Session 4

Check In

As always, check in about assigned tasks. If you don't ask about them, it sends a message to the client that these tasks are not important, which is not good. Or that you don't remember your work with them, which is even worse!

T: "Let me quickly check in with you about five things: the book, the breathing, the Fears vs Facts, the exercises, and the positive changes you're noticing. If you did any writing about unhelpful lessons from past events, I'd love to hear about that as well."

T: "What do *you* want to make sure we talk about? What do you want to do today?"

C: "I'm hoping we can do some more virtual reality."

T: "Okay. Bring me up to date about what you've done and how things are going."

C: "I'm on the last chapter of the book. I truly didn't realize before how tense and scared I was and how much my past was affecting me. When I started having panic attacks, I had no idea what was happening. They ought to teach everybody in school about panic."

T: "I absolutely agree. What else have you noticed?"

C: "Well, now that I'm not so scared of the panic symptoms anymore, they're just not happening like they used to! Or if they do happen, it's not a big deal. They don't seem as intense, and they go away faster. I use the breathing and remind myself to accept and remember the facts instead of fighting or running away or avoiding."

C: "Even the throat feelings and feeling like there's not enough air aren't as frightening. Now if they happen, I remind myself that it's just like what we practiced in here."

C: "I'm still uncomfortable on elevators, but I've started riding them anyway. I don't think I'm ready to get on a plane, but I definitely see progress. Every time I read over the Fears vs Facts, the facts seem more familiar and more convincing. I even hear myself thinking some of them spontaneously. And I'm really trying to be nicer to myself."

T: "Great. Did you happen to do any writing about past events and the unhelpful lessons your Reacting Brain could have understandably learned?"

C: "That was really interesting. I didn't know it would be that powerful. I even ended up crying a couple of times. I wrote about my mom having trouble breathing and going to the emergency room. And then I wrote about my first panic attacks; the one when I was presenting to the senior VP, and the one I had on the plane."

T: "Wow. It sounds like you've been doing a lot of really good work."

C: "Yeah. I'm feeling so much better. In fact, one of my coworkers commented that I look more relaxed and happier."

T: "That's great. Last session we talked about maybe facing some fears in virtual reality. How does that sound to you at this point?"

C: "I want to do it. It's still scary, but it's a little exciting too. On my way here today, I was thinking that's what I want to do."

VR Exposure

"Exposure" can be a scary word and concept—for therapists as well as for clients. Think of it as gentle, gradual practice for helping clients have experiences that give them increasing levels of confidence, skill, and success. Collaborate with your clients. Offer choices and get their agreement about the virtual situations and variables they will encounter.

People are more in touch with what they fear when they are *in* the feared situation. Previously unrecognized fears may surface. This is another reason to have anxiety tolerance skills in place ahead of time. It is also why you monitor client anxiety levels.

Look back over what Sophia has reported. What were her feared sensations, activities, and places? What was she afraid might happen if she had those sensations, engaged in those activities, or was in those places? What was she doing, not doing, or doing in some special way to be "safe"?

Now put that information together. If you were treating Sophia, what VEs would you suggest? What variables might be relevant?

T: "Sophia, when you first came to see me, you said you were frightened by panic attacks because they seemed dangerous, that you got scared in places you couldn't leave because you worried there wasn't enough air, and you'd stopped talking in meetings because you worried people would see signs of anxiety and judge you. Is that a good summary?"

C: "Yup. That pretty much nails it. I'm not really afraid of panic itself anymore, but I'm still uncomfortable in elevators and I'd feel self-conscious if my hands or voice shook in front of people, especially at work or while giving a presentation."

T: "Okay. Well, we have a lot of options. While you're in VR, remember the things you want to tell yourself, like 'I don't have to be afraid of being scared", "even small, crowded places have enough air', 'I can tolerate being anxious, I don't have to leave, I'm not trapped even if I can't get out right away', and 'I'll do the best I can, if my hands or voice shake and people notice, so what; they probably don't care or might even be sympathetic; most people are anxious about public speaking; I'm not going to hide away.'"

The statements above were taken from Sophia's Fears vs Facts table. They addressed her key fears and included facts that refuted unrealistic fears as well as supportive self-statements and things she would tell someone else with similar concerns.

T: "I figure we'll leave the airplane until last. Would you like to start with presenting to a group, or with going into an elevator or a subway car?"

C: "I think I'd like to practice presenting to a group."

T: "All right, let's start with a small group around a table. They're informally dressed, you're seated for the presentation, and they're smiling and nodding. How's that sound?"

C: "Good." (She enters the VE.)

T: "Look around. What's your anxiety level as you think about presenting to this group, from 0 to 10, where 0 is none and 10 is very high?"

C: "A 4."

T: "What makes it a 4 and not a 5 or 6?"

C: "Well, they look friendly, and I can hide my hands under the table if they begin to shake. But I know that's a safety action."

T: "So, what can you do instead?"

C: "I guess I'm supposed to leave them out on the table or keep gesturing even though they shake. But I worry what people will think."

T: "And what does your fear say people will think if they see your hands tremble?"

C: "My fear says they'll think less of me. That I wouldn't be anxious if I knew what I was talking about."

T: "And what can you say back to your fear brain?"

C: "Most people are anxious about public speaking. It's not that big a deal. I know what I'm talking about and I do my job well. If they think my hands shaking from adrenaline is an issue, that's their problem. I'm just going to say what I came to say. They probably won't even notice. Or if they do, they might be sympathetic. And the less I worry about anxiety, the less anxious I'll be."

T: "But what if the fear says, 'Your throat's dry! It's going to close up and you'll suffocate and die!'"

C: "I'll remind my Reacting Brain that nobody suffocates from panic. My throat has never closed up. This is an old fear."

T: "What's your anxiety level now?"

C: "It's a 2."

T: "I want you to think about what you did that made it drop to a 2 from a 4 in two minutes."

C: "I reminded myself of the facts. I told myself that panic won't hurt me. I thanked my Reacting Brain for trying to protect me but told it that I'm going to focus on my presentation, not anything else."

We repeated that virtual scenario and Sophia's anxiety level was a 1. On the third repetition, it was a 0. I then suggested that we repeat the experience with the audience wearing formal clothing. She agreed and still only reported a Subjective Units of Distress Scale (SUDS) anxiety rating of "a half or one".

T: "What if they looked bored or like they disagreed with what you were saying? Shall we do that?"

C: "Okay." (I change the virtual audience's facial expressions and reactions.) "Well, that's a little tougher, but I'm telling myself, 'I don't have to be perfect. Not every presentation is going to hit it out of the ballpark. Maybe they're having a bad day, or they disagree. I'll just give my presentation.'"

T: "What if your hands or voice shake?"

C: "So what."

When clients are succeeding, you increase the challenge level so their skills and confidence increase. This also confirms that they *are* able to cope and prepares them for reality.

Since Sophia was doing so well, I increased the exposure by taking the role of one of the listeners in VR and voicing her worst fears. In fact, I voiced those fears in such an extreme way that it became easy for her to see how ridiculous the assumptions underlying some of her fears are.

T: "What if someone pointed out signs of anxiety and said something like, 'What is *wrong* with you? Are you drunk, or just incompetent? Your hands are trembling, and your voice is shaking. Those are obvious signs that you don't know what you're talking about. The only reason anyone gets nervous is because they're incompetent or drunk.'"

C: "Wow. I don't think anyone would actually say that, but maybe they'd think it. Okay, let's see. I could say, 'You're very observant. My voice and hands are kind of shaky. Even when I know what I'm talking about, I have some public speaking anxiety like a lot of people do. If you have questions about my presentation, I'd be happy to answer them.'"

C: "And I'd tell myself, 'Just because *they're* being a jerk about anxiety doesn't mean *I* have to be a jerk about anxiety. This is just my child-like Reacting Brain trying to help by pumping out adrenaline. It'll go away. I can do the breathing and focus on what I'm saying. And if I'm anxious, I'm anxious.'"

T: "What's your anxiety level, from 0 to 10?"

C: "It spiked to an 8 for a second, but I reminded myself of what I know and listened to what I was saying, and it dropped to a 2. I would never feel comfortable if someone said those things, but I'm realizing that I don't have to be embarrassed."

T: "Great job. Do you want to do that again?"

Sophia agreed and with the second repetition, her anxiety stayed between a 2 and a 3 which she said she could cope with. She wanted to go on, so we repeated this exposure in front of larger and larger virtual audiences. Her highest anxiety level, even when being "televised" speaking to an auditorium, only briefly reached a 5 and quickly decreased.

I asked Sophia if she wanted to spend a minute somewhere relaxing in VR as a reward and she chose to go back to floating underwater. She actively looked around and was smiling. Her anxiety level underwater was 0. "I'm enjoying myself."

Fostering Progress Between Sessions

What between-session tasks might you give Sophia at this point in her treatment? What has she learned? What else do you want her to learn? What do you want her to do and notice between sessions?

T: "Keep doing what's working and notice when you're using new skills and knowledge and handling things differently."

C: "Okay."

T: "At the same time, I would also like you to notice any areas that offer you opportunities to change. Where you are still avoiding, escaping, being hyperalert for danger, taking safety actions, or trying to fight anxiety because it frightens you? Think about what your Reacting Brain is afraid of, what it needs to hear from you, and how you could change those actions and act on the facts, not the fears. Then, next session, we can continue to use virtual reality to give you practice changing fear-based actions. How does that sound?"

C: "It sounds good. I'm going to keep doing what's working. Notice what's not working and talk to my Reacting Brain about it. And I'll think about what I want to do next in VR."

C: "I'm going to make it a point to speak up in meetings. I may even offer to present to the senior level managers about my group's project. And if I get scared, so what! Right?"

T: "Right."

Session 5

Check In

This session's check in focused on two things. First, noticing progress and second, being more aware of any remaining fear-based actions.

T: "Let me check in with you. First, what positive changes have you noticed? What are you doing differently? And second, what still needs to change? What fear actions are you still taking, if any? Then, after we check in, let's talk about what you want to do today in our session."

C: "I couldn't wait to tell you. I made it a point to speak up in every meeting and I presented to one of the higher-ups. When I felt a little trembly and my voice sounded shaky, I told myself, 'He probably doesn't notice' and looked at him instead of looking away. He seemed really interested in what I was saying. My supervisor said I did a great job. And nobody said anything about shaky hands or voice. It was awesome."

T: "That's great Sophia. I'm really proud of you. It sounds like you really used what you've been learning."

C: "Yeah. I'm going to tell my supervisor I *am* interested in taking a bigger leadership role. I know that means I have to fly, so I want to work on that in here. But I can't believe I've made this much progress so quickly. Even the idea of being in a small place where I can't get out is not as scary as it used to be."

T: "You worked hard and are reaping the benefits. Unless there's something else you want to discuss, why don't we go straight into virtual reality."

Continuing VR Exposure

Take a moment to cover up the paragraphs below this one and reflect on:

- What has changed over the course of Sophia's treatment so far?
- In your opinion, does Sophia currently meet diagnostic criteria for panic disorder with agoraphobia, claustrophobia, and/or discrete social anxiety disorder?

- Do her fears and symptoms still interfere with her functioning or cause significant distress?
- If you were treating Sophia, what VR activities or situations might you recommend for exposure and skills practice? Why those and not others?
- How would you measure progress and treatment success?

Sophia has made significant progress. She reports no longer fearing the somatic sensations caused by panic. She is speaking up at work even when that causes anxiety. She no longer hides her hands or avoids eye contact. She worries much less about making a mistake, being judged, or feeling embarrassed.

On the other hand, she continues to avoid flying and still becomes anxious in enclosed spaces. Her current treatment goal is overcoming her fear of being "trapped" so she can fly.

Sophia is clear that she wants more VRET this session. Notice that I give Sophia the choice of repeating some previous VR exposures or moving ahead to new environments. If her anxiety levels had not dropped, if she hadn't been able to convincingly talk back to her social fears, or if she was still avoiding in real life or reporting distressing levels of anxiety, I would have continued to focus on VRET for social anxiety.

T: "You have some options. We could go back to the VR where you're presenting to a big audience and being televised. Or in VR we could practice being in places where you can't immediately leave. What do you think would be most helpful? What feels right to you?"

C: "I'd like to start dealing with feeling trapped. I feel like I have the tools to cope with any anxiety that comes when I'm speaking or presenting. Being anxious just isn't that big a deal for me anymore. Feeling trapped is my worst fear."

T: "Okay. There are a lot of possible situations we could use. You could be driving a car, in a large or small elevator, in a subway car, in larger or smaller rooms, or on a plane. I'm thinking the plane would be last. What do you think? We could start with you in a car on a bridge or in a tunnel where you can't just stop, or in a traffic jam where you're 'stuck'".

C: "Let's start in the car on a bridge. That doesn't seem as scary because it's open and the car is moving."

Sophia drove onto a bridge in virtual reality. She practiced driving in different lanes, since it might be harder to get off from the far lane or harder to pull onto a shoulder from the middle lane. Her anxiety levels went no higher than 3 or 4 even when I voiced her fears aloud. She repeatedly practiced responding to the fear thought that she was "trapped" with realistic reassurances such as, "I don't have to leave. There is no danger here. If I get anxious, I'll do my breathing, focus on what is actually happening, and remind myself of the facts."

We repeated this while driving through virtual tunnels and then while in a virtual traffic jam. Her highest SUDS was a 5, which dropped. By the end of the session, none of the driving situations caused more than a 1 or 2.

T: "Would it be okay if your anxiety got to a 2? Would you be able to cope with that and stay there?"
C: "I think so. It's a little uncomfortable, but I can handle it and I know now that if I get more scared, it's temporary."

Since her anxiety levels were low, I encouraged her to deliberately try to get afraid while in VR, see how high her anxiety would go, and then bring it down. When clients start to have consistent success, this suggestion is a way to increase the intensity of VR exposure, test the client's skills, and prevent relapse. Remember that the goal of treating anxiety is not so much that the client does not *have* anxiety or panic, as that the client does not *fear* anxiety or panic.

T: "Sophia, you're doing so well. I want you to try something. Try to make yourself afraid. Think or say what your primitive Reacting Brain might say. What would your fear tell you? See how scared you can make yourself right now."
C: "I'm trapped. There are cars all around and I can't get out and I can't get away. I'm stuck and trapped and something bad is going to happen, just like I was trapped as a child and bad things happened to my mom."
T: "What's your anxiety level, from 0 to 10?"
C: "It went up to a 3" (from a 1).
T: "Okay. What are you going to do and what are you going to say back to your fear? What does your Reacting Brain need to hear from you?"
C: "I tell it 'It's okay. You've got this. It doesn't matter that you can't get out of the car because you don't need to get out of the car. Look around. We're just driving. Nothing bad is happening.' I do my breathing and relax my muscles so I'm not clenching the steering wheel. I tell myself, 'This is just panic, and panic is harmless and temporary. It's probably going to go away in a few minutes. This is just the child-like part of my brain.' I tell it 'I know you're scared, but there's nothing to be scared about.'"
T: "What's your anxiety level, 0 to 10?"
C: "It's a 0. It still feels a little tense, but it just doesn't scare me. This is amazing."

At this point, we stopped VR and I asked her to "write down what you learned today: the important lessons and insights". When she finished, I had her read aloud what she had written so I could write it down as well.

Fostering Progress Between Sessions

After clients have success coping with fears in virtual reality, they nearly always begin to tell you they are starting to face fears in reality, using the same skills they learned and practiced in VR. This is a powerful validation of treatment effectiveness for both you and your clients.

At this point in VRT, you may want to remind clients that changes in VR transfer to real life. You want to balance encouraging them to face their fears (in vivo exposure) with not making them feel pressured.

T: "Sophia, look what you did today. That's really exciting."

C: "I know. It feels so good."

T: "I bet. You know, we talked about how the Reacting Brain can't tell the difference between what happens in real life and what you vividly imagine, or remember, or do in VR. So, as far as this overly protective part of your brain is concerned, you just handled being 'trapped' on a bridge, in a tunnel, and in a traffic jam and coped with anxiety without panicking or needing to leave."

T: "Between now and when we meet again, I want you to really notice all the changes that are happening. What are you doing differently? How are you feeling differently? How is your thinking changing?"

T: "Go back and reread parts of the book that might be helpful. Go over your Fears vs Facts table and add to it if there's any thought or sensation that still scares you. Keep doing what's working and use the skills you did today."

Session 6

Check In

Especially after exposure in VR, clients often begin reporting successfully tolerating anxiety and facing fears in real life. This is a terrific opportunity to have them tell you what worked for them.

Listen for any unhelpful actions that reduce anxiety short-term but feed the anxiety cycle. These would include "white-knuckling" through the fear, anxiously fighting anxiety or panic rather than accepting and tolerating it, mentally escaping or avoiding through distraction, still being hypervigilant, or taking safety actions.

Sometimes clients report problems or "failures". These are perfect learning opportunities or AFOGs (Another F*** Opportunity for Growth). By referring to the anxiety and treatment diagrams, you and the client can identify what caused the problem (i.e., unaddressed or ongoing anxiety triggers, unrecognized or unrefuted fears, unwillingness to accept anxiety, or any fear-based actions) and discuss how to correct it.

T: "I want to check in with you about what positive changes you have noticed and what's working for you. Also are there any panic sensations for which you don't have a good explanation or any fear that still scares you and you don't have a good counter for? What do you want to make sure we do today?"

C: "Well, I'm speaking up in meetings, and taking the elevator doesn't seem like a big deal anymore. I don't wait to see how many people are there before I get in and I don't even think about taking the stairs anymore."

C: "I'm giving a presentation next week and I'm not even nervous about it! Oh, and there was a major traffic jam on the bridge the other day as I was driving to work and I'm like, 'I totally got this. This is no big deal.' I let work know I might be late and then sat back and listened to the radio."

T: "Fabulous! What are you doing that's making this all possible?"

C: "Learning about what causes each of the panic sensations made such a difference. And understanding about the Thinking Brain and the Reacting Brain. Now I just put my Thinking Brain in charge. I also remind myself that I'm not that trapped, scared child anymore. The experiences in VR have been incredibly helpful."

T: "Terrific. Is there anything else you want to talk about, or do you feel ready to do more VR?"

C: "Let's do VR."

VR Exposure Therapy

As always, make VR exposure therapy a collaborative activity. Tell clients about any change in VEs or VR variables beforehand.

T: "It sounds like car situations no longer scare you. And it even sounds like crowded elevators don't scare you like they used to."

C: "Yeah."

T: "How about if we quickly do one or two elevators in VR, then maybe do a subway car or some small rooms? How does that sound?"

C: "That sounds fine. And can we get me on a plane?"

T: "Sure. Do you want to do the plane, or some of these other situations first?"

Sophia agreed to work through some other claustrophobia relevant VEs. If her anxiety levels rose and remained high in these situations, I would spend more time before moving to her most-feared activity of flying. On the other hand, if her anxiety levels never went high or else dropped quickly, we could move rapidly through them on to the virtual plane.

T: "Let's start with a large elevator that's empty."

C: "Okay".

T: "Let's say your fear says, 'What if you panic and need help and nobody's here? Or what if the elevator breaks down and you're trapped, and nobody finds you and you suffocate and die?'"

Because Sophia has been coping so well and has acquired so many skills, I can begin to voice worst-case-scenario fears. If she became anxious and couldn't counter these fears, I would coach her and teach any new skills that were needed.

C: "Well, first of all, panic is just adrenaline. It's unpleasant, but harmless, intended to be helpful, and temporary. I can do my breathing and remind myself of the facts. I don't need help because nothing is wrong. It's just a false alarm. It's the same reaction that would help save my life if I really were in danger."

C: "And elevators almost never break down. But if they do, there's always an emergency button. Someone would come open the doors and get me out."

T: "But what if it happened on a weekend or a holiday?"

C: "There's still an emergency button. Somebody always responds to that."

T: "What's your anxiety level, from 0 to 10?"

C: "It's only about a 1 or 2. Maybe 1 and a half."

T: "What was the highest it got just now?"

C: "Maybe it was a 3, maybe. It wasn't bad."

T: "How scared do you think you would have been before you came to see me?"

C: "Oh, that would have been at least an 8."

T: "And how much do you believe the things you were saying about panic and the elevator, from 0 not at all to 10 absolutely?"

C: "That's a 10. Maybe a 9 about the emergency button because I've never used one because I've never had an elevator get stuck, but it's at least a 9."

T: "How much do you believe the things the fear was saying just now, 0 not at all to 10 absolutely?"

C: "I don't believe them anymore. It's like a 0."

T: "How much would have you believed those fear thoughts before we starting meeting?"

C: "Oh, that would have been a 10."

T: "Think about what you're doing that has made that possible."

Entering a small elevator with people did not trigger anxiety. With her permission, I have the elevator break down and, speaking for the other virtual people in the elevator, had them say things like, "Oh no! We're trapped! There's no air! I have to get out! We're going to die!" Sophia was the calm, rational person who pointed out the facts and reassured everyone else.

She then quickly entered three increasingly small virtual rooms with little or no anxiety and was able to ride a virtual subway comfortably.

With ten minutes left in the session, I asked her if she wanted to start preparing for a plane ride. She agreed.

T: "You are in the car going to the airport. Think about being on the plane for several hours. What's your anxiety level, from 0 to 10?"

C: "It's low. I'm actually kind of excited and looking forward to it. There are a lot of places I'd like to visit."

T: "Okay. How about if we go to the gate area and board the plane."

C: "Yes".

T: "Look around. How are you feeling? What are you thinking? What's your anxiety level, from 0 to 10?"

C: "I'm excited. A little scared, maybe a 1 or a 2."

T: "What makes it a 1 or a 2?"

C: "I haven't done this in a long time and the last time I did it I panicked."

T: "Okay, and what can you tell yourself?"

C: "I didn't know what was happening then. I do now. I know what to do. I feel better. I'm ready to get on the plane."

T: "You're moving down the jetway. There are walls on either side of you and you're about to get on the plane. What's your fear saying? What's your anxiety level, from 0 to 10?"

C: "The fear says that the walls are really close and that I'm going to be on the plane for hours. But I tell myself that this is just a path to get on the plane. I've been in lines. I've driven in tunnels. This is just another walkway. And the plane is just a way to get from one place to another. Plus, I'm fine in elevators now and they're much smaller than planes. There's actually a lot more room on a plane."

T: "That's right. What's your anxiety level, from 0 to 10?"

C: "It went up to a 4 in the jetway, but now it's back down to a 2."

T: "You cut it in half in less than a minute. Think about what you did that made that possible and what that says about your knowledge and your ability and your skills."

Fostering Progress Between Sessions

At this point in treatment, the between-session tasks are likely to focus on noticing progress and applying the tools gained in therapy—rather than learning something new. Having clients write about how they would cope differently with a previously avoided or scary experience can build on the work done in VR.

T: "Keep doing what's working. Notice all the positive changes."

T: "If you want, you can write out a scenario of going to the airport, getting on the plane, taking a long flight, reaching your destination, and successfully coping with any fear thoughts or sensations. Include any panic sensations you might have or fear thoughts that might come to mind. Your Reacting Brain might remember that first time you panicked on a plane. What will you tell it? What will you do? Then reread it and vividly imagine it. Walk through the whole experience in your mind until you feel increasingly comfortable and confident."

Session 7

Check In

As clients make progress, they will spend more time talking about their successes. You may spend less time talking and more time validating. You can help consolidate client progress by going over the diagrams with them, highlighting the skills they used and how they are applying key treatment principles. You and they can see how they have changed from being caught in the anxiety cycle to breaking the cycle.

T: "It's been three weeks since we met. How have things gone? What have you noticed and what do you want to do today?"

C: "The work we did in the elevator was so helpful. I realized I get on elevators now without even thinking about it. And it doesn't matter anymore where I sit in a conference room. I don't have to sit next to the door or find the exits. I've stopped carrying my tranquilizer with me. In fact, one of my coworkers said he had anxiety attacks and I told him all about the Reacting Brain and the Thinking Brain and what causes the feelings he was having in his body."

C: "I just feel more relaxed and more confident generally. I like myself more. I'm feeling ready for the next step in my career. Today I'd like to actually get on the plane."

VR Exposure Therapy

As you have seen, exposure using VR can move quickly without forcing clients into situations for which they do not feel prepared. VR can begin as a way to help clients feel calmer, safer, and more relaxed. Then it can help clients learn how to cope with anxiety and finally it can provide practice and exposure helping clients succeed in increasingly challenging virtual situations.

When doing VRET, listen to clients' SUDS ratings and what they say about their readiness to move ahead. Progress may be slower—or faster—than you might expect.

Sophia had no significant anxiety during last session's VRET and she's reporting major progress in real life. She tells me she feels ready to get on the plane, so rather than repeat coping with elevators, rooms, or subways, we go straight to the airport.

T: "Shall we start at the gate?"

C: "That sounds good."

T: "Take a look around. Think about getting on the plane for several hours. What's your anxiety level, from 0 to 10?"

C: "It's nothing. It's a 0. I'm thinking about how I'll get to see my family and how I can get some uninterrupted work time while I'm on the flight."

T: "Okay. Then let's board the plane." (Sophia's avatar moves down the virtual jetway.) "What's your anxiety level, 0 to 10?"

C: "It's still 0." (She's now on the plane.)

T: "Where do you want to sit? On the aisle, in the middle, or by the window? And we can start with you sitting toward the front half of the plane, is that okay?"

C: "Okay. How about the middle seat? That's the seat I was in when I had the panic attack."

T: (I put her avatar in the middle seat.) "What's your anxiety level, 0 to 10? What's happening in your body? What your fear saying and what can you say back?"

C: "I'm feeling kind of tense, like it's hard to breathe. I think it's a 6 or a 7. I'm remembering how I panicked the last time I was on a plane. I can feel my throat closing up."

T: "Okay, so do the breathing. Relax your muscles. Breathe low and slow, low and slow. That's right. Relax the muscles around your mouth, lips, and jaw. Remember how you created pressure against your throat and could still breathe in the exercises."

C: "I'm feeling a little better."

T: "What's your fear saying and what can you say back to it?"

C: "It's saying I have to get out."

T: "And what will you say back to it?"

C: "I've coped with panic. Panic is just a false alarm. There's enough air. I don't have to get out. This is larger than an elevator. Running from fear just makes it worse. I can do this. I want to do this."

T: "Yes. You want to be free to choose. You aren't going to let the primitive, child-like part of your brain run your life. This is just your Reacting Brain and it's trying to protect you, but it's not very smart. You can thank it for trying to help but point out that you don't need it."

C: "That's right. I don't need it right now. People fly all the time. I want to fly."

T: "Right. And when you panicked on the plane, you hadn't learned about panic attacks and how anxiety works."

C: "That's right. I had no idea what happening. I thought I was dying."

T: "And what do you think now?"

C: "I know I'm not dying. There is enough air. My throat's feeling better. I'm looking around and realizing I'm okay".

T: "What's your anxiety level now from 0 to 10?"

C: "It's lower, maybe down to a 4."

T: "And what are you doing that's bringing it down?"

C: "I'm breathing and remembering that my throat feels like it's closing because it's dry and my muscles are tense. It's not really closing. I'm reminding myself that 'It's just panic' and I know how to deal with panic. I'm talking to my Reacting Brain the way I would reassure a scared child. I can feel my body calming down. It's maybe down to a 3 or even a 2."

We repeat the experience of boarding and being in the middle seat in the front half of the plane. This time, Sophia's anxiety level only reaches a 5 before dropping to a 3, then a 2. On the third repetition, her anxiety level peaked at a 3 and quickly dropped to 1.

T: "Great work! Do you want to move to a middle seat in the back half of the plane?"

C: "Yes. I feel ready for that."

T: "So now you're in the back half of the plane and your fear is saying, 'You're trapped being in the middle and so far back. You won't be able to get out.' What's your anxiety level, 0 to 10?"

C: "It's only a 4. Everybody gets off the plane eventually. There's enough air everywhere. If I have to spend a longer time before the line ahead of me moves, I can use it to call my family and let them know I've arrived."

T: "What's your anxiety level now?"

C: "It's a 1, maybe a 0."

Sophia moved to a window seat and we had her experience takeoff and being mid-flight. Her anxiety stayed at a 2 or lower throughout the entire VR experience. She looked out the window, "It's beautiful and peaceful. I'm excited. I used to love flying."

We repeated the flight, making it a night flight so there was nothing to see out the window, which might contribute to a sense of being closed in. Sophia's response was, "Whether I see out or not, it still the same plane. It's just a way to get from one place to somewhere else I want to do. I don't have to see the outside."

Relapse Prevention and Termination

By incrementally trying to activate a fear response in VR, you and your clients verify that they are no longer frightened. It is incredibly empowering for clients to deliberately try to make themselves panic—and not be afraid.

Toward the end of treatment, if anxiety triggers (other than genetics) still exist, you may focus on reducing those triggers or reducing their impact. This may involve mindfulness, acceptance, stress management, changing the narrative or self-talk, creating evidence to support more positive core beliefs or schemas, applying insights, and so on.

Continue to measure progress. Compare where the client is now to where they were when they started and where they want to be. Check that they have met their treatment goals.

T: "I'm going to use the 0 to 10 scale in a slightly different way. Looking back, before you started therapy, how much did you believe that you could cope with a panic attack, from 0, 'Not at all, I couldn't,' to 10, 'No problem, I can totally handle a panic attack.'"

C: "Oh, that would be a 0. I was so freaked out at the idea of panicking."

T: "And what about now? How confident are you that, if you have a panic attack, you could handle it, 0 not at all confident to 10 absolutely confident?"

C: "It's a 9 or even a 10. I'm doing things now I haven't done in years and things that used to scare me don't scare me now."

T: "What about flying? How confident were you before treatment that you could get on a plane for a long flight: 0 not at all, to 10 absolutely confident?"

C: "Again, that was a 0, or maybe a 7 if I took two pills and had a few drinks and knocked myself out."

T: "And what about now?"

C: "Now it's an 8 or a 9. Riding the plane in here felt so real. I didn't expect it to be so real. So, I'm pretty confident. What's going to make it a 10 is actually going on a flight. I told my family I'm coming to visit next month, and I booked the tickets. It's a five-hour flight. I'm also talking with my supervisor about flying to present at a conference."

C: "I feel ready and prepared. I'm remembering how much I enjoyed flying."

T: "Can you think of anything that might re-trigger any of your fears?"

C: "Well, I know I can be hard on myself, so if I were to be in another job with a critical boss, I know that'd be a big stress. I could be careful how I talk to myself, but I'd also listen to my body and starting planning to leave. I'm not trapped in a job and I don't have to stay. I'm not a child; I have a choice."

C: "And if I start to have panic symptoms, now I know to look at what might be triggering them. I would go back to the book and the diagrams, review my Fears vs Facts table, use my breathing, remind myself of what I know about panic, and start talking to my Reacting Brain."

C: "I just feel like I learned so much. I mean, I use these skills in all kinds of situations, not just on elevators or planes or when presenting."

We agree that she could call for another appointment in the future if she felt the need. Five weeks later, she exuberantly called to say she'd had a wonderful visit with her family and that the flights back and forth were not an issue.

References

McMahon, E. (2019). *Overcoming Anxiety and Panic Interactive Guide*. Hands-on-Guide.

Part II

Treating Fears and Phobias

This section explains virtual reality therapy for fears and phobias in general and for several common phobias:

- Specific phobias overview
- Blood-Injection-Injury phobia
- Claustrophobia (fear of enclosed spaces)
- Driving phobia (vehophobia)
- Flying phobia (aviophobia)
- Height phobia (acrophobia)
- Insect phobias (such as arachnophobia) or animal phobias

If you want to start with a quick review of some key research findings, go to the "Evidence Base" section at the end of each chapter.

DOI: 10.4324/9781003154068-7

6 Specific Phobias Overview

"Overcoming my phobia opened up my life. It freed me. I felt like I got out of jail."

As the above quote illustrates, overcoming a specific phobia can dramatically change someone's life for the better. This chapter gives an overview of using virtual reality (VR) for treating specific phobias. It builds on general anxiety treatment information presented in Chapters 2, 3, and 4.

Specific Phobias and the Anxiety Cycle

Start by understanding the factors contributing to each phobia so you can prepare clients and choose appropriate, helpful virtual experiences.

Anxiety Triggers

Genetics

Getting a family psychiatric history helps illuminate the degree to which your client may be more sensitive and reactive to phobic stimuli and generally more vulnerable to developing anxiety. Some people seem to be temperamentally more risk averse, more quickly reactive and anxious, and/or more intensely emotional.

Chemicals

Chemical factors may have triggered an initial panic attack that seemed to come "out of the blue". When clients fail to see connections between the chemical trigger and panic, they may attribute the panic response to the situation and develop a phobia.

When you identify and explain chemical triggers, a client may be very relieved, "Oh! That's what happened!" Your client's narrative about the situation may instantly change, making it much easier for them to overcome their phobia.

DOI: 10.4324/9781003154068-8

External Stress

In my experience, external stress is usually not a contributing factor in specific phobias. That being said, it is always useful to inquire about external sources of stress. High stress can exacerbate any anxiety disorder.

Self-Talk/Self-Demands

Unrealistic self-demands are usually not an important contributor to specific phobias. However, unhelpful self-talk can play a particularly important role in triggering and maintaining specific phobias.

Be alert for self-talk that emphasizes danger and/or reinforces the belief that the client cannot tolerate the phobic experience. Listen for statements such as:

- "I can't stand this!"
- "This is horrible."
- "I have to get out! Leave! This is dangerous."
- "I can't do this."

Negative past experiences can lead to this type of self-talk.

Unhelpful Lessons from Past Events

Clients' past experiences may have convinced them that they are fragile, vulnerable, or unable to cope. Client beliefs that they are incapable, vulnerable, or dependent upon others create fertile ground for phobias and other anxiety disorders.

Often specific past events created the phobia. Many clients with specific phobias vividly recall one or more frightening experiences that created or contributed to their fear. These may include a frightening experience with an animal, on a plane, with medical staff, in an enclosed space, while driving, etc.

Frightening experiences can give clients misinformation about danger or create a classically conditioned fear response. Phobias can be learned from seeing other people who are phobic or even by seeing frightening events in movies, television, or online. As always, ask about any past experiences of trauma, violence, molestation, or abuse.

Anxiety Sensations

Confronting a phobic situation, even thinking about the phobic situation, can trigger full or partial panic attacks. Ask about panic attack symptoms. Get details about the client's somatic experience.

Phobic Fears

In specific phobias, clients fear that the *situation or activity itself* is dangerous. Identify and explore those fears. For example: "The bridge will break", "The plane will crash", "There's not enough air in an enclosed space so I will suffocate", etc.

Be relentlessly curious about all the underlying assumptions and predictions associated with each fear. Ask your client—and yourself—questions such as:

- "What would have to be true for this fear to be realistic?"
- "What would actually happen if this fear were true?"
- "What is their fear predicting? What is the worst nightmare scenario or outcome?"
- "What are the underlying assumptions clients hold about themselves, other people, and/or the world generally?"

Clients frequently have more than one phobia and/or other anxiety disorders. The person who fears being "trapped" in an enclosed space is quite likely to fear and avoid activities such as driving, flying, swimming, or going to the dentist. They may fear and avoid going above a certain floor in buildings. Clients with one specific phobia frequently report other phobias when you ask.

Be alert for comorbid panic disorder or subclinical fear of anxiety. Clients may fear the bodily sensations that accompany a phobia and anxious bodily sensations may seem to support phobic fears. For example: dizziness may convince the client that heights are dangerous by reinforcing a fear of falling; shaking, sweating, or visual changes may worsen a driving phobia; chest tightness and shortness of breath may seem to confirm a claustrophobic's fear that they are suffocating due to lack of air.

Fear-Based Actions

The most common fear-based actions are avoiding contact with the phobic object, situation, or activity and leaving as soon as possible if clients are forced into contact with their phobia. When escape is impossible, clients may try to take safety actions. Efforts to not feel frightened are usually ineffective.

As a result of fearful experiences, people with a specific phobia can become very hypervigilant, especially if they cannot guarantee that they won't encounter their feared object.

Let's take fear of flying as an example:

- People with flying phobia frequently refuse to fly, go to the airport but refuse to board, or get off the plane before takeoff (avoidance or escape).
- They may try to mentally avoid through distraction, by taking medication, or by drinking (avoidance).

- When they do fly, they may have panic symptoms, cry, or even vomit (intense distress).
- They may only fly certain airlines, only fly to "safe" airports, or only fly for "safe" distances (safety actions).
- While flying, they may pay close attention to every noise and bump (hypervigilance).

Virtual Reality Therapy (VRT) for Specific Phobias

Treating Anxiety Triggers

When you and the client identify a genetic tendency to anxiety, you can emphasize how important it is for the client to understand how anxiety works, to use a combination of acceptance and anxiety management skills, and to diligently apply lessons from treatment.

The most common triggers for specific phobias are unhelpful lessons learned from one or more past events, which you may want to explore and counter. How much time and effort you spend reducing the client's anxiety *triggers* varies from client to client. Usually, however, treatment will focus *first* on treating the phobia.

Once phobic-relevant past events are identified, such as a turbulent flight or an elevator breakdown, clients can virtually revisit these frightening experiences while challenging their phobic lessons using new facts and logic.

Treating Anxiety Sensations

Phobias usually trigger full or partial panic attacks. Just thinking about the phobia may trigger anxiety symptoms. Be prepared to explain the physiological cause and intended helpful purpose of each symptom. Symptoms are covered in detail in my client workbook (McMahon, 2019). Other sources of this information include publications by Craske, et al. (2006) and Craske and Barlow (2006) among others.

Clients need to be convinced that tolerating anxiety is possible and safe. As described earlier, acceptance of "false alarms" and the resultant somatic SNS response plays a key role in overcoming fear.

Time in peaceful virtual environments (VEs) can induce or deepen relaxation and calm. VR instructions can teach techniques that help clients cope with somatic symptoms. Applying these techniques in VEs increases skill. Interoceptive exposure while in VR helps convince clients that sensations are harmless and can be tolerated.

Treating Fears

As with every anxiety disorder, fully explore client fears. Having clarified the fears and anxiety-provoking assumptions and beliefs, you and/or your clients need to uncover the facts to evaluate whether fears are realistic and in proportion to actual risk.

You will be asking clients to do things that *feel* dangerous. Clients need to be intellectually—if not emotionally—convinced that these actions are not as dangerous as they feel.

Sometimes relevant facts or convincing counter statements can be identified collaboratively with the client. Try asking questions like:

- "Is that likely?"
- "If it did occur, how bad would it really be or how would they cope?"
- "What would the client tell someone else who had this fear?"

Sometimes you need to provide specific information. For example, it helps to know facts about flying safety, or that elevators have mandated scheduled safety inspections and emergency buttons. Different phobias need different facts. The following chapters include sources of important, reassuring, relevant facts for common specific phobias.

Treating phobias is a terrific way to learn fascinating information. Why exactly *is* plane travel the safest means of transportation? How *do* planes stay up in the air? Did you know that a plane can land with only one functioning engine?

How do you evaluate likely risk? How do you help clients cope with some level of risk—because nothing is perfectly safe and we all will, in fact, eventually die of something?

Driving, for instance, involves some danger. Why is it worth it? What questions can you and the client explore to evaluate the likely risk?

Techniques from Acceptance and Commitment Therapy (ACT), mindfulness, existential therapy, and other approaches can be quite valuable. Having clients utilize these techniques while virtually facing feared situations proves their relevance and power. Clients see for themselves that the skills work.

Treating Fear-Based Actions

Many clients report, with great frustration, that they have forced themselves to confront their phobia and yet not improved. Uncovering fear-based actions may explain why their "exposure" did not work and highlight what actions need to change and why. As discussed earlier, all fear-based actions presented in the anxiety cycle diagram are commonly used by clients with phobias.

One of the primary goals of treatment is to help clients discontinue their fear-based actions and replace them with fact-based actions and non-fearful acceptance, if and when anxiety occurs. The actions clients instinctively take when afraid do not work in the long run, even if they seem to help in the short run.

Clients need to stop escaping and avoiding. They need to discontinue hypervigilance and safety actions. They need to accept some occasional anxiety or panic sensations without frantically trying to stop the somatic response.

Incorporating VR

Once you understand the anxiety cycle components of your client's specific phobia(s), VR can be used in some or all of these ways:

1 Facilitating or deepening relaxation and calm.
2 Reinforcing client attendance and involvement, including by ending sessions on a positive note.
3 Teaching diaphragmatic breathing, muscle relaxation, and/or mindfulness and/or supporting the use of imagery.
4 Providing exposure therapy following a fear hierarchy relevant to your client.
5 Identifying other relevant fears or issues by triggering previously unarticulated fears or uncovering skill deficits, such as a need for distress tolerance skills.
6 Allowing the client to practice additional new skills and knowledge in previously feared or avoided situations, if those are relevant.
7 Evaluating treatment efficacy and client response to treatment by monitoring the client's anxiety level in various VR scenarios and observing the client's ability to successfully apply new skills or learnings.
8 Minimizing risk of relapse.
9 Homework or practicing between sessions.

The first three uses of VR are often combined. Simply entering a safe, peaceful environment in VR can lead to clients achieving deeper levels of mental and physical calm. Pleasurable VR experiences are rewarding. Learning and practicing skills in VR can be easier and more memorable.

Similarly, the next three uses of VR often co-occur. You try to have clients start VR exposure only *after* anxiety management has been taught and client fears have been identified and countered. However, sometimes new fears or skill deficits come to light in VR, and it is better to have this happen in VR and in session where issues can be addressed immediately.

VR provides an emotionally powerful, realistic, yet safe, place to practice new skills. With specific phobias, this usually involves virtual reality exposure therapy (VRET): virtually confronting the phobia while accepting anxious arousal without leaving or taking safety actions.

As discussed earlier, relapse is minimized by successfully facing fears multiple times in multiple situations. VR is uniquely equipped to support repeated and varied exposure.

Depending on your client and your VR product, home practice of coping skills or exposure may be possible. There are also consumer VR self-help apps for several common phobias such as heights, spiders and other insects, flying, and public speaking, and others continue to be developed.

Each chapter on a specific anxiety disorder presents one or more case examples of applying VRT principles and tools.

Common Treatment Questions

What if the Client Has Multiple Phobias?

Clients often have more than one phobia and/or more than one anxiety disorder. Keep this in mind during your diagnostic interview and throughout treatment.

You need different facts or logic for each fear, but the good news is that the general structure of treatment remains pretty much the same across different phobias. The even better news is that overcoming one fear creates a positive "virtuous cycle".

Success becomes a "proof of concept" that treatment skills work and that the client can succeed. Client motivation, self-efficacy, and optimism are strengthened.

The same skills used to tackle one phobia can be used to tackle the next. Or, as one of my clients put it, "It's just the same process. Lather, rinse, repeat."

Treating one phobia can lead to positive changes in other phobias or other anxiety disorders even when they are not specifically targeted in treatment.

A case report by Botella and colleagues illustrates this (Botella et al., 1999). The client, a 37-year-old female, presented with claustrophobia, fear of storms, and panic disorder with agoraphobia. After eight VR exposure sessions designed to treat the claustrophobia, the client not only reported successful treatment of her claustrophobia, she also reported improvement in her storm phobia, fear of panic, and agoraphobic avoidance. The positive changes were maintained at follow-up three months post-treatment.

What if There Is No VE for the Phobia?

Ideally you will have VEs relevant to the client's phobia; however, this is not always the case. Absent a specific VE, you can always fall back on imaginal or in vivo exposure, but try the options below as well.

Use VR to teach and practice basic anxiety treatment skills even if you do not have a VE matching the details of the client's phobia.

Consider whether exposure to related or analogous VEs may help. For example, clients who fear ski lifts may benefit from virtual walks on mountain paths, looking down from virtual heights, and similar VEs, such as in the case of Barry in Chapter 11.

Remember to think about VEs in terms of their *contents*, not simply their label or intended purpose. You may have a VE that is useful for VRET even if it was not designed for the phobia you are treating.

Evidence Base

Research supporting the use of VR to help clients overcome fears has a longer history than you might expect. Therapists have used VR for specific phobias since the 1990s. Here is a brief research summary in addition to research cited earlier.

A meta-analysis of 14 clinical trials using virtual reality exposure therapy (VRET) for specific phobias by Morina et al. found "VRET can produce significant behavior change in real-life situations and [research findings] support its application in treating specific phobias" (Morina et al., 2015). A systematic literature review by Botella and colleagues found "virtual reality (VR) is an effective treatment for phobias" (Botella et al., 2017).

A meta-analysis of 33 randomized treatment studies by Wolitzky-Taylor et al. examined the comparative efficacy of exposure treatments for specific phobias:

> [E]xposure-based treatment produced large effects sizes … They also outperformed placebo conditions and alternative active psychotherapeutic approaches … Contrary to expectation, effect sizes … were not moderated by type of specific phobia … supporting the superiority of exposure-based treatments over alternative treatment approaches.
>
> (Wolitzky-Taylor et al., 2008)

North, North, and Coble conclude that

> VRT can overcome some of the difficulties inherent in the traditional treatment of phobias. VRT … can provide stimuli for patients who have difficulty imagining fear-producing triggers or are too phobic to undergo real-life experiences, and can generate stimuli of much greater magnitude than standard in vivo techniques. VRT also has the advantage of greater efficiency and economy in delivering the equivalent of in vivo systematic desensitization in the therapist's office.
>
> (North et al., 2002)

The literature review by Côté and Bouchard (2008) and the meta-analysis by Parsons and Rizzo (2008) echo the conclusions above.

References

Botella, C., Villa, H., Baños, R., Perpiñá, C., & García-Palacios, A. (1999). The treatment of claustrophobia with virtual reality: Changes in other phobic behaviors not specifically treated. *CyberPsychology & Behavior*, 2(2), 135–141. doi:10.1089/cpb.1999.2.135.

Botella, C., Fernández-Álvarez, J., Guillén, V., García-Palacios, A., & Baños, R. (2017). Recent progress in virtual reality exposure therapy for phobias: A systematic review. *Current Psychiatry Reports*, 19(7), 42. doi:10.1007/s11920-017-0788-4.

Côté, S. & Bouchard, S. (2008). Virtual reality exposure's efficacy in the treatment of specific phobias: A critical review. *Journal of Cybertherapy and Rehabilitation*, 1(1), 75–91.

Craske, M. & Barlow, D. (2006). *Mastery of Your Anxiety and Panic: Therapist Guide* (4th ed.). Oxford University Press.

Craske, M. G., Antony, M. M., & Barlow, D. H. (2006). *Mastering Your Fears and Phobias* (2nd ed.). Oxford University Press.

McMahon, E. (2019). *Overcoming Anxiety and Panic Interactive Guide*. Hands-on-Guide.

Morina, N., Ijntema, H., Meyerbröker, K., & Emmelkamp, P. M. G. (2015). Can virtual reality exposure therapy gains be generalized to real-life? A meta-analysis of studies applying behavioral assessments. *Behaviour Research and Therapy*, 74 (November), 18–24. doi:10.1016/j.brat.2015.08.010.

North, M. M., North, S. M., & Coble, J. R. (2002). Virtual reality therapy: An effective treatment for psychological disorders. In *Human Factors and Ergonomics. Handbook of Virtual Environments: Design, Implementation, and Applications* (1065–1078). Lawrence Erlbaum Associates Publishers.

Parsons, T. D. & Rizzo, A. A. (2008). Affective outcomes of virtual reality exposure therapy for anxiety and specific phobias: A meta-analysis. *Journal of Behavior Therapy and Experimental Psychiatry*, 39(3), 250–261. doi:10.1016/j.jbtep.2007.07.007.

Wolitzky-Taylor, K. B., Horowitz, J. D., Powers, M. B., & Telch, M. J. (2008). Psychological approaches in the treatment of specific phobias: A meta-analysis. *Clinical Psychology Review*, 28(6), 1021–1037. doi:10.1016/j.cpr.2008.02.007.

7 Blood-Injection-Injury Phobia

"Bleeding won't stop. There will be blood everywhere."
"The needle will get stuck in my bone and break off."
"I get light-headed and pass out."
"It's going to be really painful. It's the worst thing ever!"

Clients with a phobia of blood, injections/transfusions, and/or injury (BII) may fear other medical or dental procedures. In addition to limiting access to health care, BII phobia can restrict clients from getting vaccinations they need or cosmetic procedures they want, such as getting pierced ears or a tattoo.

This chapter explains how the anxiety cycle model from Chapter 2 applies to this phobia, how to distinguish this phobia from common comorbidities, and how to use virtual reality (VR) in treatment. Treatment is illustrated by a case example.

We also discuss how—for some people—fear of fainting may be realistic and can be prevented by specific actions.

Blood-Injection-Injury Phobia and the Anxiety Cycle

Anxiety Triggers

Genetic factors may make some people more sensitive to stimuli such as pain or generally prone to stronger emotional reactions. These clients often report that biological relatives are highly sensitive and/or have phobias, anxiety, or other mental health problems.

Negative self-talk and unhelpful lessons from past events often play key roles. Many BII phobic clients are convinced they cannot handle the pain or distress involved. This belief makes them more fearful and makes the experience and memory of past events involving needles, blood, injury, or medical care more negative. Clients often describe such negative past experiences as "traumatic" even when objectively the event seems to fall within the bounds of normal, common experience.

No one enjoys having blood drawn or getting vaccinated, but most of us would describe these experiences as unpleasant, not traumatizing.

DOI: 10.4324/9781003154068-9

Listen for unhelpful narratives and lessons about past events as described above. Listen as well for negative core beliefs or schemas. Finally, listen for past trauma, abuse, neglect, or violence. Such experiences may increase the pain response to painful experiences of any kind.

Anxiety Sensations

Some BII phobia clients have a classic panic response to these stimuli. Their heart races, their blood pressure goes up, and their muscles tense. In other words, their physiological reaction is basically the same as clients with other types of phobias.

Other BII phobia clients react very differently. A subset of BII phobia clients do lose consciousness in response to injections, blood, or injuries because their bodies have a two-phase physiologic response. First, their blood pressure and heart rate increase as you would expect; then their blood pressure and heart rate drop, and they pass out. You will learn more about this atypical response and how to train clients to change their response below.

Common Fears

Naturally, one of the fears for clients with blood-injection-injury phobia who have fainted is that they will pass out again. In addition, they may share fears commonly expressed by other clients with this phobia. Fears usually center around pain and/or misinformation about the risks of the medical procedure.

Some clients who fear the pain say things like, "It's going to be really painful" or "It's the worst thing ever!" about finger pricks, blood draws, vaccinations, injections, or other medical experiences. They describe such experiences as "awful", "the worst", "SO painful" and may label healthcare professionals as sadists who enjoy torturing them.

Misinformation about medical procedures and risks also contributes to phobic reactions. Some clients fear injections because "The needle will get stuck in my bone and break off." Others have vivid images of catastrophic, fatal, uncontrolled blood loss and fear that "Bleeding won't stop. There will be blood everywhere."

Of course, such beliefs and thoughts increase fearful hypervigilance, attention to pain, and muscle tension. These, in turn, all increase subjective discomfort.

Fear-Based Actions

Avoidance is the most common response. Typically, these clients have not had blood tests, vaccinations, flu shots, medical examinations or procedures, or dental care for many years.

When forced to confront their phobic situation, they may try to avoid mentally by not looking at the needle or blood. They may close their eyes, bring headphones and listen to music, or play digital games, essentially pretending nothing is happening. While this may help, it also reinforces the belief that they cannot cope without avoidance.

Some clients escape by leaving the clinic, medical, or dental office. Others may "try to run" or end up crouched down in a corner.

As mentioned above, fearful hypervigilant attention to possible pain increases the awareness and the intensity of the pain. Some clients grit their teeth or fight the fear and pain by counting aloud. Sadly, I have had clients tell me that counting just seems to make the experience "last forever!" Other clients try to tell themselves "It's fine," but don't really believe it. This is a form of fighting the anxiety response out of fear and dread.

Some safety actions are probably warranted. For example, for clients who pass out, it may be helpful and appropriate to have them lie down before a procedure. Of course, the hope is that after learning applied tension and completing virtual reality therapy (VRT), they will no longer lose consciousness.

Given that some people may indeed experience more pain than others, if fear of pain is the primary issue, exploring pain relief options may be warranted and humane. These clients may ask for a phlebotomist who is known to be skilled and patient with fearful patients. They may explore medical options, such as getting a prescription topical anesthetic cream to use before injections, etc.

Differential Diagnosis and Frequent Comorbidities

If your client reports episodes of losing consciousness or near unconsciousness, be sure that the client has been medically evaluated to rule out any other causes for their fainting.

As mentioned above, some of these clients seem to have more intense and therefore problematic emotional reactions generally. A general population study conducted in the Netherlands found that both fear of being alone and BII phobia each correlated more highly than other fears and phobias with overall psychological impairment and comorbidity. "The situational and blood/injury phobia subtypes appear to be a more significant index for impairments and for comorbid psychiatric disorders than the animal and natural environment phobia subtypes" (Depla et al., 2008).

This correlation suggests that you may want to conduct a more in-depth diagnostic interview with these clients, keeping these questions in mind: Is your client generally avoidant? Does your client have trouble with distress tolerance in many situations? You may wish to pay special attention to the therapeutic alliance and to client response to treatment interventions, especially those that are potentially distressing.

VRT for Blood-Injection-Injury Phobia

Depending on clients' fears and overall presentation, you may spend more time than usual using VR to help clients learn and practice relaxation and distress tolerance skills. These clients may benefit from having a greater number of positive VR experiences of deep relaxation and absorbed, focused, mindful attention before beginning exposure.

Using VR for exposure and desensitization will depend upon the virtual scenarios available to you. For example, you might use virtual environments (VEs) where the client is a passenger or driver in a virtual car on the way to a medical procedure or is in a virtual medical waiting room to address anticipatory anxiety and unfounded fears or catastrophizing.

Some VR products include videos of an actual blood draw. Some products have a VE with variables for a virtual finger prick, injection, or a blood draw with variable numbers of blood vials.

For clients who have passed out or come close to passing out, make sure the client has learned applied tension as described later in this chapter. Take exposures slowly. Use an automatic blood pressure machine to check that applied tension does, in fact, increase their blood pressure (and sometimes their heart rate) before beginning exposure. Have them tell you if they begin to feel faint and make sure they are seated in such a way as to minimize harm if they do pass out.

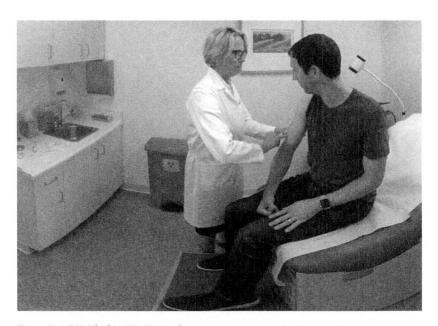

Figure 7.1 BII Phobia VE Example

Treating Anxiety Triggers

All the usual interventions for helping clients re-evaluate past experiences can be applied. Interventions for negative self-talk can be helpful to increase clients' confidence in their ability to cope. For clients who self-identify as highly sensitive people, or who seem to fit that profile, consider using some of the distress tolerance techniques from dialectical behavior therapy and/or acceptance commitment therapy.

Treating Anxiety Sensations

For most anxiety disorders, you train your clients to relax. With clients *who do not pass out*, VR can help them learn and practice anxiety tolerance skills: diaphragmatic breathing, progressive muscle relaxation, mindfulness, and/or imagery.

For clients *who do pass out*, a different approach is warranted. You want train these clients to *tense* using applied tension, as explained below.

Using Applied Tension

Clients who pass out from BII phobia have a unique phobic response. Instead of sustained intense sympathetic nervous system (SNS) arousal which raises blood pressure (BP), a transient spike in SNS arousal is quickly followed by a spike in *parasympathetic* nervous system (PNS) arousal which *lowers* their blood pressure and heart rate (HR). As a result, these clients frequently faint at the sight of blood or injury, or when getting or viewing an injection, blood test, or transfusion.

Öst et al. monitored the heart rate and blood pressure responses of 18 blood phobic patients viewing a movie about bloody thoracic operations. "The group data showed a diphasic response; an increase in HR and BP from baseline to the beginning of the film, and then a sharp drop in these parameters." Five patients either fainted or were described as on the edge of fainting. Their physiological data documented "massive bradycardia [slowed heart rate] or drop in BP or both" (Öst et al., 1984).

I explain this to clients, using terms from the anxiety cycle diagram.

> It is as if your Reacting Brain thinks your heart's blood is being pumped out on to the ground. It wants to save your life, so it drops your heart rate and lowers your blood pressure to minimize blood loss. You need to tense your muscles and mechanically raise your blood pressure.

The intervention is called applied tension (or sometimes applied muscle tension). It prevents fainting by raising blood pressure. This technique helps clients tolerate exposure and desensitization.

Applied tension can be constant or rhythmic. With constant applied tension, the client tenses their entire body and holds the tension. With rhythmic applied tension, the client tenses for 15–20 seconds, relaxes for 20–30 seconds, then tenses again, repeating the sequence of tensing and releasing five times.

To track this, use an inexpensive, over-the-counter automatic blood pressure cuff (also known as a sphygmomanometer) to measure blood pressure and heart rate. You can find blood pressure cuffs in most drug stores. I keep one in my office and use it for blood pressure and heart rate readings before and during applied tension practice to verify the increase in blood pressure and heart rate. This reassures you and the client that the applied tension is working.

NOTE: For injections and blood draws, do *not* have the client tense the area that will be used for the procedure because this can increase the pain of the procedure. Have the client practice selectively tensing all their muscles *except* the muscles of that arm.

WARNING: If there is any reason to believe that increased tension or blood pressure might be painful or dangerous, get a release of information and contact their primary care provider for medical clearance. For instance, you might want to do this for clients with migraines, hypertension, a personal or family history of strokes or transient ischemic attacks (TIAs), or similar medical issues.

Treating Fears

When clients have a justifiable fear that they will "get light-headed and pass out" because they have fainted in the past, you and they need to see that applied tension works for them. Have them practice until their blood pressure (and hopefully heart rate as well) increases reliably. Only then would you start VR exposure.

For clients who primarily fear pain or have low pain/distress tolerance, a number of approaches may be needed to prepare them for virtual reality exposure therapy (VRET). You may teach skills from acceptance commitment therapy, cognitive behavior therapy, dialectical behavior therapy, mindfulness, narrative therapy, schema therapy, and others. It is important to help clients come up with credible, alternative responses to replace thoughts that the pain will be terrible, unendurable, the worst thing ever, and that it is being intentionally inflicted by malicious caregivers.

Having identified and explored clients' misconceptions, you can offer relevant corrective information. This information must be specific in order to be convincing and effective. These clients have already received non-specific reassurances along the lines of "It'll be okay. You'll be fine. It's not that bad." Or, the worst, "It won't hurt"—when it actually will.

The more specific the examples and facts you can offer, the more credible they will be. You may need to consult healthcare professionals and search the Internet for facts, photos, or videos that disconfirm clients' fears. Carefully screen whatever you show or print for clients. Information should be relevant, believable, accurate, and helpful as opposed to overwhelming or fear-evoking.

The reality is that only minimal, transient pain and bleeding are caused by the most common medical and dental procedures. If you have concerns that this may not be the case, for example if your client is on anti-coagulants (blood thinners), has a bleeding disorder, or has a chronic pain disorder, get a release of information and consult the client's healthcare provider.

Getting facts about client fears is essential for both you and your client. The first time a client confided, "I'm afraid the needle will get stuck in my bone and break off," I didn't know what to say. The client did have very slender arms. The image of a needle slamming into a bone was pretty horrifying. Clearly, I needed reliable information to evaluate this fear.

With the client's permission, I spoke with the treating physician as well as discussing these general fears with an emergency room nurse. By the following session, I was armed with specific, reassuring facts.

In case you are interested, it is relatively rare that a needle will hit bone. When it does (remember this is rare), there is often no pain and the very slender tip of the needle is blunted. Needles do not break off and travel throughout the body causing catastrophic harm—which is what my client had feared.

VR-reinforced relaxation and repeated VR exposure are less likely to work if clients continue to believe their fears are justified.

Treating Fear-Based Actions

VR is a tremendously useful tool for treating BII phobia. Unless you work in a hospital, medical center, or dental clinic, you are unlikely to be able to arrange graduated in vivo exposures, whereas VR make controlled, graduated, repeated exposures easy. Even if your VR product does not have all the specific scenarios you would wish, you may be able to use parts of VR videos or environments designed for other fears.

You may have VR videos of actual blood draws and injections. Or a VR product that has VEs with variables for a virtual finger prick, injection, or blood draw with more or fewer vials of blood.

When clients confront a blood draw or other feared medical procedure in VR, you help them cope with fear without avoiding, escaping, or safety actions. While they are in the immersive experience, you can coach them to use their new skills, new facts, and changed self-talk. You help them let go of unneeded safety actions and reduce hypervigilance.

Treatment Challenges

There are several treatment challenges you may encounter. Some of these are unique to BII phobia.

Fainting

One challenge is knowing what to do for clients with blood-injection-injury phobia who faint. Luckily, now you know the recommended intervention: applied tension.

I have never had a client pass out during treatment, but you might consider taking some precautions. If you or the client think they *may* faint, have them safely seated and leaning back during VRET, confirm that they can raise their blood pressure by tensing, and agree to stop VR and have clients put their head down lower than their heart if they feel like they're going to faint. Ask how much time the client usually has between first feeling faint and actually passing out. For clients in teletherapy who fear they may faint, discuss whether they would like to have a trusted person present in case of fainting.

No VR for the Specific Fear

Another treatment challenge is that you may not have virtual scenarios that match a specific client's fears. For example, at this time, there are no VEs for dental fears. Often you can find something similar enough. And more VR experiences are being designed to meet common therapeutic needs. By the time you read this, more VEs will exist.

If you search the Web or YouTube for relevant VR content such as 3D VR videos, preview the entire video to ensure that contents are appropriate for your client.

Realistic Threat of Pain

A third treatment challenge is that sometimes reality seems to support and validate clients' fears. Many medical and dental procedures *are* truly painful, at least temporarily.

This challenge is similar to challenges presented in treating driving phobia. Clients must learn to accept some level of risk or discomfort. Injections and certain medical procedures present the risk of some pain. Interventions may include: uncovering and challenging unrealistic beliefs about the amount and duration of pain, teaching distress tolerance skills, increasing motivation, and taking practical steps to decrease pain.

Relapse Prevention

A final treatment challenge involves factors that are not under your control. As part of relapse prevention, you want to prepare clients to cope if they encounter healthcare providers who may not be understanding or supportive.

Some healthcare professionals may not believe clients' reports of passing out or be unwilling to alter their procedures to take this into account. Some healthcare professionals are brusque or unsympathetic. Others may be rushed. Some are less skilled or less gentle than others. Some lack the understanding or patience to cope with the intensity of these clients' fear and distress. They may be unwilling to take the time to explain procedures or to apply a numbing cream.

Role play how clients could assertively respond and effectively cope with the issues described above. You can speak for the virtual healthcare providers and provide graduated exposure: moving from being an understanding, supportive, patient provider to virtually interacting in ways that are increasingly dismissive, brusque, unsympathetic, impatient, and unwilling to accommodate. Throughout this process, you monitor client anxiety and coach clients to be appropriately assertive and active in obtaining what they legitimately need.

The goal is that clients leave treatment prepared to cope without relapsing into avoidance or other fear-motivated actions.

Case Example

"I did it! I actually did it!"

Brittany

I mostly work with adults, but will sometimes treat intelligent, motivated older teenagers who are referred for VRT of a specific anxiety issue. Brittany is a case in point.

Her parents called me asking about VRT for needle phobia. She was terrified of needles. Getting mandated immunizations was a major issue, provoking tears and arguments for weeks beforehand. They were seeking phobia treatment because Brittany's pediatrician was considering acupuncture.

After talking with her parents, I spoke with Brittany. She was ambivalent about getting injections and acupuncture but was very motivated to get her ears pierced. "All my friends have pierced ears. I tried three times, but I chickened out each time. I started to feel faint and was just too scared."

Since her primary fear was of passing out, I taught her applied tension. Brittany learned quickly and was intrigued and encouraged to see the increase in blood pressure readings. This reassured her that she would not pass out.

I used the anxiety cycle diagrams to explain the rationale for VR exposure and had her say aloud her reasons for getting over her fear of needles. She seemed motivated and ready.

We did a mix of in vivo, imaginal, and VR exposure. Once she could handle a syringe and imagine receiving an injection, we began VRET.

Brittany progressed through a hierarchy of VR exposures. First, we tackled her anticipatory anxiety by having her sit in a virtual waiting room, waiting to be called for an injection. I had her describe her thoughts and reactions and periodically asked about her anxiety ratings. She watched as other patients were called in by the nurse. As her anxiety dropped, she felt ready for the next step, entering the exam room and having a procedure that involved a needle.

I controlled and viewed the events in VR from my computer and had Brittany mirror her avatar self's position. When her avatar was called into the virtual procedure room, I asked Brittany to stand. When the avatar sat down for the procedure, I had Brittany sit.

As I took her step by step through a series of virtual activities involving needles and blood, I repeatedly checked her anxiety level, reminded her to use applied tension, and had her repeatedly talk back to her fears aloud. If she had trouble refuting a fear, I prompted her until she was able to respond to fears confidently and convincingly.

Her self-reported anxiety levels on the Subjective Units of Distress Scale (SUDS) dropped from a 7 to 1. I always got permission before moving her to the next level and I described what that level would involve.

When her avatar in VR had a finger stick for a drop of blood, I touched the same finger in real life with the tip of a pen. Adding tactile stimuli made the experience more real and increased the likelihood of change transferring to the non-virtual world.

After three repetitions of exposure to a virtual finger stick, she gave permission to have an injection. In anticipation, her anxiety increased to a SUDS of 6 so I helped her use her new skills and knowledge to bring it down before actually starting the virtual injection. Her SUDS dropped with each repetition.

The next step on her fear hierarchy was having a virtual blood draw taking one tube of blood. I added kinesthetic stimuli by touching her skin with the tip of a pen where the needle was used in VR.

After her anxiety dropped, we moved to a blood draw with two tubes of blood. SUDS levels dropped from 8 to 3 with an occasional 2.

I saved watching a two-dimensional video of an actual blood draw for last. Although it was less immersive because it was two-dimensional, it was more fear-evoking because it was a video of a real person experiencing a real blood draw. I pointed out that the person in the video was not frightened and didn't have intense pain. I also continually praised her use of her new skills and encouraged her to "think what this means that you are able to decrease your anxiety!" Although the video continued to be anxiety-provoking, she was able to tolerate watching rather than closing her eyes or looking away.

In the end, the pediatrician decided that acupuncture was unnecessary. Injections continue to be dreaded, unpleasant events but are endured with less anticipatory anger and distress.

On the plus side, I received an exuberant text that she had gotten her ears pierced, which had been her real treatment goal all along. And she did it without passing out.

Evidence Base

While little research exists about VRT for BII phobia, two pilot studies (Jiang et al., 2020; Wiederhold et al., 2005) support its possible usefulness. VR exposure to blood and injection stimuli elicited self-reported anxiety and physiological arousal, suggesting that VR exposure is "an effective method of cue exposure for individuals who experience anxiety in situations related to blood and injections" (Wiederhold et al., 2005). Self-reported fears decreased in a randomized controlled trial of single-session VRET for BII phobia (Jiang et al., 2020) See these references for more information about applied tension (Bodycoat et al., 2000; Öst et al., 1991; Öst & Sterner, 1987; Öst et al., 1989).

References

Bodycoat, N., Grauaug, L., Olson, A., & Page, A. C. (2000). Constant versus rhythmic muscle tension in applied tension. *Behaviour Change*, 17(2), 97–102. doi:10.1375/bech.17.2.97.

Depla, M. F. I. A., ten Have, M. L., van Balkom, A. J. L. M., & de Graaf, R. (2008). Specific fears and phobias in the general population: Results from the Netherlands Mental Health Survey and Incidence Study (NEMESIS). *Social Psychiatry and Psychiatric Epidemiology*, 43(3), 200–208. doi:10.1007/s00127-007-0291-z.

Jiang, M. Y. W., Upton, E., & Newby, J. M. (2020). A randomised wait-list controlled pilot trial of one-session virtual reality exposure therapy for blood-injection-injury phobias. *Journal of Affective Disorders*, 276, 636–645. doi:10.1016/j.jad.2020.07.076.

Öst, L.-G., Fellenius, J., & Sterner, U. (1991). Applied tension, exposure in vivo, and tension-only in the treatment of blood phobia. *Behaviour Research and Therapy*, 29(6), 561–574. doi:10.1016/0005-7967-91-90006-o.

Öst, L.-G. & Sterner, U. (1987). A specific behavioral method for treatment of blood phobia. *Behaviour Research and Therapy*, 25(1), 25–29. doi:10.1016/0005-7967(87)90111–90112.

Öst, L.-G., Sterner, U., & Lindahl, I.-L. (1984). Physiological responses in blood phobics. *Behaviour Research and Therapy*, 22(2), 109–117. doi:10.1016/0005-7967(84)90099–90098.

Öst, L.-G., Sterner, U., & Fellenius, J. (1989). Applied tension, applied relaxation, and the combination in the treatment of blood phobia. *Behaviour Research and Therapy*, 27(2), 109–121. doi:10.1016/0005-7967(89)90069–90067.

Wiederhold, B., Mendoza, M., Nakatani, T., Bullinger, A., & Wiederhold, M. (2005). VR for blood-injection-injury phobia. *Annual Review of CyberTherapy and TelemedicineTelemedicine*, 3, 109–116.

8 Claustrophobia

"The idea of being stuck or trapped terrifies me. I don't even like to think about it."
"I have to get out!"

Clients with claustrophobia tend to fear any situation where they cannot easily or immediately leave. As you imagine, this can interfere with every area of their lives. Claustrophobic clients have lost jobs, refused promotions, strained or limited family relationships, and restricted their lives. Let's explore how virtual reality therapy (VRT) can help.

Claustrophobia and the Anxiety Cycle

Anxiety Triggers

I suspect there may be an innate component to claustrophobia. Our ancestors would have wanted to see approaching danger and be able to escape. It may be that an atavistic remnant of this instinct remains with us today.

While infants often enjoy being swaddled, they also enjoy kicking their legs and waving their hands. From a very young age, humans appreciate being able to move freely and generally dislike being restricted or held down. If you have ever had to physically restrain a toddler from running into the street, you know exactly what I am talking about.

Even feeling visually "closed in" or "trapped" can impact us, as shown in a fascinating study by Fich et al. Researchers tracked physiological indicators of stress in participants who were exposed to psychosocial stress in two types of virtual rooms: one was a "closed room" with no visible windows or doors; the other virtual room had a view of the outdoors. The results are intriguing. The closed room did not trigger a stress response in the subjects in and of itself, but the setting did influence subjects' reaction to stress. "[P]articipants in the closed room responded with more pronounced cortisol reactivity to stress induction, and continued to show higher levels throughout recovery, compared to participants in the open room" (Fich et al., 2014).

Genetics can, of course, make someone generally more likely to develop an anxiety issue of any type. Chemical factors are not commonly a direct

DOI: 10.4324/9781003154068-10

trigger for claustrophobia but might contribute to claustrophobia if they trigger symptoms such as shortness of breath. External stress, negative self-talk, or unrealistic self-demands increase the overall likelihood of anxiety issues but are not usually direct claustrophobia triggers.

Unhelpful lessons from past events are the most common anxiety triggers for claustrophobia. While taking a history, listen for and ask specifically about frightening experiences that may have created or contributed to claustrophobia. These may include things that happened to the client personally, things they observed, and even things they heard about, read about, or saw in movies or on the news.

Movies and media highlight emotionally compelling stories. Stories of miners trapped underground by a cave-in, rescued victims who had been imprisoned and abused, students trapped in an underwater cave, survivors trapped in collapsed buildings after earthquakes or bombings, and similar stories are given vivid, compelling, and repeated coverage. The horrors and dangers of being trapped are emphasized.

What unhelpful lessons did your client draw—consciously or unconsciously—from such experiences? What connections were made? How did these contribute to claustrophobic fears? What needs to be explained and addressed during VRT?

Anxiety Sensations

Certain somatic sensations seem particularly common with claustrophobia. Asking about and connecting these sensations to clients' fears helps your clients understand why their fears seem credible.

Listen carefully for anxiety sensations such as feeling:

- Short of breath
- Chest tightness or pressure
- Lump in the throat
- Hot
- Sweaty
- Dizziness and/or visual changes
- Restless and muscle tension

Feeling short of breath seems to be evidence of insufficient air. This combined with chest tightness or chest pressure can make a client feel like they are unable to breathe.

Tensed muscles also contribute to feeling unable to breathe. Experience this for yourself. Tense all your muscles and try to breathe. Even tightening the abdominal muscles alone can create a feeling of "not being able to get a deep breath".

A "lump in the throat" sensation can make the client fear their throat is closing up, blocked, or swelling shut.

Feeling hot or sweaty can contribute by making the room feel "stuffy". Dizziness and/or visual changes can make clients fear they are passing out (perhaps from lack of oxygen) and visual changes can also create a sense of "the walls closing in".

Restlessness and general muscle tension can create a feeling of needing to move, feeding clients' belief that they must escape.

Common Fears

Claustrophobic clients often misinterpret somatic sensations as proof that they could (or are about to) suffocate, pass out, and/or die due to lack of oxygen or throat closing. They may believe there is not enough air on a plane, in an elevator, in a closed room, etc. and that they must get out. They may fear that a hot, humid, or stuffy environment means they cannot breathe.

Muscle tension and restlessness can lead to fears that they could "start screaming" or do something "crazy", "out of control", or "violent" to escape.

Often, however, clients initially find it hard to identify fears other than frightening thoughts of being "trapped!" "stuck!" or "can't get out, can't escape!" These are such emotionally evocative words they may even make *you* anxious and tempt you to agree that panic is justified.

Explore clients' fears in more detail. Uncover, articulate, and explore all underlying assumptions and predictions. Make the feared outcomes more explicit.

Ask questions such as:

- What exactly do you mean by being trapped or stuck? What does your Reacting Brain think will happen? What "danger" (use air quotes here) is it trying to protect you from?
- What would be the worst thing about being unable to leave? If you did not or could not leave, what would happen?
- Why does your fear say you need to get out? What is it afraid would happen if you couldn't?

Repeatedly follow up with questions like:

- And if that did happen, what does your fear say would happen next?
- And then what?
- And then what?
- And then what does your protective, but primitive, Reacting Brain think might happen?

By the end of this process, you and your client should have a much clearer understanding of their claustrophobic fears and this understanding will allow you to re-evaluate those fears both in real life and while in virtual reality (VR).

Specific, concrete fears can be evaluated against evidence and logic. Vague threats cannot.

Fear-Based Actions

Claustrophobia typically leads to multiple fear-based actions that can impact a client's health, career, relationships, leisure, and overall quality of life.

Escape

Clients have walked out of dental and medical appointments. They have pleaded to have airplane doors opened and gotten off planes after boarding. They have left meetings, movies, concerts, and other gatherings.

They have gotten off elevators if an elevator became "too crowded" or, conversely, if they were left alone in an elevator with no one there to help them if needed.

They have demanded that cars pull over so they could get out. They have left because an environment felt hot, humid, or closed in.

Since I practice in California, many of my clients have visited Disneyland. Lines for rides are often underground and even outdoor lines (at least when not during a pandemic) can be incredibly long and congested. I have had claustrophobic clients who tried to take their children on a ride only to frantically demand to leave and/or refuse to board the ride at the last minute. Clients may not even feel able to remain on the tram or train.

Avoid

Claustrophobic clients have refused lucrative job offers because reaching the office would require taking an elevator. They have declined job interviews and avoided meetings because the meeting might take place in a small room without windows.

Some of my clients routinely walked many flights of stairs rather than take an elevator, to the annoyance and disbelief of family and friends. Clients have demanded a hotel room on a lower floor just to avoid the elevator or a larger hotel room to avoid feeling trapped.

Clients with claustrophobia may avoid driving in certain lanes or on certain roads. They may avoid driving at certain times to avoid traffic jams. They may refuse to sit in the backseat of a car, or in the middle or window seat if they fly. They may avoid buses, subways, trains, trams, and planes altogether or may avoid routes that go underground or go "too long" between stops.

Claustrophobia can ruin family vacations. Clients have restricted destination choices or refused to go. They have ended up waiting alone for hours while family members go on rides at amusement parks, take underground tours, or ride elevators to famous sites.

Avoidance is not always physical; it can be mental. For example, clients may mentally avoid by playing games on their phone or otherwise trying to avoid noticing their environment. "I tell myself, 'Don't look'. I try to imagine that I am not there."

Hypervigilance/Look for Danger

People with claustrophobia tend to know the location of every exit, stairway, window, and door. They may be hyperaware of room size and number of people.

They may constantly monitor their body sensations. They may listen intently as they ride an elevator, concerned that routine noises indicate an imminent breakdown. They may anxiously look for brake lights indicating a traffic slowdown, watch the numbers of cars, or check traffic maps due to fear of being "stuck" in traffic.

Safety Actions

Clients may only ride elevators that move quickly or that have a "safe" number of other passengers. They may ride elevators only for a limited "safe" number of floors or only when accompanied by a loved one.

They may turn the air vent on planes to high, carry their own fan, only sit in "safe" aisle seats near the front, or only fly short distances. Clients may only drive in outside lanes on a highway so there is room to pull off at any time. Or they may only drive certain routes they feel are safe.

They may only sit in the front seat of a car and open car windows or turn on air conditioning to reassure themselves that there is enough air. They often sit near the door in meetings or close to the exit on buses, subways, or trains, reassuring themselves they can leave immediately if necessary.

Clients may seek reassurance. They may anxiously ask whether an elevator has ever broken down or whether flight attendants have supplemental oxygen they can receive if needed. They may reassure themselves: "I could always pull the emergency cord or plead with the driver to let me out, saying I'm having a medical emergency."

Such reassurances and plans are safety actions. They often indicate unrealistic demands for a perfect guarantee of safety and rarely decrease phobic fear in the long run because anxiety can always come up with another "what if...?" "Yes, this elevator has never broken down before, but *what if* this time is the time the elevator stops?!" or "Yes, they have oxygen on the plane but *what if* the flight attendant doesn't believe me when I say I need oxygen or what if the oxygen runs out?!" or "Yes, but what if the driver won't stop and let me out?!"

Watch that getting facts about objective safety does not morph into seeking absolute guarantees. The benefits of VR exposure will be undermined by such actions.

Fighting the Anxiety Response

Some clients respond to anxiety by telling themselves to "Relax! Relax!" in a frightened effort to make the anxiety stop for fear of what might happen. Or they respond to perceived shortness of breath by taking big, "deep" breaths *in an effort to make the feared sensation go away.*

You now understand—and can use the anxiety cycle diagrams to explain—why this does not work.

Whenever clients tell you they are taking deep breaths or doing diaphragmatic breathing, have them demonstrate. Often clients who think they are breathing with their belly are breathing with the chest. This method of breathing—sometimes called overbreathing—can actually increase feelings of not getting enough air and create tingling, tension, numbness, dizziness, and/or visual changes.

To recap the points made above, using relaxation techniques, or even reviewing facts, is unlikely to be effective unless it is done with an attitude of acceptance and an understanding that what is happening is an unpleasant, but essentially well-intentioned and harmless, response to misinformation.

VRT for Claustrophobia

Build a coherent case formulation using the anxiety cycle diagram. Then organize treatment, including VR, using the treatment diagram to target your client's specific triggers, sensations, fears, and actions.

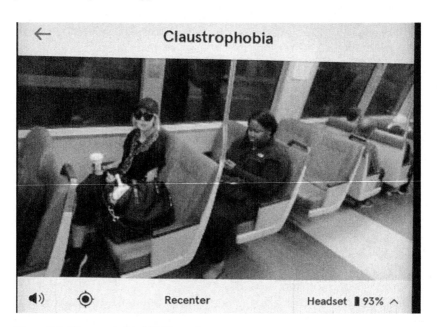

Figure 8.1 Claustrophobia VE Example

Think about your clients with claustrophobia. Consider the various ways VR could support treatment. In the case example of Debbie below, VR was primarily used for exposure.

Treating Anxiety Triggers

You may use any of several interventions to help clients re-evaluate and change the impact of their past experiences which created claustrophobia.
Listed alphabetically, these might include:

- Cognitive behavioral therapy (CBT) to challenge lessons from past events.
- Eye movement desensitization reprocessing therapy (EMDR).
- Imagery rescripting.
- Insight into how past events are negatively impacting the present and how the client is repeating the past.
- Narrative therapy techniques.
- Writing about past events while focusing on drawing different lessons and incorporating new information.

You may suggest clients imagine, write about, and/or discuss in session questions such as "If you could go back in time, what would you tell your younger self that you wish someone had told you so you didn't become so frightened?" or "What would you tell someone else who had a similar experience?"

Reviewing new cognitions, new insights, or new narratives may be easier and more memorable while the client is in a calming virtual environment (VE). You may use VR stimuli for EMDR if your VR system supports that option.

If a phobia-relevant experience occurred at a specific location, you might have the client revisit that location virtually if the option is available. This can increase the immediacy and emotional impact of new lessons learned as well as offer an opportunity for exposure and desensitization. For example, I might have had Debbie revisit the Eiffel Tower or the Empire State Building.

Treating Anxiety Sensations

Although this was not the case for Debbie, VR programs teaching progressive muscle relaxation are often more effective than diaphragmatic breathing for claustrophobia. Mindfulness can also help. For some clients, focusing on breathing makes them more hypervigilant about feeling short of breath.

Some VR programs can aid interoceptive exposure by mimicking shortness of breath through the sound of loud, fast breathing, or dizziness and visual changes by blurring or otherwise changing the visual display in VR.

Treating Fears

First you uncover the fears and explore *both* the feared predicted outcomes or worst-case scenarios *and* the underlying—usually unvoiced and unrecognized—assumptions that must be true for the fears and predictions to be true. Then, once you have specifics, you help your clients evaluate the accuracy of their fears, predictions, and assumptions.

You can ask questions such as:

- How likely is it that your feared situation will occur? This does not require an answer of zero, it focuses on the relative likelihood. For example, an elevator can break down and stop between floors, but how often does this happen compared to the number of elevators and elevator trips?
- If this did occur, what would actually happen? How bad would it really be? How long would it last? What actions could the client take?
- What have other people done when "trapped" in one of the client's feared claustrophobic situations? Why do they act and react like they do and not like you do? What happened to them? What conclusions can you draw from that? What does that tell you about the situation?

The "what ifs…?" of fear thoughts always need to be addressed. These might include thoughts like "What if there's a traffic jam and I can't get off the road?" "What if the windows can't be opened?" "What if I feel hot and short of breath and think I can't breathe?" "What if I can't get an aisle seat?" and so on.

Elicit such thoughts using a curious, nonjudgmental voice and tone. Evaluate them collaboratively with your client in the context of the two of you working together to re-educate and re-train their well-meaning, but childish, Reacting Brain.

If a client doesn't know exactly what they're afraid will happen, cautiously putting them—with their permission—into a VE that sparks a phobic response may quickly clarify their fears.

By the end of this treatment stage, clients should be starting to identify and question their fears and convincingly to talk back to them. This will be important when they face claustrophobic situations virtually.

Treating Fear-Based Actions

As clients become less frightened of and more tolerant of somatic symptoms, it is easier to encourage them to drop safety actions, reduce hypervigilance, and remain in virtual enclosed places without escaping.

The relief and increased confidence that clients feel after successful VR exposure is tremendously rewarding for them and for you. Such experiences vastly increase the likelihood that clients successfully change their behaviors outside the office in real life where it counts.

During virtual reality exposure therapy (VRET), you will target each of their relevant fear-based actions as discussed below.

Fighting Anxiety Sensations

Using VR to teach, practice, and reinforce anxiety management and distress tolerance skills gives clients alternatives to frantically fighting the anxiety response. If clients have trouble using these skills during VR exposure, you may have the option of playing recorded skill instructions in VR. Or, of course, you may guide them yourself, prompting them to use their skills.

Avoiding

Using your knowledge of their fears, guide your clients through a series of VR experiences using a formal or informal hierarchy, monitoring their anxiety at each step. Encourage them to actively pay attention to their surroundings, their emotions, their body, and their thoughts so they are mindfully present and accepting, rather than mentally avoiding or escaping.

Hypervigilance/Looking for Danger

While encouraging clients to notice what is actually happening in VR, point out everything that disconfirms their fears. Prompt them to replace fearful expectations of danger with fact-based, more realistic risk evaluations.

Challenging clients' fears reduces hypervigilance, as does objective mindful awareness of the VE. Hypervigilance is further reduced when you highlight decreases in clients' Subjective Units of Distress Scale (SUDS) ratings.

Safety Actions

As part of graduated, controlled VR exposure, you modify their VR experiences to decrease and then discontinue safety actions. For example, you can move a client from a "safe" aisle seat on the virtual airplane to a middle seat and then a window seat, or vice versa depending on which makes the client increasingly anxious. You may place the client in a series of virtual rooms that are smaller, more crowded, or have fewer windows.

Escaping

By the time you begin VRET, clients should grasp how anxiety works, know what is required to overcome their phobia, understand the goal and rationale of exposure, and have effective coping tools. You should have a strong, collaborative working relationship and trust. The client's urge to flee should be decreasing.

Even so, check in with clients throughout their VR experiences and ask before changing environment variables or VEs.

Treatment Challenges

One of the challenges in treatment is evaluating whether or not client fears are warranted. Two other challenges discussed in this section are dealing with clients who have anxiety about donning the VR headset or using VR when your system does not have VEs specifically designed for claustrophobia.

True Alarm? Actual Danger?

For claustrophobic clients who fear suffocation, ask about medical conditions, especially any that might actually cause breathing difficulty. Examples are asthma, serious allergic reactions such as anaphylaxis, and cardio-pulmonary (heart and lung) diseases such as chronic bronchitis, chronic obstructive pulmonary disease (COPD), chronic heart failure (CHF), emphysema, etc.

If you or your client have any concerns that symptoms might indicate a medical problem, get the client's permission and have their healthcare provider provide a thorough evaluation and recommendations. It is vital to determine whether a client's feeling short of breath is caused by phobic anxiety or by a medical issue like an acute asthma attack or allergic reaction. The appropriate treatment interventions are very different!

Client Anxiety About the VR Headset

This has not occurred in my practice, but it is possible that a client might feel trapped and claustrophobic at the thought of wearing a headset. If this is the case, begin by exploring the fears and assumptions the client has about the headset. For example, are they afraid the headset could get stuck and be unable to come off? Do they fear the headset will obstruct their breathing? You can demonstrate on yourself that the headset goes on and off easily and does not cover the nose or mouth.

You can create a hierarchy of headset exposure experiences. For example:

1   Watching *you* don the headset, breathe with the headset on, then remove the headset.
2   If you and client are physically in the office, having the client put the headset on you and take it off you.
3   If possible, having clients put their face farther and farther into the headset without fitting the straps on their head.
4   Setting the headset straps for maximum looseness, then gradually tightening.

No VE for Claustrophobia

If your available VR products do not include a VE specifically for claus-trophobia, look for relevant content within VEs designed for other uses. For example, VEs of elevators for height phobia, of planes for flying phobia, of offices or rooms of different sizes for public speaking, job interviews, etc., or MRI machines or medical exam rooms for blood-injection-injury phobia. These environments may all be used for claustrophobia exposure. Remem-ber to look at the VE content, not just its label or intended purpose.

Case Example

Debbie

> *"It was fine. It was really fine."*

When Debbie came to see me, she had avoided riding elevators for decades. And that was perfectly fine with her.

Her friends and family all knew she "had to" take the stairs. Hotel rooms were carefully selected to be on a lower floor. She stayed on the ground during vacations while her family went up the Eiffel Tower, rode the London Eye Ferris wheel, or visited the observation deck of the Empire State Building. She only saw doctors and dentists whose offices could be reached by using the stairs. Her claustrophobia had even limited her job choices.

She was okay with all of that—until her only daughter got pregnant. She knew her daughter would need her help after the baby came and she really, really wanted to spend time with her grandchild—but her daughter lived in a penthouse apartment on the tenth floor. Now she was motivated to get over her claustrophobic fear of elevators.

Evaluating her anxiety triggers, it seemed as if genetics may have a role. Several family members had anxiety and she herself was a self-described "terrible worrier". While not meeting diagnostic criteria for generalized anxiety disorder (GAD) or depression, she tended to ruminate and focus on the negative.

Relevant past events included learning about claustrophobia by hearing two close relatives with claustrophobia talk about their fears and seeing them avoid elevators and refuse to sit in the backseat of cars. She also learned unhelpful lessons from her first panic attack—which happened to occur during a business trip while riding an elevator.

Debbie was jet-lagged, working long hours, and stressed about meeting a major deadline. It was her first job and she had heard rumors of impending layoffs.

She got on the elevator to meet with the client, thinking, "If this doesn't go well, I'm going to lose my job!" As more people boarded the elevator at each stop, she became increasingly anxious and worried that she would be late for the meeting.

> I began to feel hot, and sweaty, and like I couldn't breathe. It seemed like the elevator ride was taking forever and I started to think "I have to get out now. I can't stand this. This is unbearable." I made it to the meeting, but when I went to ride the elevator back down, I thought, "I can't do it." I walked down ten flights of stairs, all the way down thinking, "What if that [panic attack] happens again? That was awful!"

Then she began to worry:

> What if the elevator had stopped because there were too many people? That's a lot of weight. What if it broke down and I was trapped? With all those people, there wouldn't be enough air. I might pass out. And if I couldn't get out, I could go crazy! I felt really out of control.

These thoughts terrified her and at that point she stopped riding elevators (avoid). On the rare occasions when she could not avoid, she picked the elevator with the fewest passengers and stood right next to the door (safety action). If she got too anxious, she got off and waited for another elevator. "I never rode more than one or two floors before getting off. I was too afraid." (escape).

The first therapist she saw emphasized using relaxation and breathing techniques to "control" the somatic symptoms (fighting the anxiety response). Sometimes it worked, but sometimes it didn't. "I was always checking whether I felt hot or short of breath or anxious (hypervigilance) and when I noticed any of those things, I left right away." (escape).

Before continuing, think how *you* would use VR if you were treating Debbie.

Our first two sessions were devoted to getting her history and using the anxiety cycle and treatment diagrams to understand what had happened and what treatment would involve. I explained the causes of her somatic symptoms to help her convince herself that they were uncomfortable but not dangerous. I emphasized that they did not indicate that she was in danger; they were the result of a false alarm because her Reacting Brain misinterpreted the situation.

I acknowledged that she did not control her Reacting Brain and so panic symptoms could occur but that even though that aspect of her anxiety cycle *was* "out of control", *she* was not out of control. She could change her response to anxiety.

She already used diaphragmatic breathing; what needed to change was her intent. I encouraged her to use the breathing to help "surf the wave" of adrenaline and minimize her discomfort, without fighting or being frightened by it. She practiced thinking about her breathing in this way while standing on a virtual beach or by a virtual waterfall. I did *not* have her vir-tually swim underwater since that would have likely triggered a claus-trophobic response. At home, she continued to practice breathing with thinking about a different approach to panic.

Two sessions were spent exploring and refuting her fears about elevators. I explained that elevators have scheduled maintenance and call buttons in case of emergency. We discussed that there is always air flow because elevators have heating and air conditioning. I had her think about the fact that she had never heard a news story about people dying in elevators because of lack of air.

We identified relevant variables as part of developing a fear hierarchy. She was more comfortable in a large elevator than a small one, with some people rather than many or none, and riding a few floors rather than many.

We reviewed VR exposure options and she chose to start with waiting for a virtual elevator in order to tackle her anticipatory anxiety. In the VE, I had her first state a fear about either riding the elevator ("I'll be trapped") or experiencing anxiety ("I can't breathe. I must leave!") and immediately counter the fear ("Elevators rarely break down. If it did, I would press the emergency button, and someone would come." "There *is* enough air. This is a false alarm. There is no danger. I don't have to leave.") Over three repetitions, her SUDS dropped from 5 to 2.

When she said she was ready to board, I had her enter a large virtual elevator with a few people, ride one floor, and get off. Her SUDS returned to a "5 or 6" with the thought, "What if the elevator doors don't open?" I responded, "And what *if* the elevators doors don't open? How likely is that? Does that usually happen? And what would be the worst if the doors didn't open?"

She got better and better at confidently refuting her fears. Her SUDS dropped to 1 and she began taking longer and longer elevator rides.

Over the next few sessions, she took virtual rides to more floors, first with more people, then alone, and first on the larger elevator, then on the smaller elevator. With each change, her SUDS would briefly increase, but the increases tended to be smaller and SUDS began dropping more quickly.

By our sixth session, she commented, "I think I can do this." I encouraged her to think about everything she had learned and experienced. She scheduled the next session for a few weeks later, "to give me time to practice".

By our next meeting, she had taken several elevators up to as many as four flights. She would tell herself, "The door is going to open. People take elevators all the time." She also confided that she was "trying to be more realistic" about things generally rather than worrying.

We repeated the VR exposures and her SUDS stayed in the 1–3 range. She commented, "The more you do them [feared activities], the more fear goes down." Naturally, I agreed.

Outside of sessions, she began practicing taking the elevator to and from her daughter's apartment. First, she had her husband go with her "just in case". Then, she had her husband take the elevator and wait for her while she took the elevator alone to join him. Next, she went alone but called her daughter before getting on the elevator. She tended to discount her progress, but her family was amazed and delighted. Although never entirely comfortable in elevators, by the end of treatment she was routinely riding the elevator to her daughter's apartment ("although I still don't like it") and had stayed in a hotel room on an upper floor for the first time in many years.

The focus of treatment then moved to dealing with her other life stresses and worrying in general. Occasionally something like being stuck in traffic in a tunnel briefly reactivated claustrophobic anxiety but she told me when that happened, "I felt a little scared, but I didn't panic." She was no longer afraid of anxiety and fighting it. She was no longer avoiding or escaping. Her life was less restricted. And she loved showing photos of her holding her granddaughter.

Evidence Base

Over 20 years ago, Botella et al. published a case report of successful VRT for claustrophobia (Botella et al., 1998) and followed up a year later reporting that after VRT of claustrophobia, the authors

> observed a generalization of improvement from claustrophobic situations to the other specific phobic and agoraphobic situations that were not treated ... VR exposure was effective in reducing fear in closed spaces, in increasing self-efficacy in claustrophobic situations, and in improving other problems not specifically treated.
>
> (Botella et al., 1999)

In 2003, Bouchard et al. published reports from a clinical trial using VR to treat children presenting with claustrophobia or fears of heights or spiders (Bouchard et al., 2003) offering support that VRT is effective with phobic children as well as adults.

A literature review by Côté and Bouchard (2008) pointed out that while many of the 39 studies reviewed had methodological limitations (e.g., case studies or small sample sizes, no control or comparison), the majority of studies reviewed concluded that VR exposure was effective in treating specific phobias (Côté & Bouchard, 2008). The studies included subjects treated for fears of claustrophobia, driving, flying, heights, and spiders.

A study by Shiban et al. focused specifically on claustrophobic subjects' response to VR stimuli and emphasized VR's potential for effective exposure when treating claustrophobia (Shiban et al., 2016).

References

Botella, C., Baños, R. M., Perpiñá, C., Villa, H., Alcañiz, M., & Rey, A. (1998). Virtual reality treatment of claustrophobia: A case report. *Behaviour Research and Therapy*, 36(2), 239–246. doi:10.1016/S0005-7967(97)10006–10007.

Botella, C., Villa, H., Baños, R., Perpiñá, C., & García-Palacios, A. (1999). The treatment of claustrophobia with virtual reality: Changes in other phobic behaviors not specifically treated. *CyberPsychology & Behavior*, 2(2), 135–141. doi:10.1089/cpb.1999.2.135.

Bouchard, S., Robillard, G., St-Jacques, J., Côté, S., & Renaud, P. (2003). An update on the first 18 months of clinical studies on anxiety disorders at the UQO cyberpsychology lab. *CyberTherapy*. www.vrphobia.com/imi/conference2003/downloads/CyberTherapy_Program_4_Dec_2002.pdf.

Côté, S. & Bouchard, S. (2008). Virtual reality exposure's efficacy in the treatment of specific phobias: A critical review. *Journal of Cybertherapy and Rehabilitation*, 1(1), 75–91.

Fich, L. B., Jönsson, P., Kirkegaard, P. H., Wallergård, M., Garde, A. H., & Hansen, Å. (2014). Can architectural design alter the physiological reaction to psychosocial stress? A virtual TSST experiment. *Physiology and Behavior*, 135, 91–97. doi:10.1016/j.physbeh.2014.05.034.

Shiban, Y., Peperkorn, H., Alpers, G. W., Pauli, P., & Mühlberger, A. (2016). Influence of perceptual cues and conceptual information on the activation and reduction of claustrophobic fear. *Journal of Behavior Therapy and Experimental Psychiatry*, 51, 19–26. doi:10.1016/j.jbtep.2015.11.002.

9 Driving Phobia

Fear of driving, sometimes called vehophobia, is a common reason for seeking treatment.

Driving Phobia and the Anxiety Cycle

> *"I'm worried the other cars won't see me or that I'll lose control if I drive the speed limit."*
>
> *"I feel like the car is going to fly off the curve on an entrance ramp."*

Anxiety Triggers

When genetic vulnerability, chemical triggers, and/or external stresses result in panic symptoms and those symptoms happen to occur while driving, clients can quickly develop a driving phobia. Having once experienced fear while driving, driving may become a conditioned stimulus for fear. Even if the cause of the panic symptoms was entirely unrelated to driving, feeling frightened while driving can convince clients that driving is dangerous, or that driving while anxious is dangerous.

Negative self-talk can lead clients to overestimate risks, including the risk of accidents, whether through their fault or that of others. For clients who routinely expect the worst and/or worry, driving may seem to offer constant opportunities for accidents.

Clients with unrealistic self-demands (perfectionism or rigid high ideals) will unfairly criticize their driving abilities. Anything less than perfect attention may be considered dangerously lax. They are also likely to view other drivers' speed and behaviors as "unsafe".

Clearly past events play a major role in this fear. An orthopedic surgeon asked about virtual reality exposure therapy (VRET) for driving, saying, "After an automobile accident, I fix their bones, but many of my patients are too afraid to drive again." Many driving phobic clients will have been in at least one motor vehicle accident, either as driver or passenger. Get the details of all

DOI: 10.4324/9781003154068-11

the accident(s) or near accident(s) because the specifics may explain the circumstances driving your client's fear.

Factors such as the time of day, weather conditions, or type of road may now be anxiety triggers. The Reacting Brain tends to automatically respond to everything associated with an accident as a signal that another accident may occur.

If clients were rear-ended, they are likely to fear being rear-ended again. If they saw an accident on a highway during a rainy evening, they may now be anxious about driving in the rain, at night, or on the highway. Growing up with fearful drivers can send the message that driving is dangerous and something to fear.

You can also see how broader beliefs about oneself, other people, and the world play a role. Driving requires a great deal of trust. Clients need to believe they are safe drivers. They need to believe in their mechanic and their car. They need to have reasonable faith and trust in other drivers.

Listen empathically for experiences that may make it difficult for clients to see themselves as competent and resilient—or lead them to believe that others are thoughtless, inattentive, uncaring, or malevolent and not to be trusted.

Has your client experienced emotional or physical abuse, loss, or trauma? Did your client grow up in a dangerous neighborhood or experience discrimination? Was the client raised by a parent with substance abuse issues, uncontrolled bipolar disorder, or borderline personality disorder? These, and similar experiences, can easily lead to the belief that the world is a chaotic unpredictable place where bad things happen, and so one must always be on the alert.

As a therapist, you can listen and help clients gain insights and become aware of learnings from the past that are often unarticulated, unexamined, and/or unconscious. You can help articulate them, explore and question them, and bring them to conscious awareness.

In my experience, the biggest factor in overcoming a driving phobia is the client's motivation and determination. Many clients are distressed by how their fear restricts their lives while simultaneously deeply ambivalent about taking the "risk" of driving.

Driving phobics may struggle with general self-mistrust and be perfectionistic and self-critical. They may have trouble forgiving themselves for past behaviors, especially if they drove dangerously, made bad decisions, or caused an accident in the past.

Depending on the individual case, techniques from cognitive behavioral therapy (CBT), forgiveness therapy, narrative therapy, psychodynamic therapy, schema therapy, self-compassion therapy, and/or guided writing may help address the lingering harmful effects from the past and change clients' problematic beliefs. Interventions used for PTSD such as cognitive processing therapy (CPT), eye movement desensitization and reprocess (EMDR), or prolonged exposure (PE), etc. may be appropriate.

Understanding how and why the past contributed to driving fears may help clients benefit from virtual reality therapy (VRT).

Anxiety Sensations

Combining anxiety reduction skills with distress tolerance may be especially important for driving phobia treatment. Consider the challenges that clients face in overcoming fear of driving. First, clients must be willing to enter situations that have some real potential for danger. On top of that, you are asking your client to repeatedly choose to continue driving, in the face of constantly available opportunities to escape.

Acceptance commitment therapy (ACT), dialectical behavior therapy (DBT), motivational interviewing (MI), or other interventions may be useful. They can provide additional distress tolerance skills and strengthen the client's motivation to continue despite distress.

As mentioned earlier, simply experiencing anxiety while in a car can lead to subsequent fear of driving because it is natural to assume that you are in danger if you feel afraid.

These somatic symptoms may convince clients that they are unable to safely operate a car or are going to pass out:

- Sweaty hands
- Shaking, especially in hands or legs
- Weakness, "jelly legs"
- Muscle tension, feeling "paralyzed"
- Shortness of breath
- Dizziness
- Visual changes
- Decreased concentration

It is important to identify these sensations so you can explain their cause and harmless nature.

Common Fears

The basic fear is being in another motor vehicle accident. Some clients fear they will cause an accident; some clients fear that other drivers will cause an accident. Some believe certain driving conditions are dangerous. Some believe that driving while anxious is unsafe. Let's examine some of the most common fears.

Fear of Driving While Anxious

Clients may fear that simply being anxious renders them unfit to drive. You can often find direct connections between clients' somatic symptoms and their driving fears.

Here are some examples:

- My sweaty hands will fail to grip the wheel and I will lose control.

- My hands or legs may tremble so much or be so weak, I'll be unable to use them to operate the steering wheel or pedals.
- My arms or legs feel so tense that they feel "paralyzed", and I won't be able to move them.
- Shortness of breath or dizziness are signs that I am about to pass out and crash.
- Visual changes caused by anxiety mean that I can't see well enough to drive.
- Decreased concentration is dangerous because I must always pay complete attention.

Fear the Car Is Unsafe or Unreliable

Clients who fear they will be the cause of an accident may believe *their car* is unsafe. They do not trust the car to function. Car-focused fears include fears that:

- Brakes will fail.
- Tires will not grip.
- Cars will "fly off the road" if driven on a curve or above a certain speed.
- Cars will skid if there is any rain on the road.
- Windshield wipers will malfunction impairing visibility.

Fear of Being an Unsafe Driver

Clients may not trust *themselves*. They may fear they are unsafe drivers. Self-focused fears include fears such as:

- My vision is not good enough, even with corrective lenses or after being reassured by an optometrist or ophthalmologist.
- I will be distracted.
- I will hit a car in my blind spot or otherwise fail to see another car, even though they check their mirrors frequently.
- I won't hit the brake in time and will hit someone.
- I will react too slowly or too quickly. My reaction times will be too slow or too fast.
- I will get lost or confused and make unsafe or illegal driving decisions.

Fear of Other Drivers

Clients may also not trust *others*. They fear that other drivers will:

- Brake so fast the client will be unable to stop in time.

- Drive too fast or follow too closely and won't have time to brake, hitting the car in front, causing a chain reaction of accidents, including the client's car.
- Rear-end the client's car.
- Not see the client when merging or changing lanes and hit them.
- Drive dangerously because they are "unsafe" or "stupid," are "driving dangerously", "changing lanes too often", and so on.

Fear of Certain Driving Conditions

Clients often believe that certain roads, road characteristics, or traffic conditions are inherently unsafe such as driving:

- At night
- In rainy or stormy weather or with reduced visibility
- On a wet road
- On a bridge, overpass, or curve
- In the outside lane near a sharp drop-off, such as a cliff edge or mountain road
- Through a tunnel
- On certain roads or in certain lanes
- At certain speeds
- When there are more cars

Fear-Based Actions

Escape

Clients who fear driving will often escape by pulling over to the side of the road and stopping, or by taking the nearest exit and getting off the highway. If someone is in the car with them, they may demand that the other person take over driving.

Avoid

Some clients avoid any driving whatsoever; most have partial avoidance. They drive minimal distances. They avoid driving certain roads (usually freeways) but are willing to drive on others. They may demand to be the driver and avoid being a passenger—or the opposite.

Hypervigilance

When these clients do drive, they are likely to be hyperalert and expect the worst. Anxious hypervigilance increases the client's sense of danger, leading the client to misinterpret normal driving experiences as risky or signaling imminent threat, and react accordingly.

They anxiously monitor the sight of brake lights ahead as a sign that a multi-car crash is imminent. They repeatedly check their mirrors. They monitor cars all around them for fear of being hit.

They can quickly become hypervigilant to anxiety sensations and mis-interpret them as well. They may monitor their body sensations.

While a passenger, they may point out "dangers". They may repeatedly, anxiously, remind the driver of stoplights, stop signs, and so on. They may even scream warnings or shout directions.

Safety Actions

You can probably guess the common safety actions taken by people with driving phobias. Often, they will only drive the "safe" slow lane, at a "safe" slow speed, or follow the car ahead at a farther than usual "safe" distance. They may look several times before changing lanes or leaving a stop sign. They may only drive on "safe" roads or under "safe" driving conditions.

They may repeatedly wipe their hands, so the hands are not "too" sweaty. They may open windows, turn off the heat, or turn on the air conditioning to reassure themselves that there's enough air.

Fighting Anxiety Sensations out of Fear

People with driving phobias try the usual ways of stopping feared anxiety sensations. They may take deep breaths and end up hyperventilating. They may use relaxation techniques, mindfulness, or mantras in a frightened attempt to make themselves relax. They may repeatedly try to reassure themselves—which tends to be ineffective when it is motivated by fear—rather than reviewing reassuring facts with an attitude of accepting some anxiety.

Frequent Comorbidities

Since we tend to think we are in danger when we feel frightened or panicky, full or subclinical panic disorder often accompanies or creates fear of driving. Clients who have been in an auto accident may have posttrau-matic stress disorder (PTSD). Clients with generalized anxiety disorder (GAD) will worry about driving, just like they worry about most things.

VRT for Fear of Driving

There are two compelling reasons to make virtual reality (VR) part of driving phobia treatment. First, these clients need to be able to tolerate anxiety while engaging in an activity that does actually present some danger.

VR makes learning and practicing anxiety tolerance techniques more engaging, vivid, immersive, and memorable so skills may be more easily learned and perhaps more powerful.

Second, VR is the most feasible option for monitored practice and exposure. It is the rare therapist who accompanies phobic clients on drives. With VR, you can accompany clients safely and as often as needed while they gain confidence.

Treating Anxiety Triggers

More compassionate and realistic self-talk can be practiced as a way to reduce the anxiety triggered by negative thinking and unrealistic demands. Practicing this new thinking may be easier at first in a tranquil virtual environment (VE). This is very true for some clients, like Michael in the first case example below.

Exposure to VEs reminiscent of experiences that contributed to developing driving phobias may be helpful in challenging the lessons, narratives, and conditioned responses created by those experiences.

Treating Anxiety Sensations

Anxiety management skills like diaphragmatic breathing, progressive muscle relaxation (PMR), and mindfulness can be taught and practiced first in safe,

Figure 9.1 Driving VE Example

calming VEs. Learning can be fostered by listening to the VR program's recorded instructions and watching avatars practice these skills.

I often find that PMR is particularly helpful with driving phobia because these clients may be tensing their entire upper body while driving—both virtually and in real life.

During VRET, you can remind clients to use anxiety tolerance techniques. You can either coach them yourself or with clients who responded well to the recorded instructions, you may have the option of playing those instructions while clients virtually drive. Simply hearing the recording may help clients feel calmer or be more tolerant of anxiety.

Ideally, your client's interpretation of and response to anxiety sensations will change as you encourage them to accept and manage the symptoms without fearing them.

Treating Fears

Preparing for successful virtual exposure means arming clients with facts that disprove their fears or otherwise justify driving.

What degree of fear is appropriate? How do you and your client decide whether driving despite anxiety is justified, their car is safe, their skills are adequate, and the risks inherent in driving are worthwhile?

Answering these key questions can be tricky. At first glance, many of the fears voiced by clients seem quite reasonable. Since cars can hydroplane on wet, slippery, or icy roads, does that mean clients should never drive under such conditions? If "distracted driving is dangerous driving" (as the "don't text and drive" ads say), does that mean clients should have total attention on the road at all times?

Explore all unvoiced assumptions. Skeptically examine and question these predictions. Ask lots of questions so that you and your clients can unemotionally and objectively evaluate the reality of their concerns.

What would have to be true for their fear to be realistic? What would happen if their fear were true? Is that likely and how bad would it be really?

Does the client drive while drunk or high, while texting, or when so sleep-deprived that s/he is falling asleep at the wheel? Is the client thrill-seeking or risk-averse?

Is the client's car well-maintained? Do the brakes and accelerator work? What about the lights, wipers, mirrors, and so on? Do the tires have sufficient tread? Does the steering wheel work?

How long has the client been driving? What is the client's driving record? How is the client's hearing, vision, and ability to turn their head?

When a car going the speed limit accidentally hits a guard rail, does the car hit it head on and plunge through the railing? How many broken railings has the client actually seen on highways, bridges, or overpasses?

Do cars all slide and crash in the rain? How often do merging cars collide? Is there a multi-car crash every time there is a rash of brake lights? Are all accidents serious? Do other drivers wake up in the morning thinking, "I'd like to have a car accident today"? Or are most other drivers just trying to get to work, or get home, or run their errands?

Questions such as these help you and your clients better gauge the level of actual risk. Questions should directly address clients' fears including fears about driving while anxious or panicky. Be sure to explain how anxiety and panic work and the protective intent of every panic sensation. Use the anxiety and treatment cycle diagrams. Clients need to know why panic is not dangerous even when they are driving and why facing their feared situations, even when frightened, is necessary and justified. Review earlier chapters as needed.

Michael and Ruth, in the case examples at the end of this chapter, responded well to questioning their fears.

Even after intellectually disputing fears, clients are likely to have a visceral response to driving and may continue to be reluctant to drive when anxious. Virtual driving is a way to transition from an intellectual understanding that driving is relatively safe to an emotionally felt, visceral understanding. VR can activate somatic and affective responses, allowing them to be processed.

Driving in VR is real enough to bring fearful thoughts to the forefront of the client's brain. What can feel theoretical when discussed in session feels far more threatening and credible during a "dangerous" VR driving situation. Listen for new fears or old fears that still seem convincing.

Treating Fear-Based Actions

VR allows clients to "drive" during sessions with you. This gives you the ability to gradually and collaboratively help clients *enter* feared driving situations, rather than avoid, and *remain*, rather than escape.

Because of the immersive nature of VR, virtually facing fears nearly always creates a vivid "lived" experience. If clients are not responding, encourage them to "make it real; pretend you are actually driving" and verbalize their fears (or you say them).

Because VR can activate somatic, affective, and cognitive experiences of fear, therapeutic interventions can have an especially powerful impact.

When you both agree they are ready and with their permission, have clients gradually confront previously feared or avoided driving situations. Depending on your VR program, you may be able to recreate specific conditions by adjusting weather conditions, type of road, highway lane, and/or traffic density.

As clients practice driving while accepting anxiety (which should be decreasing) and challenging their fear thoughts, have them discontinue safety actions and reduce excessive hypervigilance. Virtual driving exposure lets clients safely take more and more "risks" until, ideally, they can drive in any weather, on any road, in any lane, and in any traffic condition with appropriate caution but without excessive fear, hyper-alertness, safety actions, or the urge to escape or avoid.

Successful immersive, engaging, and affectively evocative experiences in VR vastly increase their willingness and ability to drive in real life.

Treatment Challenges

In my experience, flying phobia treatment is straightforward and quick: often three to five sessions total, including VR exposure practice. In contrast, driving phobia is often harder to treat, takes longer, and even with VR the success rate seems to be lower. Mason, the second case in this chapter, provides an example.

It is not entirely clear why driving phobia is harder to treat than flying phobia. Perhaps it is because once the plane takes off, clients with flying phobia have fewer choices. They can't leave and so may conclude "I just have to deal with it" and use the skills learned in therapy.

On the other hand, when a client with driving phobia gets into a car there are near-constant opportunities to change to a "safe" lane, slow down to a "safe" speed, move onto a "safe" road, or pull over and stop.

And, of course, driving is actually more dangerous than flying. Accidents *do* happen. Most of us have witnessed and/or experienced at least one accident and, while the majority of accidents are minor fender benders, serious and even fatal accidents can occur.

As a result, there is an existential component to treatment. Overcoming driving phobia requires coming to terms with uncertainty and risk. Even when you drive competently and defensively in a well-maintained, safe car, you cannot control other drivers.

Think about the techniques you use with other presenting problems and how to use them with driving phobia. How do you help other clients accept uncertainty and deal with the absence of guaranteed safety in life? How do you encourage them to focus on quality and values and create a life worth living?

Case Examples

Michael

> *"I have to be able to drive. I have to get over this fear."*

Michael came to treatment in great distress. When he had been younger, he had frequently driven while "buzzed" and taken risks even when not using substances. He had loved the thrill of driving 100 miles an hour while weaving in and out of traffic. "It made me feel like Superman. It was such a rush." Right up until he rear-ended a station wagon with three children in it. "It was just luck no one was killed. I saw the mom sitting there in shock with blood streaming down her forehead and the children crying. I thought, 'My God. What have I done?'"

At that point, he entered a 12-step program, stopped drinking and using, and lost his license for a few years. Even after getting back his license, he rarely drove. Images of that accident haunted him whenever he got behind the wheel. He used public transit to commute to work, took cabs or a car service, or had his wife drive.

Now in his 40s with children of his own, he was even more horrified by his past actions. The less he drove, the more frightened he became of driving.

What brought him to therapy was that his wife was facing surgery that would limit her ability to drive. She would need him to drive her to and from medical appointments. He would need to drive their children to and from school and after-school activities. He would need to drive to do the shopping. He was fearful and deeply ambivalent about resuming driving, but knew he had no choice.

We matched his personal experience to the anxiety cycle diagram and prepared for VR by tackling unhelpful lessons from the past.

The first four sessions focused on helping him forgive himself for past actions and contrast his past self with his present self. He spoke and wrote about how the man he is now differs from the young man he had been at the time of the accident and I discussed how the brain develops through the mid-to-late 20s. A combination of self-compassion therapy, guided imagery, cognitive challenging and reframing, narrative therapy, and writing techniques helped.

Next, we described various VEs designed to be relaxing and identified those that he through he would prefer. He found the beach especially calming. While deeply immersed and calm on his virtual beach, he learned and practiced diaphragmatic breathing and PMR.

Next, while he was deeply relaxed in on his virtual beach, I had him say aloud the lessons he had taken from therapy so far including new ways of thinking about his past actions, a more realistic view of his current self, and his reasons for confronting and overcoming his fear.

Over two sessions, we collaboratively explored, questioned, and countered his fear thoughts. Together in session, we created a two-column table with multiple rows: a Fears vs Facts dialogue table. His fears, one per row, were written in the left column; new ways of thinking were written in the right column. Each fear-countering statement needed to be true and helpful.

Michael found it helpful to write what he would say to his children when they reached driving age if they had similar fears. He did not want them to be as restricted and fearful as he was—which was another source of motivation.

As we created the Fears vs Fact table, I pointed out holes in his logic or the absence of supporting evidence. We made the counter statements as powerfully convincing as possible. At home, he repeatedly reviewed the table, practicing replacing fear thoughts with facts and added any additional fears that arose as well as additional facts to refute his fears.

At this point, we agreed he was ready to go "driving". The prospect still made him afraid, but now he convincingly said that he knew this fear was unjustified. "I'm not the man I was then. I don't take risks. I'm careful and thoughtful. This fear isn't helping me or my family and I need to get over it. I need to do this."

Given the extent of his fear and years of avoidance, I started VR exposure slowly and prepared to move very gradually. Since any driving was anxiety-provoking, I began by using a 3-D VR still photo of being inside a car on an uncrowded suburban street.

This virtual car was not moving (because this was a photo, not a video) but because it was VR, he was "inside" the car and could look around. This felt real enough that his Subjective Units of Distress Scale (SUDS) self-report spiked to an 8. I encouraged him to relax his muscles, slow his breathing, and look around carefully. After ten minutes, his SUDS dropped to a 5.

I had him take a break and remove the headset while we reviewed what he had done that had helped. When he re-entered the same photo VE, his SUDS only rose to a 6 and quickly dropped to a 2. After sitting in the virtual car three times and thinking about driving (but not virtually driving), his SUDS was a 1 and he was feeling more hopeful.

I had him experience a few other VR photos of driving in different traffic conditions, included on a crowded city street. He worked on reducing his anticipatory anxiety. I confirmed that he was able to tolerate and decrease anxiety and convincingly dispute his fears. His SUDS dropped to 0.

At this point, I moved to using VR videos and VEs in which he was "driving". Although he did not actually control the car's movement, he could look around and check his mirrors. The virtual experiences were "real" enough that again his initial SUDS was quite high (8 to 10), but these spikes were tolerated and transient. He began to gain confidence.

We moved from driving suburban streets to driving city streets. We added driving past a bicyclist and driving in the rain with decreased visibility.

From there, we moved on to highway driving. This was more challenging, so I went back to 3-D VR still photos of entering a freeway and driving on a freeway. His SUDS only went to 5, and within one exposure had dropped to 3, then 2, then 1.

We repeated the same exposure two more times until his highest SUDS was a "two or a three" which quickly decreased to 1. He confirmed that an anxiety level of 2 would be tolerable. "That wouldn't keep me from driving."

We continued to progress through increasingly difficult scenarios in VR until he could enter a highway, change lanes, increase or decrease speed, and pass other cars. He practiced driving alone and then with virtual passengers in the car.

He kept "driving" despite sweaty hands, some increased heart rate, and muscle tension. I began testing his abilities and progress by starting to say his fears aloud while he was driving.

Throughout all the VR exposures, I talked to him, encouraging him to use his new skills and knowledge and checking on his self-reports of anxiety. As he improved, I had him voice his fears and counter them. If he had trouble successfully countering his fears, I reminded him of what he knew. Toward the end of this phase of treatment, I would voice his fears while he refuted them without any prompting from me. Actively engaging with clients during VR exposure does not seem to disrupt their immersion and, in fact, seems to support their progress.

As we made progress during VRET sessions, he started driving in real life. First, he practiced driving to the hospital and the school alone because he still worried about putting his loved ones "in danger" if he drove.

I encouraged him to add gradual in vivo exposure as homework to reinforce what we did in sessions. His successes in VR gave him the confidence to apply the same approach in real life.

By the time he was driving comfortably in all the VR driving scenarios, he had driven his wife to her doctor's appointment and had begun driving the children. "That was huge for me. When I could do that, I knew things had really changed." He told me his wife was grateful for the change and had remarked that he seemed happier overall. "I could never have done this without VR."

Mason

In contrast to Michael, Mason requested VRT for driving phobia but his distress over not driving seemed to be outweighed by his fearful beliefs about driving.

Mason seemed to be chronically tense and generally avoidant in several areas of his life. He had never married, had no family close by, and appeared to have few close friends and few leisure activities. In his profession he had been trained to look for and expect negative outcomes. He lived in a city with extensive public transit. His goal was to be able to drive after he retired, but retirement was several years in the future.

I thought it likely that he met diagnostic criteria for dysthymia and avoidant personality disorder, but he made it clear that he was not willing to consider anti-depressant medication and was uninterested in exploratory psychotherapy. "I've seen therapists in the past and they don't do anything."

I confirmed that he had a driving phobia, explained how anxiety works, and reviewed the rationale and strong evidence supporting exposure-based treatment. He did not want to explore his anxiety triggers nor discuss past experiences, although he did maintain that he wanted to proceed with therapy in order to drive.

He had never caused an accident or been in one. He acknowledged that his car was well-maintained, but still worried the brakes might give out or that any less than ideal visibility made driving dangerous.

We spent two sessions trying to teach anxiety management skills and counter his fears. He had difficulty relaxing although we tried different approaches and had him experience a variety of VEs that most other clients find relaxing. He found the VR relaxation skills instructions "boring".

His phobia-supporting beliefs were strongly held and fairly ego-syntonic. He stated flatly that driving was dangerous. "I can see the traffic from my window. Everyone's driving crazy. They nearly have accidents all the time. People barely stop for stop signs and traffic lights. And when it rains, cars might not be able to stop."

I suggested that he gather evidence by counting the number of cars and comparing it to the number of actual accidents he observed. As with most of the suggested homework, he did not do it. Attempts to question and challenge these beliefs were met with grudging skepticism.

He cancelled the next two appointments. When he next came in, he wanted to drive in VR. I began VRET, hoping that virtual driving might change his affective response and cognitions.

His SUDS were mid-range rather than high but did not decrease. At the next session, he reported that he had driven a few blocks. I praised and encouraged this change and encouraged him to explore what he had done that had made that possible. We resumed driving in VR, but he seemed less engaged. He declined to schedule another appointment, saying he was too busy and did not really need to drive now but that he might return when he reached retirement age.

Ruth

Ruth felt trapped. Trapped in an unhappy marriage. Trapped by family obligations. Trapped by her driving phobia.

Throughout childhood, she had been told it was her job to take care of her younger siblings. "It's like I had to be the mom." Now adults, her siblings were financially irresponsible and repeatedly came to her for loans (which they never repaid) despite earning good incomes. Her mother called daily complaining about Ruth's father and Ruth's siblings. "Nothing I say makes a difference. She doesn't seem to want to change. She just wants to complain."

At 18, Ruth had married her 20-year-old boyfriend after dating for two months, "to get away". Her husband, who had seemed "fun-loving" when they were dating, turned out to be an alcoholic. He also had a gambling addiction and was financially irresponsible. He kept promising to quit but never did for longer than a few months. He refused to attend a 12-step program, enter rehab, or go to therapy.

Ruth finally went to therapy to increase her self-esteem and decrease her codependency. She had begun setting limits with her family and was ready to leave her husband but needed to drive the freeways. At this point the therapist she saw for ongoing therapy referred her to me for adjunctive VRT.

Ruth quickly recognized various anxiety triggers. Several family members had anxiety, suggesting a genetic factor. She was more anxious during the premenstrual phase of her cycle and had noticed that she was more anxious if she had had one or two drinks the night before.

She felt under chronic external stress. With her therapist, she continued to work on changing the self-demands and lessons from the past that had contributed to years of codependency. Now she was ready to change her driving as well.

She combined avoidance and safety action by only driving surface roads, even though this added over an hour to her commute and limited her possible jobs and earning capacity. She was eligible for a much higher paying job, but the commute would require highway driving. She was highly motivated and ready.

She found diaphragmatic breathing easy to learn and loved the depth of relaxation as she practiced in a virtual meditation garden. She practiced diaphragmatic breathing at home and while driving her usual routes.

In the second session, we focused on the list of driving fears she had brought in. Her fears centered around concern that driving at highway speeds was inherently dangerous. I pointed out that driving is driving and that if she was a safe driver at slower speeds, she would be a safe driver at higher speeds because it is the same skill. We also discussed that on highways it was actually safer to drive with the flow of traffic rather than at slower speeds and emphasized that out of the thousands of cars and drivers commuting every weekday, the vast majority of them reached work and home safely.

Together we created a list of self-statements that she found reassuring and credible. She practiced them at home and by the next session, was ready to start VRET. We went directly to driving onto the highway. She was able to quickly refute her fears and her SUDS went from a 7 to a 5, then a 3, then a 2, then a 1. "I'm driving and it feels okay!"

In that one session, she repeatedly entered the freeway and drove at freeway speeds. During the second VRET session, I used a highway driving VE created using computer-generated imagery (CGI) so I could control more aspects of her virtual driving experience—with her permission ahead of time. I had her change lanes, increase the car's speed, and pass other cars. I pointed out that she was in control the whole time. The highest her SUDS was a 4, which quickly dropped to between 1 and 0.

We agreed to meet in a month. She came to the appointment saying she had accepted a new job after several interviews. She had driven to these interviews on the most direct freeway route without significant anxiety before or during. "When I start to get scared, I do the breathing and remind myself of what we talked about."

She had also filed for divorce and made plans to move out. "I love my new apartment. I just signed the lease. I can't believe what a difference this has made to my life."

We agreed that she had met her treatment goals and terminated our treatment. She continued working with her referring therapist for support through the contentious divorce.

Summary

Michael, Mason, and Ruth provide contrasting examples of responses to treatment. Their stories highlight many of the factors that influence treatment outcomes and illustrate how VR is a powerful treatment tool, but is only a tool, not a stand-alone, fix-all treatment. Client and therapist variables always matter.

Evidence Base

Wald and Taylor (2000) was one of the earliest case reports of VRET for driving phobia. Three treatment sessions were held over ten days including "practice of four VR driving scenarios". Ratings of anxiety and avoidance decreased, and the patient reported less interference in daily functioning. Treatment gains were maintained at follow-up seven months later.

In 2004, Wald reported less positive results on a series of five patients, concluding: "VRET may be most useful as a supplement or preparatory intervention for in vivo exposure, rather than a stand-alone intervention" (Wald, 2004).

Walshe and colleagues explored the importance of immersion in treatment of driving phobias. In 2003, they treated 14 subjects who had developed driving phobia after a car accident with "the combined use of computer-generated environments involving driving games (game reality) and a virtual reality (VR) driving environment" to provide exposure therapy. Only seven out of 14 subjects experienced immersion, but in those subjects,

> Pre- and post-treatment comparisons showed significant post treatment reductions on all measures SUDS ($p = 0.008$), FDI [Fear of Driving Inventory] ($p = 0.008$) ... Further analysis of the FDI showed significant reductions in all three subscales: travel distress ($p = 0.008$), travel avoidance ($p = 0.008$), and maladaptive driving strategies ($p = 0.016$).
>
> (Walshe et al., 2003)

It is important to note that positive results occurred despite comorbid PTSD and depression. In 2005, they concluded "There is a small but growing body of research supporting the effectiveness of computer-generated environments in exposure therapy for driving phobia" but again cautioned that some patients may not feel virtual driving environments are "real enough" to create sufficient immersion (Walshe et al., 2005).

A more positive report was published in 2007 by Beck et al. on a case series of six driving phobics with "full or severe subsyndromal PTSD [who] completed 10 sessions of VRET". Significant reduction in PTSD symptoms was achieved. "[H]igh levels of perceived reality ('presence') within the virtual driving situation were reported, and patients reported satisfaction with treatment" (Beck et al., 2007). Increases in presence or immersion may reflect changes in VR technology between 2003 and 2007 and VR has improved greatly since then.

References

Beck, J. G., Palyo, S. A., Winer, E. H., Schwagler, B. E., & Ang, E. J. (2007). Virtual reality exposure therapy for PTSD symptoms after a road accident: An uncontrolled case series. *Behavior Therapy*, 38(1), 39–48. doi:10.1016/j. beth.2006.04.001.

Wald, J. (2004). Efficacy of virtual reality exposure therapy for driving phobia: A multiple baseline across-subjects design. *Behavior Therapy*, 35(3), 621–635. doi:10.1016/S0005-7894(04)80035–80032.

Wald, J. & Taylor, S. (2000). Efficacy of virtual reality exposure therapy to treat driving phobia: A case report. *Journal of Behavior Therapy and Experimental Psychiatry*, 31(3–4), 249–257. doi:10.1016/S0005-7916(01)00009-X.

Walshe, D. G., Lewis, E. J., Kim, S. I., O'Sullivan, K., & Wiederhold, B. K. (2003). Exploring the use of computer games and virtual reality in exposure therapy for fear of driving following a motor vehicle accident. *CyberPsychology & Behavior*, 6 (3), 329–334. doi:10.1089/109493103322011641.

Walshe, D., Lewis, E., O'Sullivan, K., & Kim, S. I. (2005). Virtually driving: Are the driving environments "real enough" for exposure therapy with accident victims? An explorative study. *CyberPsychology & Behavior*, 8(6), 532–537. doi:10.1089/cpb.2005.8.532.

10 Flying Phobia

"I can't believe it. I was so relaxed I fell asleep on the plane."
"It makes me so happy that I can go on vacations now with my family."

In my experience, fear of flying (also called aviophobia) is probably the specific phobia that causes the greatest number of clients to seek treatment.

Unwillingness to fly places limits on clients' educational options, job and career opportunities, and ability to visit distant family or friends or accompany them on vacations. Every area of clients' lives can be impacted.

The good news is that flying phobia can be treated and incorporating virtual reality (VR) definitely facilitates treatment. VR offers the valuable ability to practice flying during session. I love it when a new client calls with flying phobia because virtual reality therapy (VRT) is often fast, straightforward, and effective.

Flying Phobia and the Anxiety Cycle

"My brother is a nervous flyer too."
"Flying always made me a little anxious, but after 9/11 it got worse and then there was this really turbulent flight. I've been scared to fly ever since."

Anxiety Triggers

In addition to individual differences in vulnerability to anxiety, I suspect that certain fears, like fear of falling or being trapped, develop particularly easily. Flying involves both being high up in the air and being restrained and unable to leave.

Chemical factors and stress can play a role in triggering a flying phobia. Several clients have reported that their phobia developed during a flight when they were flying while jet-lagged, sick, or hungover. Flying anxiety often first occurs during a period of stress, i.e., dealing with stressful work projects or deadlines, flying with a critical boss, flying after an argument or breakup, or flying to a stressful, dreaded family gathering.

DOI: 10.4324/9781003154068-12

The most common self-talk or self-demand trigger seems to be the need to be in control. Flying phobics frequently confide how hard it is for them to "give up control" to the pilot and co-pilot. Some clients have ruefully told me that they constantly grip the armrests as if they are "keeping the plane aloft". Others report, "I am always listening in case something goes wrong; in case I need to do something," even though they lack the knowledge to determine normal from abnormal sounds and couldn't fly the airplane in any case.

Fear of flying often begins following a frightening experience such an unusually turbulent flight. Simply hearing about others' bad flight experiences can create anxiety because the Reacting Brain learns lessons from what is seen and heard, as well as from what is personally experienced.

Does the client have family members who are afraid to fly? What has the client heard friends or coworkers say about flying? People often share stories about "awful, terrible" turbulent flights, neglecting the key fact that the reason they are sharing the story is because the plane landed safely. And they don't talk about all the other boring, less turbulent flights, at all.

News stories and movies can contribute to clients' fears. News media present a skewed view of the world by selectively highlighting emotionally compelling stories. After a plane crash, the media repeatedly broadcast horrifying images of wreckage and detailed, emotion-laden, heart-rending stories of death, near-death, fear, and terror. Viewers can easily be left with a distorted sense of the dangers of routine air travel.

Anxiety Sensations

Certain anxiety sensations may be particularly frightening when they occur during a flight. For example, shortness of breath, chest tightness, dry throat, lump in the throat, and/or feeling hot may be interpreted as evidence that there is not enough air. Clients can misinterpret panic symptoms as meaning that they are "out of control" or "losing it", the prospect of which can feel especially scary were it to occur during a flight.

While flying, there are times when passengers are asked to remain in their seats with their seatbelts fastened, times when all restrooms are in use, or the aisle is blocked by service carts. Nausea, queasiness, "butterflies" in the stomach, other GI symptoms, or restlessness seem far more threatening when clients cannot be guaranteed the freedom to get up, walk around, or immediately access the restroom.

Common Fears

Flying phobic clients believe that *flying itself* is dangerous, but even with classic flying phobia, specific fears about flying vary. Some fears, like fear of turbulence, are very common; others are less common.

I have heard all the fears listed below:

- Because planes are so heavy, they could fall out of the sky at any time.
- Turbulence is dangerous and could drop planes out of the sky; bumps mean the plane is plummeting toward the ground.
- Planes cannot fly through storms, snow, or lightning.
- Noises indicate a dire problem and are signs of imminent catastrophe.
- Planes are likely to crash into one another in the sky.
- Flying is dangerous so it is irresponsible of me to fly; it will be my fault if my children lose their parent.
- Because flying is dangerous, I will likely die in a plane crash which would be the worst, most unbearable death.
- A terrorist could be on the plane and plan to blow it up or make it crash.
- There is a limited amount of air on a plane; I could suffocate.

Fear-Based Actions

Clients with flying phobia often simply refuse to fly. Others try to fly. They book flights. They may even go through security and reach the gate before turning around and leaving (avoid).

Other clients board planes but leave in a panic before takeoff, sometimes even demanding to be let out after the airplane doors have closed (escape).

If clients do fly, they often try to *mentally* avoid or escape. They draw the window shade and refuse to look out. They close their eyes, put on headphones, and pretend they are not flying. I hope it is clear to you how different this is from putting on headphones to entertain yourself because flying is boring.

Other clients go to the other extreme. They are hyper-attuned to everything about flying, expecting disaster to strike at any minute (hypervigilance). They track the flight path looking for "dangerous" turbulence or storms. They watch flight attendants and other passengers and analyze the pilot's voice during announcements, looking for signs of a problem. They may listen intently to every noise or monitor the intensity or frequency of every bump, convinced that each one is an indicator or precursor of catastrophe.

Some clients, like Jose in the case example later in this chapter, do force themselves to fly, but they "white-knuckle" through each flight, remaining tense and fearful.

Some clients only fly certain "safe" airlines, planes, routes, or durations (safety actions). They may fly only during "safe" clear weather. Clients may ask flight attendants to reassure them about flying safety, distract them, check on them, or promise to deliver supplemental oxygen. Some clients ask to meet the pilot before boarding to reassure themselves that the pilot is trustworthy—even though this gives them no actual information about pilot competence.

Other clients use a mix of avoiding, safety actions, and/or fighting the anxiety. They drink before and during flights or take prescription anti-anxiety medications (often along with alcohol despite warnings not to do so). They tell themselves frantically to "Relax! Relax!" and desperately try to get anxiety sensations to stop.

Differential Diagnosis and Frequent Comorbidities

Flying phobia is particularly interesting diagnostically. When a client calls saying they have a "flying phobia", the problem *may* actually be fear of flying, e.g., fear of plane crashes, fear of insufficient air on the plane, fear of terrorists, fear that turbulence is dangerous, or fear that normal noises mean something is wrong. However, it may be another phobia entirely or a mixture.

The problem may be claustrophobia because the plane is an enclosed space. Or acrophobia (fear of heights) because the plane is up high.

It may be panic disorder ("What if I have a panic attack!?!"). Or social anxiety ("I have to talk to these people and I'm not going to know what to say and embarrass myself. What if I pass gas and everyone knows!").

It may be obsessive compulsive disorder (OCD) ("There are germs on this plane."). Or generalized anxiety disorder (GAD) ("I worry about flying like I worry about everything"). I have treated at least one client who had comorbid emetophobia and was afraid of vomiting on the plane or hearing or seeing another passenger vomit.

Some clients presenting with "flying phobia" have panic disorder with resultant agoraphobic avoidance. They are more afraid of panic than of flying. Clients may believe that having a panic attack on a plane is more dangerous than having one somewhere else. Delve into what they imagine would happen if they panicked on the plane.

Do they fear that panic will cause a heart attack, and that panicking on an airplane is more dangerous because they could not get to a hospital? Do they fear that panic will make them go crazy and do something dangerous like open an emergency exit door? Are they concerned that others would see their fear and misinterpret their anxiety as signs that they are terrorists? Do they think they will be arrested or that, if they hyperventilate, they will somehow suck up all the available oxygen?

Some clients be afraid to fly due to fears that they will vomit or lose bowel control and be unable to reach a restroom. There *are* times when passengers are asked to remain in their seats with seatbelts fastened, when all restrooms are in use, or when the aisle is blocked by service carts.

Ideally gastrointestinal symptoms and restlessness will decrease in frequency, intensity, and duration with treatment, but such fears still need to be evaluated. Get objective information about whether and how often clients have *in actual fact* vomited or lost bowel control, as opposed to fearing or anticipating that they might.

Listen carefully as clients respond to your questions. Do they tell you, "I almost…" or "If I hadn't gotten to the restroom in time, I would have/ might have…" and so forth? Or do they say, "I vomit every time I travel on a boat, fly on a plane, or am a passenger in a car on a winding road." Have they lost consciousness or lost bowel control? Do they have a medical problem that causes the feared symptoms and, if so, what is their healthcare provider's advice about treatment and activities?

Flying can also activate personality issues and schemas about needing to be in control, having trouble trusting, and/or fearing death. Issues with trust or distress tolerance may become the focus of treatment, either after treating the fear of flying, or if they interfere with treating the flying phobia.

The good news is that Kahan et al. report that VRT for flying fears can be successful *even when comorbid anxiety disorders are present* (Kahan et al., 2000). The authors also make the point that clients may continue to have some anxiety after treatment, but that they are able to tolerate the anxiety and fly.

VRT for Fear of Flying

Virtual reality has been a game changer when it comes to treating fear of flying. It offers significant advantages over the alternative treatments of medications, fear of flying classes, and therapist-accompanied flight.

Medications like anxiolytics (usually a benzodiazepine) or beta blockers (like propranolol) may or may not work. Clients often tell me, "The medicine didn't work," or only worked "sometimes" which can increase anticipatory anxiety and hypervigilance to somatic symptoms.

Even when medications suppress the emotional and somatic anxiety response, taking medicine can reinforce the client's belief that they cannot cope, which can feed the anxiety cycle ("Look, flying is so anxiety-provoking or dangerous that I need to be medicated or sedated to do it").

Figure 10.1 Flying VE Example

Clients neither learn ways to manage their anxiety nor learn facts about flying safety. They do not learn to articulate and successfully question their fears.

Some airports offer group programs for fear of flying that include a brief round-trip flight at the end. The information given during such courses is valuable and many attendees may benefit. However, these classes may or may not be run by licensed mental health professionals trained in diagnosing and treating anxiety disorders. The pace of treatment is predetermined, and participants do not receive information and interventions tailored to fit their individual needs and stage of readiness in a group class.

It is rare (and expensive) to have a therapist accompany a client on a flight and I have actually treated clients who paid for this service and then discovered that having the therapist with them had become their safety action. They were still frightened at the prospect of flying alone.

Treating Anxiety Triggers

Sometimes simply gaining insight into anxiety triggers helps clients decrease their fear of flying. Past anxiety on a plane may be attributed to chemical factors (like drinking too much the night before) or external stresses, not flying itself.

Some VR products include virtual environments (VEs) where clients can practice alcohol refusal skills. VR can help teach stress management skills. It can also provide opportunities for your clients to virtually practice assertiveness, making them less likely to be pushed into stressful situations.

Human memory is malleable. When fear of flying developed after a frightening flight, consider using VR to create an "alternative memory" of that flight—somewhat like using nightmare rescripting where clients change (rescript) the details of a nightmare.

Have your client recall the original flight while on the virtual plane, then re-imagine the flight removing or modifying those aspects that made it frightening. Concurrently, you manipulate relevant VE variables to first recreate the conditions of the past flight as closely as possible, then gradually change those conditions to create a feeling of safety.

Treating Anxiety Sensations

VR can help clients learn and practice relaxation, but this may not be needed. In my experience, clients with a simple flying phobia and no other issues learn diaphragmatic breathing quickly and easily. I often teach breathing during the first session after obtaining a history and reviewing the anxiety and treatment cycle diagrams.

With clients who have additional issues, harnessing the power of VR may make learning anxiety tolerance skills easier, more effective, or more palatable. VR can deepen relaxation and increase absorption in mindfulness. Enjoyable VR experiences can reduce baseline anxiety at the start of a session and provide a rewarding experience at the end.

Treating Fears

As a therapist, you can provide a counterweight to fear-inducing influences and misinformation. The more detailed facts you know about air travel safety, the more effective and convincing you will be.

Explore clients' fears, assumptions, and predictions. Different fears about flying require different sets of facts.

Correcting clients' misinformation or lack of information about flight safety, especially regarding turbulence, can be tremendously therapeutic. I highly recommend spending an hour or so researching basic information about flying safety and creating a client handout. The time and effort involved are minimal and the payoff is worth it.

Know simple answers for common client fears. For example, is turbulence actually dangerous, and if not, why not? How *can* airplanes fly even though they are heavy? What are some of the noises that indicate that the plane is functioning normally, such as changes in engine noise during take-off and leveling out, or as the landing gear is retracted after takeoff and released before landing? Do people pass out and die because there is not enough air or oxygen in airplanes? Is outside air brought into the plane or is the plane a hermetically sealed container?

For relapse prevention near the end of therapy, I will have clients in VR and say, "Now I'm going to be your primitive Reacting Brain and say all the things your fear might tell you." I then proceed to verbalize clients' previously reported fears in a strong, anxious voice and check that clients can counter these fears and no longer believe them. When clients confidently, fluently talk back to their fears, both they and I feel optimistic about their ability to successfully do so independently in real life.

Treating Fear-Based Actions

After identifying and intervening to reduce your client's anxiety sensations and fearful beliefs about the dangers of flying, you use VR so they can apply everything they have learned.

You and the client formally or informally create an exposure hierarchy, a list of situations related to flying that are likely to trigger more or less fear. Clients progressively confront these situations within VR. VR allows you to match the content and speed of treatment to the individual client's needs so exposure proceeds at an optimal pace.

Begin virtual reality exposure therapy (VRET) by presenting the least fear-inducing activity or situation and moving to more feared situations as your client progresses. For example, you might start VRET using still 3-D VR photos (or stills from VR videos) of being in a car going to the airport or having just arrived at the airport to evoke and reduce anticipatory anxiety. Flight phobics often endure days or weeks of worry and insomnia anticipating a flight.

During VRET, ask about physical symptoms and anxiety using the Subjective Units of Distress Scale (SUDS), and fear thoughts. Check carefully for any increase or decrease in anxiety and monitor client responses. Encourage clients to use their anxiety management skills and new facts. Confirm that anxiety and somatic symptoms decrease over time and that fear thoughts become less credible.

Once at the virtual airport, you can have clients wait at the gate, observe flights taking off and landing, or board through the jetway. Once they are comfortable with these steps, you can have them sit in various sections or seat positions on the plane and experience virtual taxi, takeoff, mid-flight, and landings.

Depending on your VR products, you may be able to control the time of day, weather, and degree of turbulence. At each step along the fear hierarchy, check clients' progress using SUDS. Continue changing the variables of the VR experience so clients can become increasingly comfortable with all aspects of flying under feared conditions.

Use VRET to prepare clients for future flights. For example, "Now imagine that you are getting on the plane for your upcoming business trip."

Self-Guided VRET at Home?

A handful of my clients have used flight simulator games at home or even gained access to a flight simulator like those used to train pilots. They reported positive experiences, which helped viscerally convince them that flying was safer and easier than they had imagined: "I had no idea how easy it is to fly and land a plane. My ten-year-old could do it."

Their experience on the simulator was helpful, although it did not cure their phobia. They felt the need to continue VRT and benefited from it.

Some clients ask about watching VR or 2-D videos available on internet sites. In general, I warn clients against videos from the internet. Such videos were not filmed with a therapeutic purpose in mind. In fact, most seem selected to elicit maximal emotional reactions—usually fear, shock, horror, or at best, excitement and thrills. I screen any video before recommending it to a client.

The one exception *might be* the amazingly reassuring video of a Qantas plane sustaining a direct lightning strike while flying. The plane continues to fly steadily and placidly as if nothing had happened. If you are interested, the URL for that video is: www.youtube.com/watch?v=036hpBvjoQw.

CAVEAT: I only show this video to clients *during a session*. I do not send them home to look it up because of all the other, non-reassuring videos that will be suggested alongside and immediately after it.

Treatment Challenges

In my experience, flying phobia presents fewer treatment challenges than many other anxiety disorders. With clients who present with a simple flying phobia, VRT is usually straightforward, short, and successful. My overall clinical experience is that when you have convincing replies to the common flying fears and use VR for exposure and practice, the majority of flying phobics complete treatment in three to eight sessions.

Naturally, treatment can be longer and more complex when additional issues are present. Negative schemas, personality disorder traits, or attachment issues can impede the development of a therapeutic alliance, undermine client motivation, make it difficult for clients to complete recommended homework or tolerate distress, and may need to be addressed in longer-term therapy.

With some clients, the fear of flying is simply one manifestation of another concurrent anxiety disorder such as agoraphobia, generalized anxiety and worry, obsessive compulsive fears, panic disorder, post-trauma symptoms, or social anxiety, to name the most common. These issues may need to be addressed before clients can overcome their flying fears.

But remember that flying phobia can respond to VRET, even with co-occurring anxiety disorders (Kahan et al., 2000).

Case Examples

> *"I opened the shade and thought how beautiful the sky and clouds were. And then I watched a movie."*

Jose

Jose was the youngest child by several years. As he put it, "I was a surprise bonus baby." Despite a gap in age, he was very close to his older siblings and extended family. Family events were celebrated with large family gatherings and attending them meant he had to fly long distances.

In the past, flying to visit relatives across the United States and in other countries had been no problem. "I *enjoyed* flying"—until one mid-winter night flight returning to college in Boston.

Takeoff was delayed because of bad weather. Jose was tired, worried about his upcoming exam, and a bit hungover from partying the night before. He was stressed about getting back later than planned. "I kept thinking about everything I needed to do."

The plane finally got off the ground, but the pilot warned that the flight was going to be "a little bumpy". The seatbelt signs were on for the entire trip.

Jose had just dozed off when, "Suddenly there was this huge drop that jolted me awake." Fellow passengers screamed and, for the first time in his life, Jose had a panic attack. He spent the rest of the flight tensely monitoring the plane's progress, waiting for another drop, and texting farewell messages to family "just in case we didn't make it".

He forced himself to continue flying but his trepidation kept increasing. Smooth flights did not reassure him because he remained tense throughout the flight, awaiting possible turbulence and disaster. Bumpy flights, winter flights, and night flights became increasingly scary.

He started avoiding family gatherings if he couldn't drive to them. When he did fly, the day and weeks leading up to the flight were pure misery. "I kept thinking about it and worrying. I would want to cancel the flight. I couldn't sleep at all the night before." After reading a blog about VRT for fear of flying, he called me.

Jose already did daily mindfulness meditation and knew diaphragmatic breathing from doing yoga, so I skipped using VR to teach those skills. In our first two sessions, I completed a diagnostic evaluation, discussed his fears, shared reassuring facts about flying safety and turbulence, and used some brief interventions targeting his past experiences. We quickly agreed he was ready to "fly".

As a result of exploring Jose's fears and past experiences, I knew what increased his anxiety and used this to create an informal hierarchy. Flying was scarier than anticipating flying. Flying at night felt more dangerous than flying during the day. Flying in rain or stormy weather felt more dangerous than flying in clear weather. Being in a window or middle seat felt more dangerous than an aisle seat because, "I couldn't get to an emergency exit if we crash." And, of course, turbulent flights were more frightening than smooth flights.

To deal with his anticipatory anxiety, we began with him being driven in a virtual taxi (or being a passenger or driver in a virtual car) going to the airport. He used belly breathing to manage his physical sensations. I had him repeatedly say his fears aloud and respond by giving objective facts about flying.

During this process, I also prompted him to voice and talk back to impulses to avoid ("I don't really have to go. I could say I'm busy, or sick, or I could drive ten hours"), to escape ("I'm already anxious just going to the airport. I need the car turn around right now. I can't deal with this anxiety. I'm leaving"), or to take safety actions for anxious reassurance ("It's only a short flight on a safe plane. I have a safe seat. I checked the weather and can double-check it every 15 minutes before boarding").

His SUDS started at 5 and, with repetition, moved to a 4, then a 2, then a 1. At this point, we agreed to go to the flight check-in area in VR and, when that triggered very little anxiety, he moved to the gate area.

I instructed him to physically stand whenever his virtual self was standing in VR, and to sit down whenever his virtual self was sitting. Having clients mirror their avatar's physical position increases the subjective reality of the VR experience, known as "presence".

I moved Jose's virtual self to the window at the gate so he could watch the planes taking off and landing and continue to reduce his anticipatory anxiety. When his SUDS remained at a 1 or 2, we agreed to start boarding.

When Jose joined the line to board the aircraft, he reported "a little anxiety spike" that peaked at a 6. His avatar moved down the jetway onto the plane. We repeated this virtual experience twice until his anxiety dropped back to a 2. He felt ready to take off.

We began with Jose in an aisle seat flying on a clear, sunny day without turbulence. The VR experience included the sounds of airplane engines revving and the noises that occur during taxiing, takeoff, flight, and landing. He was pleased to find that his anxiety got no higher than a 5, even during takeoff and landing, and quickly dropped to a 1 on his second repetition.

With his permission, I began to change the weather. A smooth night flight was fine. His SUDS did not increase.

I moved Jose to the middle seat on the plane, and then, when that did not increase his anxiety, to the window seat. He continued to be calm in the window seat for the smooth night flight. By this point, he was excited by his progress and eager to try turbulence.

To help create turbulence, I had him change seats in my office to a chair I could jostle. The movement of the chair added kinesthetic stimuli of turbulence to the auditory and visual stimuli available in VR. (Depending on your system, your VR equipment may provide kinesthetic stimuli via a vibrating platform.)

Jose was now in a window seat during a stormy night flight with some mild-moderate turbulence. In a rather shaky voice, he said, "This really reminds of that flight to Boston. It's kind of scary, but I know we landed safely, and I now know planes are designed to fly through turbulence." He used mindfulness to stay focused in the present experience. I reinforced his use of skills and knowledge.

At first, he was visibly tense, gripping the chair's armrests. His SUDS spiked to a 9, then steadily lowered to 8, then 7, then 5, then 4, and finally to 1. We repeated the VR experience with the same variables. This time, his SUDS peaked at 6 before dropping.

With his permission, I kept increasing the intensity of the turbulence and his anxiety kept decreasing. "This is amazing. Incredible. I actually feel good!"

In our last session, he repeated the stormy, bumpy night flight. At its highest, his anxiety briefly reached a 4 before dropping to a 1 and remaining between 1 and 0. "I don't worry about riding in a bumpy shuttle. I don't have to worry about riding in a bumpy plane." He was looking forward to a family reunion on the east coast and had booked flights for a vacation in Europe.

A few weeks later, he sent me a selfie of him smiling with his sibs at the vacation home they'd rented for their family reunion.

Muhammad

Muhammad wanted to overcome a flying phobia so he could visit extended family in India. As an engineer in a tech company, Muhammad was both intrigued by VRT and somewhat dubious about whether it would work for him.

Muhammad was diligent about practicing the skills taught in therapy and we quickly agreed he was ready for a virtual flight. As he donned the VR headset, his face displayed a combination of cautious hope mixed with definite skepticism. He was willing to try but waiting to be convinced.

He had very little anxiety traveling to the virtual airport, at the gate, and boarding the virtual plane and initially, he was not particularly immersed or present. I encouraged him to "pretend it is real". He did become more immersed over time, commenting after a few minutes, "It's feeling more real."

After takeoff, his SUDS surprised us both by shooting up to a 9. His shoulders tensed. His hands clenched the arms of the chair.

He tolerated the anxiety as we challenged his fears. By the end of the session, his SUDS had decreased from a 9 to a 3.

As I put away the equipment, he disclosed that the VE had brought back forgotten memories of "flying through a monsoon".

In the next session, we discussed how frightening flying through a monsoon had been. He gained insight into its lingering impact and was able to rethink the unhelpful lessons and reactions it had created.

As he continued to fly in VR, Muhammad was delighted to find that his thoughts and reactions quickly changed. After three more VRET sessions, he booked a flight and successfully visited his relatives.

Like Muhammad, many clients find that VR is more real than they expected.

Evidence Base

Case reports, research studies, literature reviews, and meta-analyses have provided a strong evidence base supporting the use of VR exposure therapy for overcoming fear of flying (Cardoş et al., 2017; Krijn et al., 2004; Rothbaum et al., 2000; Triscari et al., 2015; Wiederhold et al., 2014).

In a 2017 quantitative analysis of 11 randomized studies, the authors reported (italics added):

> the *superiority of VRET* vs. classical evidence-based interventions at post-test and follow-up. Results revealed similar efficacy between VRET and exposure-based interventions at post-test, and showed *better treatment gains over time when using VRET ... The present meta-analysis supports the efficiency of VRET in flight anxiety and encourages the use of this type of exposure ... in clinical practice.*
>
> (Cardoş et al., 2017)

References

Cardoş, R. A. I., David, O. A., & David, D. O. (2017). Virtual reality exposure therapy in flight anxiety: A quantitative meta-analysis. *Computers in Human Behavior*, 72, 371–380. doi:10.1016/j.chb.2017.03.007.

Kahan, M., Tanzer, J., Darvin, D., & Borer, F. (2000). Virtual reality-assisted cognitive-behavioral treatment for fear of flying: Acute treatment and follow-up. *CyberPsychology & Behavior*, 3(3), 387–392. doi:10.1089/10949310050078832.

Krijn, M., Emmelkamp, P. M. G., Olafsson, R. P., & Biemond, R. (2004). Virtual reality exposure therapy of anxiety disorders: A review. In *Clinical Psychology Review*, 24(3), 259–281). doi:10.1016/j.cpr.2004.04.001.

Rothbaum, B. O., Hodges, L., Smith, S., Lee, J. H., & Price, L. (2000). A controlled study of virtual reality exposure therapy for the fear of flying. *Journal of Consulting and Clinical Psychology*, 68(6), 1020–1026. doi:10.1037//0022-006x.68.6.1020.

Triscari, M. T., Faraci, P., Catalisano, D., D'Angelo, V., & Urso, V. (2015). Effectiveness of cognitive behavioral therapy integrated with systematic desensitization, cognitive behavioral therapy combined with eye movement desensitization and reprocessing therapy, and cognitive behavioral therapy combined with virtual reality exposure therapy methods in the treatment of flight anxiety: A randomized trial. *Neuropsychiatric Disease and Treatment*, 11, 2591–2598. doi:10.2147/NDT.S93401.

Wiederhold, B. K., Bouchard, S., & Loranger, C. (2014). Fear of flying (aviophobia): Efficacy and methodological lessons learned from outcome trials. In *Advances in Virtual Reality and Anxiety Disorders* (65–89). Springer US. doi:10.1007/978-1-4899-8023-6_4.

11 Height Phobia

"Everyone was so excited, talking about the amazing views. It brought home to me how much I was missing."

I live and practice in a city with tall buildings, surrounded by hills and hiking trails with breathtaking views, and within easy driving distance of ski slopes. Clients with height phobia (also called acrophobia) may be motivated to overcome their fear for work or leisure reasons.

Height Phobia and the Anxiety Cycle

Anxiety Triggers

Humans may be particularly susceptible to fearing heights. "Visual cliff" studies with infants support that fear of heights is easily learned, although Bowlby's original hypothesis that fear of heights is innate was not supported by further research (Campos et al., 1978). Some clients will tell you they have "always been" afraid of heights for as far back as they can recall.

Any of the anxiety triggers can contribute to fear of heights. In the first case example at the end of this chapter, Brenda's anxiety triggers included external stresses, self-talk, and self-demands.

It is always worthwhile asking about frightening past height-related experiences. Clients may have observed people acting fearful or heard them talk about being afraid of heights. Phobia-triggering past events can include scary height-related movie scenes—of which there are many!

What fear-promoting, unhelpful lessons did a client with height phobia draw from their past experiences? What connections were made?

Anxiety Sensations

It is important to note that most people respond with physiological arousal (such as rapid heartbeat, increased skin conductance, muscle tension) when exposed to heights, whether or not they have acrophobia. A key difference between people who develop fear of heights and those who don't seems to

DOI: 10.4324/9781003154068-13

be what they tell themselves about this physiological arousal (i.e., the unhelpful lesson).

People who interpret arousal as "excitement" or "an adrenaline rush"—and mean that in a positive way—are not frightened. Sensations tend to plateau and become a non-issue. These people either ignore symptoms or actively enjoy them as signs of pleasurable excitement or exhilaration without worrying about or anxiously monitoring their bodies.

In contrast, clients who worry about a bodily response to heights are likely to react with fear-motivated hypervigilance. Their rapid, pounding heartbeat, sweating, or tension are interpreted as signs of fear and danger rather than excitement. In turn, this fear triggers more bodily symptoms as the brain responds by releasing more adrenaline.

Both adrenaline and muscle tension can cause shaking, trembling, feelings of weakness, and trembling legs. Pupils can widen, contributing to visual changes and a sense of unreality.

Clients may start hyperventilating. Even slight hyperventilation contributes to visual changes and can cause dizziness, tingling or numbness, and a sense of derealization or depersonalization or not being fully present. The sense of not being present increases when clients focus attention on their body's reaction rather than their environment.

As clients fearfully notice and interpret bodily sensations, these sensations continue or increase and can snowball into a panic attack. This combination seems to prove to clients that they were right to be afraid; either because the environment itself is dangerous or their bodily symptoms are dangerous if they occur in this environment. And so, a phobia of heights is created.

Common Fears

Connections between sensations commonly experienced and fears commonly expressed are easy to see. Clients misinterpret muscle tension, trembling, shaking, dizziness, tingling, numbness, a sense of weakness or "jelly legs" as indicating that they are going to collapse or pass out and fall from a dangerous height. Clients often think these sensations mean they are unable to control their legs or their body. They may believe these symptoms will render them unable to move or get to safety.

Clients can be convinced that visual changes mean they are about to pass out, especially when visual changes are accompanied by a pounding heart, tingling, numbness, dizziness, and sense of derealization or not being present. Clients may misinterpret these symptoms as signals that they are about to have a seizure or other serious medical problem.

Since clients do not *choose* to have anxiety, they may conclude that they are "out of control" which, in turn, fosters fears that they might "go crazy" or "do something crazy" like jump from a height. This, combined with the sense of restlessness (feeling a need to fight or flee), can easily lead clients to believe they will act impulsively in ways that will be embarrassing or dangerous.

Clients begin, consciously or unconsciously, looking for threats and subsequently believe their body sensations, the environment, or their own thoughts are dangerous.

Three misinterpretations can co-occur and build on each other:

1   Clients misidentify what is happening in their body as dangerous in itself or a sign of danger.
2   Clients may decide the setting is inherently unsafe for some reason since they are afraid.
3   Clients may become frightened by their own mental images of jumping or falling.

Since the main danger in a high location is falling or jumping, thoughts or images of falling or jumping are easily evoked. Many people spontaneously have such images in high places. Most people can ignore such thoughts and are not upset by them.

Anxious clients, however, very easily misinterpret such mental images as terrifying indications that they are *going* to fall, that they are *tempted* to jump, or they are *likely* to jump. This is not the case—especially when clients are horrified by the possibility.

Similarly, scary thoughts or vivid images of the structure (e.g., building, bridge, overpass, elevator) collapsing and falling can spontaneously come to mind. In turn, these powerful, evocative images make the feared outcome seem imminent and likely.

As with every anxiety problem, thoroughly explore the assumptions and predictions that fuel their fears. Help the client question and rigorously evaluate fears, reviewing actual experience, logic, and facts.

Fear-Based Actions

Explore what activities or situations each client refuses to do because of their fear of heights (avoid). For example, clients may refuse to:

- Ride Ferris wheels or similar amusement park rides.
- Take elevators or go to hotel rooms, apartments, or offices above a certain height.
- Visit tourist destinations that involve heights or overlooks.
- Hike in varied terrain.
- Go skiing or ride ski lifts or gondolas.
- Fly in an airplane or hot air balloon because of the height.

Clients may initially enter a feared situation only to leave (escape). They turn back from hikes, leave sightseeing groups, cancel meetings, or make excuses to leave, and get off elevators, trams, or planes.

When acrophobic clients *do* enter feared situations, they are likely to quickly leave or make frightened attempts to stop the fear response. Clients may become overly focused (hypervigilant) on aspects of the external environment or their internal experience.

Clients may anxiously monitor how high they are, how steep the steps, stairs, or trails are, how narrow, muddy, or rocky the path is, how close they are to the edge, whether there are guardrails and how strong and safe the railings seem, and so on.

Multiple safety actions are common. Clients may:

- Carry unneeded walking sticks.
- Walk as far from the edge as possible at all times.
- Always have a companion "in case".
- Never look down.
- Stay far from windows or balconies.
- Stay close to exits in case they have to leave.
- Only hike "safe" trails.
- Only go to a "safe" height, and so on.

Similarly, clients may anxiously monitor their internal experiences, fearfully checking for signs of dizziness, weakness, tension, shaking, trembling, vision changes, or feeling unreal or out of control.

Some clients fight their somatic anxiety symptoms, thinking those symptoms present some kind of danger. When a client responds to anxiety sensations by tensing or hyperventilating, their actions can create more sensations.

When a client uses relaxation, diaphragmatic breathing, or distraction techniques *because* of fear, these techniques may provide short-term relief but also entrench the misunderstanding that anxiety is dangerous or intolerable. This, of course, strengthens the cycle of anxiety.

Differential Diagnosis and Comorbidities

Just because a client comes to you for psychotherapy is not proof that their symptoms are caused psychologically. Ask in the first session about any medical diagnoses and about medication and substance use. Several medical conditions can create vertigo or dizziness, and some conditions can put clients at risk for falling or passing out. If either you or your client suspect a contributing physiological factor, urge clients to get a thorough work-up to rule out medical causes.

Relevant medical issues can range from benign and transient to quite serious. A partial list of medical causes of dizziness, light-headedness, vertigo, or falls includes acoustic neuroma, allergies, benign paroxysmal positional vertigo, cancer, circulatory problems or heart disease, colds or influenza, dehydration, epilepsy or other causes of seizures, hypoglycemia, inner ear problems, Meniere's disease, Parkinson's disease, and postural hypotension (also called orthostatic hypotension).

Apart from the above, it is common for clients with acrophobia to have either subclinical fear of panic symptoms or diagnosable panic disorder. Be alert for comorbid anxiety disorders accompanying or contributing to fear of heights.

Virtual Reality Therapy (VRT) for Height Phobia

Fear of heights is another phobia for which virtual reality (VR) is an invaluable treatment tool. It expands exposure options beyond having clients imagine being in high places, physically accompanying clients to locations and doing therapy in public, or trying to persuade clients to place themselves in frightening heights situations without you.

Treating Anxiety Triggers

Since past events frequently play a role in creating a height phobia, help your clients re-evaluate these events. How did these events, whether experienced or observed, influence them? What lessons were learned, consciously or unconsciously? Are these lessons and resulting behaviors still appropriate and functional? Are their phobic reactions warranted?

Treating Anxiety Sensations

All my acrophobic clients are frightened by the physical symptoms of anxiety they experience in response to height. You might use VR to teach,

Figure 11.1 Height VE Example

practice, and reinforce whichever anxiety management skill(s) your client finds most effective.

One or all of the three common anxiety management skills can be helpful. For some clients, diaphragmatic breathing works well; for others, tensing then relaxing muscles, or just relaxing muscles works best; for others, mindful awareness and acceptance is the key.

Since height evokes a bodily reaction in most people, your goal is for clients to notice physical symptoms and feel confident about tolerating and responding to them. Focus on those sensations the client finds scariest, often dizziness or shaking.

Even mild hyperventilation can cause dizziness, visual changes, tingling, and numbness. Slow, low diaphragmatic breathing is the opposite of hyperventilating and can reduce or reverse these symptoms. Breathing in this way also activates the parasympathetic branch of the nervous system which may reduce the overall somatic anxiety response.

Shaking or trembling is often described as having "jelly legs" or feeling "weak". Muscle tension—along with adrenaline—contributes to these sensations. This tension can also give clients the mistaken impression that they are paralyzed or can't move. Progressive muscle relaxation (PMR) can be very effective for this. Teaching and practicing PMR in "safe" virtual situations can make learning easier and more engaging.

Mindfully noticing what is *actually* happening can be a powerful skill. Teaching mindful awareness while a client is immersed in a relaxing or neutral VR setting can make mindfulness easier to learn and understand. VR can make a difference with clients who might otherwise find mindfulness training "boring" or find it hard to maintain focus and concentration.

Treating Fears

You want to correct fears based on misinterpreting somatic symptoms. You don't want your clients to just endure by gritting their teeth (mentally, or physically!) and "white knuckling" through each experience.

Feeling scared is easy when the client's SNS has been triggered and adrenaline is coursing through their body. The client's narrative about what is happening is pivotal.

Elucidate the physiological cause of each sensation (adrenaline, changes in blood flow, breathing, muscle tension, etc.), and logically explain why each sensation is not dangerous. For example, you might clarify that while the fight-or-flight response *can* make muscles tense, tremble, and shake, it does *not* cause paralysis, inability to move or use muscles, falling, or collapse because none of those would help the person fight or flee. Muscles don't suddenly become weak at heights and regain strength when not at a height. Compare the number of times they have feared they would fall, collapse, jump, etc. to the number of times these have actually happened.

Check that your client understands what is happening in their body. Confirm that they *believe* the explanation, logic, and evidence—at least intellectually.

Some height phobic clients fear that the building, deck, walkway, bridge, overpass, etc. may collapse, that the elevator will fall, hurtling them to their death, and so on. Gather reassuring information to share with clients. You may want to estimate with clients the total number of tall buildings, decks, overpasses, elevators—whatever their feared structure is—and compare this rather astronomical total to the number of actual collapses.

Continue to ask clarifying questions such as: how likely are such events, under what circumstances would collapses be likely, and how likely would the client happen to be there at that time? Use facts, numbers, and logic to combat client fears.

This still leaves the classic anxiety response, "Yes, but what IF it happened?!?" This is where a discussion about the impossibility of perfect safety and the decisions of how to live one's life comes into play.

I talk about the fact that we have a choice about how we live our lives: whether we live a full life—or a life restricted by fear and anxiety, often asking, "Who do you want running your life? You? Or your childlike, primitive, caveman Reacting Brain?"

If clients respond, "Yes, but I shouldn't take foolish risks and going someplace high is a foolish, unnecessary risk," I encourage them to review the actual risk and remind them of the reasons they decided to seek treatment.

Proceeding to VR exposure can reveal gaps in skills or knowledge. Previously undetected fear thoughts may become evident. An unsuspected need for additional anxiety management or distress tolerance skills may become clear.

Treating Fear-Based Actions

By this point, clients should have facts and logic that contradict their fears, as well as techniques for minimizing and tolerating anxiety. Still, even armed with these tools, facing fears demands some courage. You might suggest your clients briefly recall why they came into treatment, and why confronting their fear (exposure) is required.

What are they missing? What do they want to achieve? What motivates them? Do they want to share special memories with their family or friends? Do they want to be able to accept a job located on the higher floors of tall office buildings?

What have they learned about how anxiety works? Why does avoiding, or fighting, or taking safety actions and staying alert for danger not work? Why is it necessary and helpful to act on facts and deliberately face fears?

Thus prepared, clients should be ready for VR exposure. The two of you might rate the expected fear response to each of 10–20 feared situations to create a formal hierarchy or you could use your knowledge of their fears and fear actions to create an informal fear hierarchy.

Choose among your VR options and start with situations likely to evoke mild up to moderate anxiety. Select the virtual situation or environment and adjust the variables (e.g., height, weather, distance from an edge or railing) to gradually move up their hierarchy of feared situations until even their most highly feared situation no longer triggers significant anxiety. For more phobic clients, you may want to start with 3-D still photos, before moving to 2-D videos, and ending with 3-D VR videos or computer-generated imagery (CGI) virtual environments (VEs). Repeat virtual exposures as often as needed until fear decreases. See Appendix A for information on using different VR content types.

Before each change in exposure, get the client's permission. Ask for frequent self-reports of anxiety using the Subjective Units of Distress Scale (SUDS) and adjust treatment accordingly.

During virtual reality exposure therapy (VRET), encourage clients to continue to test their fears. If clients fear the height environment itself, have them review the facts, logic, and self-talk that counters the fears.

For clients who fear certain physical responses while at a height, encourage them to use their skills, the facts, and to "run experiments". For worry about trembling legs, urge the client to notice whether or not they actually fall and remind them that their leg muscles still function, even if they are trembling or tense. You can instruct clients to alternate tensing and relaxing their leg muscles, to alternate lifting one leg and then another, to bend and straighten, or to perform other physical movements to provide proof that their legs still support them and function. As you will read in the case example of Ray, I have even sometimes encouraged clients: "Dare yourself to fall; try to fall right now."

Because VR "feels real" the virtual height is likely to trigger a physiological response, giving clients repeated opportunities to acclimate to bodily sensations and to test and disconfirm previously held fears about the consequence of physical symptoms such as trembling legs, feeling weak, etc.

After clients can convincingly refute previous fears and have little anxiety during VRET, you can challenge them to *try* to make themselves as afraid as possible. This tests treatment efficacy and helps guard against relapse. Frequently ask for SUDS to check that they do not, in fact, become very afraid. The paradoxical effort of deliberately trying to induce fear while in VR—and failing—is deeply reassuring to clients.

Self-Help VR Apps for Height Phobia

Self-help VR programs for fear of heights featuring automated avatar guides have been developed by researchers in Korea and England. Acrophobia may be particularly amenable to automated treatment because only three variables are manipulated during exposure: height, distance from edge, and direction of user gaze. When programs based on this research become commercially available, clients with height phobia as a presenting problem or comorbid issue may benefit from using such a program as an adjunct to therapy.

Hong et al. explored the use of a VR system that captured heart rate, direction of user gaze (i.e., whether the user was looking down), and subjective fear ratings (Hong et al., 2017). The study's goal was to test the efficacy and safety of a "self-training" system on 48 volunteer subjects. Subjects were divided into low-fear and high-fear groups depending on their Acrophobia Questionnaire (AQ) scores and completed a four-session program over two weeks. They concluded, "This mobile program may be safely applicable to self-training for individuals with high scores on the fear of heights by repeated exposure to virtual environments with the embedded feedback system."

Freeman and colleagues used radio advertisements to recruit 100 subjects with fear of heights (Freeman et al., 2018). Subjects were randomly assigned to either "usual care" which would not have included VRET or to an automated cognitive therapy program guided by an avatar virtual coach for 30-minute sessions up to two to three times a week over two weeks with a four-week follow-up. Subjects in the VR program reported a statistically significant decrease in fear maintained at follow-up.

Treatment Challenges

The first challenge is ruling out medical conditions that might increase the client's risk of falling, as described above. After that, the biggest challenge is keeping the client motivated to complete treatment.

Part of this second challenge is that avoiding heights can be relatively easy. Clients can request hotel rooms on lower floors, sit far from windows in high offices, and decline to go on hikes or visit high places. You may need to be particularly attentive to maintaining client motivation and belief in treatment.

A third challenge is that clients must accept a certain level of physiological activation because, as mentioned earlier, most people respond to heights with physiological arousal.

Research shows that even subjects without a phobia of heights have increased heart rate in a VR heights environment. Diemer et al. matched 40 acrophobic patients with 40 non-phobic control subjects and exposed them all to a height environment in VR. "Unexpectedly, controls, who reported no subjective fear, also showed an increase in heart rate and skin conductance" (Diemer et al., 2016). While phobic subjects reported more fear than control subjects, levels of physiological arousal as measured by heart rate and skin conductance increases were not significantly different.

In other words, it seems as if pretty much everyone has a physical response to VR heights exposure. The good news is you can share this information with clients to help combat their misinterpretation of and fear of physiological arousal. The bad news is clients may continue to have a physical response to heights. Consequently, part of treatment will be helping them re-interpret and accept this bodily response.

A final treatment challenge is that your available VEs, photos, or videos may not match the specific feared environment your client wants to enter in real life. For example, at present I am not aware of any VR environments for riding a ski lift or gondola. On the other hand, this is not necessarily a barrier to successful therapy, as you will see when you read about Brenda in the case example following.

Case Examples

Brenda

Brenda was initially referred for public speaking anxiety. A statuesque woman with a commanding presence, her recent promotion meant giving presentations to top-level management and she was expected to present at conferences. She responded well to VRT, at which point she asked if VR could help with her fear of heights.

In college, Brenda had been a competitive skier and loved nothing more than being out on the slopes. She was still athletic and active, but between raising two children and juggling the demands of her work, she had not skied in several years.

She told me, "I was thrilled when it turned out I had a half-day free at a winter conference in Colorado. I couldn't wait to get up on the mountain."

Then the unthinkable happened, she panicked on the ski lift. To her dismay, she had developed a phobia of heights. To say she was puzzled would be a vast understatement. It was more like she was flabbergasted. How could this have happened?

We spent some time exploring her possible anxiety triggers. She faced stresses from both parenting and her job and wanted to do her best in every area of her life. Since becoming a parent, she worried more. Life can feel riskier when you are responsible for the welfare of others.

We talked about how becoming a parent can make you more aware of potential dangers. You feel more vulnerable: "What if something happens to them? What if something happens to me and they lose their mother?"

The demands of being a working mother were amplified by her self-talk and self-demands. Brenda's job was rewarding, but often stressful. Her manager and coworkers were demanding, and she wanted to meet all their expectations. At times this was impossible and her unrealistic demands for perfection contributed to professional success, but also to her personal anxiety.

Brenda found this intellectually interesting, but her bottom line was, "I want to be able to ski again." She and her partner had planned a ski vacation and now she was afraid that she wouldn't be able to enjoy it.

I explained that I did not have a VE for ski lifts so I wasn't certain that VRT would help, but that I did have VEs for other heights situations we could try. Brenda wanted to try.

She was determined to overcome her fears and actively participated in treatment. We prepared for exposure and began exposure using every available VE that involved heights. We had Brenda look out the windows of offices, take indoor and outdoor elevators, go to rooftops, and step out onto the outdoor decks of high-rise apartments.

She watched VR videos of hiking mountain paths, standing near cliffs, and walking across swaying bridges over caverns. Her anxiety levels occasionally spiked to an 8 or 9, but generally were in the 4 to 6 range and dropped fairly quickly. By the end of the three sessions we were able to schedule before her vacation, her SUDS were reliably between 0 to 2.

The VRET was successful. I received a gleeful email from her with a photo of the ski lift she'd ridden up along with a picture of the sign describing the lift as one of the highest and longest in the United States.

Ray

Ray was a typical case of heights phobia. He was in his early 40s and had been fearful of heights all his life. When he even got close to a window in a high building, he felt scared and dizzy. He sat far from windows and tried not to look out.

His wife and teenage sons loved mountain hiking. Ray tried going with them, but often turned back partway. When he did hike, he stayed as far from the edge as possible. "I'm afraid of fainting or falling."

We reviewed key facts to estimate Ray's risk of falling or losing consciousness. Ray had *never* fallen. He was in excellent health and had no medical problems affecting his balance, vision, or muscle control.

He was, however, horrified by mental images of falling or throwing himself off a height. He was not suicidal, impulsive, or risk-taking. I had no concerns that he would deliberately jump or fall due to carelessness or inattention.

Because Ray had been frightened and avoidant for so many years, I began VRET very gradually, starting with 3-D VR still photos. Even so, his SUDS immediately hit a 5 and it took the rest of the session to bring it down.

We started the next VRET session with the same VR photo. This time, his anxiety only increased to a 3, and quickly dropped to between 0 and 1. We moved on to using 3-D photos of other heights environments, but I stayed with each photo until none of them elicited much fear.

Given his positive response to the photos, I began using VR videos, starting with the least fear-inducing one available. Ray's anxiety bounced up to a 6 and we had to take some breaks when he got slightly queasy. With short, repeated exposures to the VR video, his anxiety decreased.

By the next session, he felt ready to enter a heights VE. Even the lowest option was much "higher" than the scenes in the VR videos.

Almost immediately Ray began to sweat. His legs felt weak and "wobbly like I'm going to fall over". His anxiety spiked quite high ("It's a 9") but he remained determined. Diaphragmatic breathing in the VE did not help, so I had him switch to tensing and relaxing his muscles. When he remarked, "My legs are full of adrenaline," I combined instructions to tense and relax his leg muscles with suggestions of tension and adrenaline draining out of his legs with each relaxation.

Ray's anxiety dropped to a more manageable 7 and he said his legs felt stronger. I then encouraged him to test his fear that his legs would "give out" and that he would fall. With his permission, I put my hands on his shoulders and had him "dare the fear" to make him fall. I coached him and modeled saying things like, "Go on. Make me fall. Make me fall right now."

When he remained standing, I encouraged him to taunt his fear, "You're not making me fall. What's the matter? I thought you said I was going to fall. I'm not falling." This quickly cut his anxiety in half, down to a 3 or 4.

At this point, Ray began coming up with his own ways to test the validity of his fears. As I stepped back and gave him room, he lifted first one leg, then the other. He jumped up and down. He squatted down and bent over. No falling—except for his anxiety level, which had dropped to a 2.

During our last session, Ray went through all the VR heights options, including photos, videos, and VEs, while reporting little or no SUDS. His gains in VR had transferred to real life. Since our last session, he had deliberately looked out the window from the tenth-floor conference room, remaining until his anxiety disappeared. He happened to ride a glass elevator and actually looked out, instead of looking down in a panic as in the past.

He felt ready to enjoy the family hikes and said he didn't think he could have done it without VR. I agreed.

Evidence Base

VRT for acrophobia has a strong evidence base. As Coelho et al. comment in their literature review, VR "has been used in the psychological treatment of acrophobia since 1995 … It is now known that virtual reality exposure therapy (VRET) regimens are highly effective for acrophobia treatment" (Coelho et al., 2009).

Coelho et al. (2008) reported that height phobic subjects exposed to virtual heights environments made "significant improvements … on the Behavioural Avoidance Test, the Attitudes Toward Heights Questionnaire and the Acrophobia Questionnaire". The authors also pointed out that treatment times were "considerably shorter" with VRET compared to in vivo exposure (Coelho et al., 2008).

In a chapter on acrophobia, Bouchard et al. (2014) conclude that VR shows "equal efficacy with in vivo treatment in controlled studies completed to date. Treatment usually lasts between three and four sessions and is conducted using affordable computer and VR equipment" (Bouchard et al., 2014).

References

Bouchard, S., Wiederhold, B. K., & Bossé, J. (2014). Fear of heights (acrophobia): Efficacy and lessons learned from psychophysiological data. In *Advances in Virtual Reality and Anxiety Disorders* (119–144). Springer US. doi:10.1007/978-1-4899-8023-6_6.

Campos, J. J., Hiatt, S., Ramsay, D., Henderson, C., & Svejda, M. (1978). The emergence of fear on the visual cliff. In *The Development of Affect* (149–182). Springer US. doi:10.1007/978-1-4684-2616-8_6.

Coelho, C. M., Silva, C. F., Santos, J. A., Tichon, J., & Wallis, G. (2008). Contrasting the effectiveness and efficiency of virtual reality and real environments in the treatment of acrophobia. *PsychNology Journal*, 6(2). www.psychnology.org.

Coelho, C. M., Waters, A. M., Hine, T. J., & Wallis, G. (2009). The use of virtual reality in acrophobia research and treatment. *Journal of Anxiety Disorders*, 23(5), 563–574). doi:10.1016/j.janxdis.2009.01.014.

Diemer, J., Lohkamp, N., Mühlberger, A., & Zwanzger, P. (2016). Fear and physiological arousal during a virtual height challenge—effects in patients with acrophobia and healthy controls. *Journal of Anxiety Disorders*, 37, 30–39. doi:10.1016/j.janxdis.2015.10.007.

Freeman, D., Haselton, P., Freeman, J., Spanlang, B., Kishore, S., Albery, E., Denne, M., Brown, P., Slater, M., & Nickless, A. (2018). Automated psychological therapy using immersive virtual reality for treatment of fear of heights: A single-blind, parallel-group, randomised controlled trial. *The Lancet Psychiatry*, 5(8), 625–632. doi:10.1016/S2215-0366(18)30226–30228.

Hong, Y.-J., Kim, H. E., Jung, Y. H., Kyeong, S., & Kim, J.-J. (2017). Usefulness of the mobile virtual reality self-training for overcoming a fear of heights. *Cyberpsychology, Behavior, and Social Networking*, 20(12), 753–761. doi:10.1089/cyber.2017.0085.

12 Insect and Animal Phobias

"I'm never going to like them, but I'm not terrified of them anymore."

People can become phobic of any living creature: bees, birds, cats, cockroaches, dogs, snakes, spiders, etc. My impression is that fewer clients seek treatment for these phobias compared to others, perhaps because they don't realize that effective treatment is available or because they fear that treatment would require horrifying exposure.

Insect/Animal Phobias and the Anxiety Cycle

Anxiety Triggers

Some clients report being phobic "for as long as I can remember" which makes me wonder whether humans are predisposed to fear creatures like snakes and spiders. It may be no coincidence that many horror movies feature people being attacked by animals, insects, or creatures with exaggerated animal- or insect-like characteristics.

Negative self-talk along the lines of "I can't stand this" or unrealistic demands that insects or animals never be encountered may play a role. Clients who experience themselves as weak, helpless, vulnerable, or unable to tolerate distress are at greater risk for any anxiety disorder.

Past experiences may create conditioned fears or leave clients with misinformation about the phobic object. Clients can also learn fear-based behaviors from watching others.

Many clients report specific triggering past events, such as being bitten by a dog, scratched by a cat, frightened by a "huge" and presumed venomous spider, bug, etc. In addition to asking about personally experienced events, it is worth asking about frightening movies or other media experiences that may have contributed to a client's phobia.

Clients' location, occupation, and leisure activities can influence the development or impact of phobias. Insects may be more prevalent in warm humid climates with abundant vegetation. Fear of snakes or lizards is more likely to present problems for clients living near desert habitats

DOI: 10.4324/9781003154068-14

in the western United States or swamps in Florida, compared to clients in urban settings.

Anxiety Sensations

The most common somatic response when confronted by a feared insect or animal is a full or partial panic attack, which reinforces the idea that the phobic object is dangerous and can lead to comorbid panic disorder.

Clients with insect phobias may report muscles tensing in instinctive withdrawal—as opposed to preparing to fight. They may "shudder" and experience skin sensations like twitching, unpleasant tickling, or their skin "crawling" as if the insect were touching them.

Common Fears

Clients with these phobias usually fear being attacked and injured. The phobic animal is viewed as hostile, unpredictable, dangerous, and ready to attack.

Fear of animal bites are not entirely unreasonable. About 1% of US emergency department visits are for animal bites, predominately from dogs and less commonly from cats. Fatal injuries are rare, but even minor bites are an infection risk (Maniscalco & Edens, 2019).

Clients with insect phobias may report similar fears of being attacked and injured—even though most insects are harmless—but these clients' emotional reaction is often more emotionally complex. In additional to fear or panic, clients often report "disgust" and "revulsion" as well as—or even instead of—fear. The thought of an insect on their skin or in their hair repels them.

Fear-Based Actions

Clients confronting their feared insect or animal quickly move to escape and ask others to remove the animal or insect. They are usually avoidant and hypervigilant, staying alert to escape or avoid. They may have chronic insomnia because they are afraid to relax and let down their guard while sleeping. Hypervigilance may contribute to tension and stress symptoms.

Clients may be constantly on the lookout for sights or sounds of their feared creatures. They may avoid going to zoos or museums, going to certain areas of the house or neighborhood, or going on vacations. In extreme cases, they may be reluctant to leave home.

As your clients describe their experiences with feared animals or insects, listen for any safety actions they may be taking. Such actions make sense in light of their fears and beliefs. Exploring safety actions can help you uncover previously unrecognized fears or beliefs.

I don't worry that clients will not respond to virtual stimuli. If anything, you may have to desensitize clients before presenting virtual animals or insects. Some clients are too frightened to even look at photos of the feared animal or insect, including from children's books. Even small, unlifelike stimuli, such as a towel folded into the shape of a snake, triggers the fear response for some clients.

Virtual Reality Therapy (VRT) for Animal/Insect Phobias

Treating Anxiety Triggers

The anxiety triggers most likely to be relevant include genetics, self-talk, and unhelpful lessons from past events. For clients who seem predisposed to anxiety or intense emotional reactions, a number of interventions may be helpful, including practicing acceptance for innate temperament, learning coping and relaxation skills, addressing fear of panic symptoms, and correcting misconceptions regarding the phobic sensations.

Past experiences may have given clients misinformation about the phobic animal or insect, or a view themselves as helpless, vulnerable, or unable to cope with emotional distress.

Explore and correct unhelpful lessons learned from past encounters with the feared animal or insect. Help the client unpack what actually happened versus their memory and look at how they might handle this situation now.

Treating Anxiety Sensations

Experiment with different ways to cope with anxiety. Sometimes encouraging clients to deliberately maintain a moderate level of tension, which makes them feel strong and able to cope, works better than trying to achieve relaxation.

Figure 12.1 Dog Phobia VE Example

Treating Fears

Identify clients' specific fears and help them evaluate their fears against the best available evidence, facts, and logic. Help the client explore the actual likelihood and seriousness of any danger, based on their individual situation.

Avoid the pitfall of trying to guarantee perfect safety. Life never offers such guarantees.

Where there is realistic danger, help them plan for reducing their risks. For example, clients may believe that all snakes are venomous, and all snakebites result in death. Neither of these beliefs is true. More than 85% of snake species are non-venomous. Only five deaths result from 7,000 to 8,000 venomous snake bites each year in the US (CDC, n.d.).

Where there is actual risk, help clients formulate a reasonable plan. This might include learning which insects or animals live in their area, how to determine if they are actually dangerous, how to avoid dangerous insects or animals, and appropriate protective actions—based on facts, not simply fear.

To combat revulsion or disgust, encouraging the client to use distress tolerance skills or to act on their values despite distress may be more effective than recommending relaxation.

Reflect on your *own* emotional reactions. If reading this section triggered negative emotions, consider following these treatment suggestions yourself. Reducing your own discomfort prepares you to be a more effective therapist for these phobic clients.

Augmented reality (AR) can superimpose images of insects on a scene viewed through a smartphone. The first several times I saw cockroaches or spiders crawling around my desk in AR, I reflexively startled and dropped the phone! It took several repetitions for me to become comfortable. This was a good example—and a good story to share with clients—of the need for deliberate, repeated exposure.

Treating Fear-Based Actions

The goal of treatment is to replace phobic avoidance with appropriate caution or tolerable dislike. Phobic clients may never become animal lovers or entomologists, but they no longer need respond with such intense terror, disgust, or avoidance that it interferes with their activities.

Information from research studies, government and academic websites, and other reputable sources, can be helpful sources of reliable facts. Clients' fears may be completely unfounded, blown greatly out of proportion, or, in some cases, realistic.

Be alert to actual danger. For example, if your client is frightened of a neighbor's dog and reports that the dog has lunged at or attacked him or someone else, the dog may present a real danger. Similarly, it is generally advised that young children not be left unsupervised with a dog.

Although serious risks from insects are rare, they do occur and should be taken seriously when realistic. For example, some areas have poisonous or venomous insects (like black widow spiders or fire ants) or insects likely to carry serious diseases (such as Lyme disease or Zika virus).

Some people have severe allergic reactions to many types of insect bites or bee stings. If your client has a history of severe allergic reaction to an insect sting and is at risk for anaphylactic shock, suggest that the client ask their healthcare provider about carrying an epinephrine autoinjector and medical ID jewelry with their allergy information.

Explore factors that influence how frightened the client feels. Relevant features for animal or insect phobic clients include:

- Proximity to the animal/insect
- Safety barriers or restraints (i.e., muzzled or on a leash, in a cage or terrarium)
- Size of the animal/insect
- Number of animals/insects
- Whether the animal/insect is moving
- Speed and/or suddenness of movements

Use this information to tailor an exposure hierarchy. Use gradual, repeated exposures to help reduce clients' cognitive and emotional responses. Adjust each virtual reality (VR) experience to let your client successfully confront and overcome their fears, without feeling overwhelmed.

Notice whether clients respond better to relaxation techniques or to mindful acceptance (acknowledging and detaching from the thought and emotion in a nonjudgmental manner). Some clients tolerate exposure better when they remain somewhat tense, coupled with suggestions that they are strong, determined, and physically much larger than the feared creature.

You may create a hierarchy collaboratively by having the client rate how frightening several scenarios would be on a scale of 1 to 10 or 1 to 100 (where higher number indicate more fear). Perhaps several small spiders moving rapidly in a terrarium would be a 50 but a large spider outside a terrarium and close to the client might be an 85. Various factors can interact in client ratings. Creature size, number, movement, distance, and barrier all play a role.

In a majority of cases, you will succeed with this goal if you follow the treatment steps as outlined. The case examples of Cindy and Jessica at the end of the chapter demonstrate this. However, unexpected sometimes problems crop up, as the case of Steve exemplifies.

Treatment Challenges

As with many anxiety disorders, one challenge is making the correct diagnosis and identifying any comorbid conditions (like those mentioned above) that might interfere with phobia treatment. Another challenge, also mentioned above, is obtaining accurate information so you and the client can realistically evaluate any risks posed by the animal or insect. Be sure to draw your facts from reputable websites which give a balanced view of actual risks.

Challenges addressed below include lack of tactile stimuli, dealing with disgust and revulsion, and/or lack of phobic-specific VR content.

Lack of Tactile Stimuli

Clients with insect phobias often fear the tactile sensations of an insect on their skin and have a "skin crawling" component to their somatic response. You may want to add tactile stimulation to the VR exposure hierarchy, based on client readiness and with their prior agreement.

Combining tactile stimuli with VR exposure makes the experience more realistic. Making a client's experience more realistic makes reactions more intense and fear-inducing, moving the experience higher on the client's fear hierarchy. Take this into account because you want exposure to be gradual and tolerable. As a general principle avoid big leaps in fear, whenever possible.

For clients who are afraid of furry animals like a cat or dog, you can provide a small fuzzy blanket or furry stuffed animal. With the client's permission, have them pet the blanket or stuffed animal while close to the virtual animal.

For insect phobic clients, you can simulate the sensation of the insect landing on them by lightly brushing the skin with a small paint brush or makeup brush. You may take a scrap of paper or a bit of tissue and put it on a client's hand or arm. Doing this allows the client to see that they can quickly "brush off" the insect. If they fear the insect will cling, the sticky side of a small, crumpled sticky note or a piece of tape can be useful.

Disgust and Revulsion

As mentioned earlier, clients may react with disgust or revulsion in addition to, or instead of, fear. Accompanying thoughts may be describe the phobic creature as "dirty", "nasty", "disgusting", "icky", or similar adjectives.

Disgust can be harder to overcome than fear. Acceptance commitment (ACT), distress tolerance, or mindfulness techniques may help increase client willingness and ability to tolerate feelings of revulsion.

It may help to emphasize that clients need not *like* the phobic creature, just be able to cope with it without the phobia controlling their actions or restricting their lives.

No VR Content of the Feared Creature

If your VR system does not include virtual content of the client's specific phobic animal, insect, or arachnid, here are two options to try:

- Look for VR content with creatures that look roughly similar or have enough salient features to be used for virtual reality exposure therapy (VRET). For example, cockroaches might be used with a client who is phobic of stink bugs. During VRET, have clients imagine that the virtual creature displayed is their feared creature or have them focus on the similar features.
- Select virtual environments (VEs) where the feared creature might be found in real life. Have clients go to those locations virtually and imagine encountering their phobic object. For example, subway stations might be relevant for clients who fear rodents, cockroaches, or feral cats. Parks, open spaces, or even city streets might be relevant for fear of dogs or birds. Forest or marsh scenes might be used for fear of birds, snakes, insects, or spiders. Rooms indoors might be useful for mice, insects, or spiders.

In some virtual environments you can increase or decrease lighting levels. When that is the case, gradually making the environment darker can increase the exposure intensity.

Case Examples

Steve: Spider Phobia

Let me share the cautionary tale of a spider phobia client, lest you get the mistaken impression that every case progresses smoothly and inevitably to total success.

Steve wanted to overcome his fear of spiders, especially tarantulas. He didn't allow his children to bring nature books home from the school library because they might have pictures of spiders. He left the room if he saw a spider. He wouldn't accompany his wife and children to the park, the zoo, or on a walk in the woods. And there was absolutely no way he was going camping, even in an RV. If a spider was ever seen in the house, he made his wife or children capture or squash it.

Steve felt bad about making his family members deal with spiders, and he didn't want to pass his fear on to his children.

When questioned, he reported no family history of anxiety or other psychological problems. He had no other phobias and did not panic at any other time. His job was somewhat stressful, but this was not presented as a problem. He was not depressed.

Both his wife and children and his family of origin were described as loving and supportive. Steve did not present as overly self-critical or perfectionistic, although he was hard-working, conscientious, and took a cautious, risk-averse approach to life. In short, there seemed to be no genetic, chemical, external stress, or self-talk triggers.

The *primary* anxiety trigger identified was a past experience when he was six years old. While on a camping trip with his parents, a large spider got inside their car without anyone noticing. Steve was in the backseat, leaning his head against the window, when the spider crawled up the window toward him. He yelled in fear and began crying. His parents finally stopped the car and put the spider out, but Steve was terrified. His parents' calm explanations that the spider was large, but harmless, made no difference. "They told me it was harmless, but it was so huge. It had all those legs. It was ready to jump on me!"

He had Googled spiders and already knew intellectually that they were generally harmless to humans. Reviewing facts did not help. Nor did the various anxiety management skills we tried.

Since this phobia seemed to stem from a rather traumatic past event, we agreed to use eye movement desensitization and reprocessing (EMDR) in which I had been trained by Dr. Francine Shapiro (Shapiro, 2017). I used both traditional EMDR and the flash technique (Manfield et al., 2017). The memory of the experience faded, and he felt calmer. I encouraged Steve to practice mindfulness and in session we practiced relaxation paired with positive suggestions and imagining a changed response to spiders.

Steve's positive initial result from EMDR waned over time. I repeated EMDR and continued to identify his fears (e.g., "A spider will bite me and inject venom") and counter them with facts (e.g., "Spiders in our area are not venomous").

We agreed to start using VRET at the next session. I discussed options of AR or VR exposure. Steve preferred VR. I used two different VR products to make exposure as gradual and tolerable as possible and was careful to explain to him in advance what he would see in the VE.

Steve first looked at a cartoon drawing of a spider in VR, which triggered an anxiety level of 1. When he moved to looking at a more realistic black-and-white drawing of a spider, his anxiety increased to 2. He used diaphragmatic breathing which created a feeling of "peace" and dropped his anxiety to 0.

We moved to a color photo of a real spider. He used breathing, facts, and mindfulness and kept his anxiety to a 1. He was doing well, and we wanted to continue.

I was concerned that the next step in the program we had been using would be too frightening because the virtual spiders appeared very close to the client, so I changed to a different VR program which showed spiders farther away.

The first option was to show a single, small, virtual black and red spider in a terrarium on the far end of a virtual desk. The sight of the spider triggered a 3 on the Subjective Units of Distress Scale (SUDS), spiking to a 6 as soon as the spider moved. I played the recorded instructions for diaphragmatic breathing. Within five minutes, his SUDS was a 2.

To end the session on a positive, reinforcing note, with Steve's agreement, I put him in a virtual underwater scene, thinking to combine relaxation with some mild exposure because there were creatures with arachnid-like features: a crab crawling along the seabed and an octopus with trailing legs swimming by. Steve calmly observed and commented on the spider-like aspects of the crab and octopus. His anxiety started at a 1 and moved to 0. We were both encouraged.

By the next session, Steve said he had watched his children's DVD of the movie *Charlotte's Web*, pausing the film as needed and using breathing and mindfulness for anxiety control. "I did what you talked about. I just paid attention to it." He had moderate but tolerable anxiety that went down somewhat, from a 6 to a 4. By session 5, Steve had watched the spider close-up scene in *Charlotte's Web* and anxiety had dropped further from a 4–5 to a 1 or 2. He was also doing imaginal rehearsal of dealing with large spiders.

I again discussed various virtual exposure options: 2-D videos of spiders, AR, or either of the two VR programs we'd used previously. Steve chose to use the VR program of the spider in the terrarium. Keeping the variables set to only one spider in the terrarium at maximum distance away, the small spider only triggered an anxiety of 1. We moved up to the next size "medium" spider. Again, the anxiety level was tolerable, a 3.

This is where, in retrospect, I wish I had had Steve stay in this VE until his anxiety decreased to a 1 or 0. But things had been progressing well, so I changed to a video of the next size larger spider.

As always, I explained what to expect and got permission before changing VEs or variables. However, the moment the larger moving spider came into view, Steve yelled in panic and tore off the VR headset, throwing it aside and hyperventilating. Just the opposite of what I wanted to have happen.

I apologized and we talked over what had happened. Before Steve left, he watched a video of a spider without distress, but he was clearly shaken by his virtual experience. He cancelled the next session, reporting that his fear had increased.

I reached out to him and we rescheduled. After processing the experience, we resumed VR exposure with the agreement that he would spend more time at each level, that we would use the first VR product, not the one that had scared him, and that we would set a goal of achieving an anxiety level of 0 whenever possible.

I also made a point of getting an anxiety level *before* each exposure as well as getting his permission to advance. I wanted to make sure he did not enter any exposure already highly anxious.

Steve quickly worked his way through the cartoon drawings of spiders. We did not move to the next step until his anxiety was 0, even when the peak anxiety level was only a 1. The black-and-white drawing, which he had seen before, caused an anxiety of 2 which he brought down to 0. The photo of a real spider resulted in anxiety of 3, which he again quickly brought down to a 0.

The hardest jump was going to be the next step, so we discussed it in detail beforehand. He would see a small, animated spider at a distance, but it would be moving. The combination of size and movement seemed to be his primary fear triggers.

As expected, the moving spider created more fear, an anxiety level of 5. Using diaphragmatic breathing and reviewing the facts to counter his fears and misconceptions, his anxiety dropped to a 0.

In our next session, we repeated the same VR exposures and were able to go three additional steps: a medium moving spider far away, a larger moving spider that came closer, and a small faster-moving spider that came closer. His maximum anxiety was a 3 and dropped to either a 0 or 1. We then repeated the entire sequence. Steve's anxiety response to all but one of the VEs was 0. One VE triggered a 2 which decreased to 0.

Unfortunately, the negative emotional impact of that frightening experience lingered and, despite what seemed like two subsequent successful sessions, he discontinued treatment. Cost was a contributing factor, but he specifically cited the frightening session as a major factor in his decision to stop.

Important take away lessons from this case:

- Remain aware that innocuous looking content may terrify the person with the phobia. For me, the difference in size between the medium and large spider was not much, but for my client, the larger spider was a "huge giant".
- VR experiences have the potential to sensitize, rather than desensitize, as this case example demonstrates. I encourage you to describe in advance as clearly and specifically as possible the details of what the client will experience and to get the client's permission before moving forward.
- Spend sufficient time processing any negative reactions and work to repair therapeutic ruptures. I thought I had done this, but in hindsight, we might have spent more time processing what had occurred.
- Finally, remember that, despite the poor outcome in this particular case, research does show that VR (and AR) can effectively treat animal and insect phobias.

I included this case example so that you can learn from my experiences, the bad as well as the good, as you integrate VR into your practice. Bad experiences are rare, but they are the reason I repeatedly emphasize preparation prior to exposure.

Cindy: Spiders and Insects

Cindy reacted to insects and spiders with a combination of panic and disgust.

There are lots of insects and spiders where I live. They look repulsive and I'm afraid they're going to jump on me! Even though I have the pest control spray every month, I still see them outside sometimes. I even saw them once or twice in the house. I screamed and ran outside. I wouldn't go back in until my father came and killed them. I can't go on like this. I'm getting more and more afraid.

We worked on diaphragmatic breathing and discussed using a combination of "staying in the moment" and some progressive muscle relaxation.

We identified which insects were more and less fear-inducing and created a fear hierarchy starting with looking at cartoons, then drawings, and then photos beginning with her less-feared insects moving up to her most-feared. I got children's books from the library to find cartoons, drawings, and photographs, organized them from less scary to more, and used them to provide graduated exposure.

We reviewed in detail why her phobic creatures were not harmful to humans. We also agreed that she could continue to dislike them and take appropriate actions to minimize their appearance in her house.

She began to imagine responding in an appropriate, non-phobic manner to seeing an insect or spider, deliberately imagining what she would tell herself, how she would manage her anxiety, and what she would do. Only after she had those skills and had practiced using them successfully in imaginal exposure, did we move to exposure in virtual reality.

For exposure, we started with a VR video before moving to more immersive VR environments. The VR headset I was using held a smartphone and had detachable straps. I removed the straps before I gave Cindy the headset so she could choose how close it would be to her face and feel more in control. This decreased her immersion but also reduced the risk of an experience being too frightening, as had happened with Steve. As Cindy felt less afraid, she held the headset flush against her face and eventually wore the headset on her head, while sitting at a desk, and placed her hands on the desktop to mirror the position of her avatar's hands in the VE.

At each step, I asked permission before changing a VE or a variable. During each exposure, I waited until Cindy's SUDS was down to a 1, and most of the time I waited until her anxiety had decreased to 0. At the start of each session, I repeated a few of the previous VR exposures to reinforce progress and confirm that the improvements were maintained.

I double-checked with Cindy at every point before changing a variable and offered her choices of which variable to change whether type of insect, size of insect, number of insects, or distance from the insects.

VR control variables for insect type, size, number, and distance from the avatar allowed me to create a hierarchy of exposures by gradually bringing the insects closer without changing their size or number, increasing the number of insects without making them bigger or bringing them closer, or making the insects bigger without increasing the number or changing the distance. These variables could be controlled for each of type of virtual insect.

What seemed to work best was to desensitize first to one *size* of insect and gradually bring that size insect *closer* before increasing the number of insects or their size.

Near the end of treatment, I added tactile stimulation. When the virtual insect was closest to Cindy's virtual hand, I would lightly tap the appropriate place on her hand or finger with a small brush. Cindy also practiced "flicking them away". We agreed that the insects and spiders were "stupid" and "absolutely harmless". She commented, "If they get on me, it's because they're curious or lost and I can brush them off." She continued to dislike insects and be disgusted by them but was no longer terrified.

Jessica: Dogs

Jessica sought treatment for her dog phobia when the city built a dog park next to her favorite library. She lived in an urban neighborhood with lots of singles and families, many of whom had dogs, so she frequently encountered dogs while out running errands. She wanted to be more at ease.

Genetic factors may have contributed to her phobia. Her sister was afraid of flying. Her mother tended to worry about her health. Her nephew got anxious before giving presentations at work. Clearly anxiety ran in Jessica's family.

She denied any significant external stresses, negative self-talk, or unrealistic self-demands and did not recall any relevant past events when I asked about these in our first session.

Whenever she saw a dog, Jessica's heart sped up and her muscles tensed. Her primary fear thought was that dogs were "just tamed wolves" who could "revert" at any time. All dogs were viewed as ready to attack, regardless of training, breed, or size. The dog park was an especially big source of anxiety because dogs were off leash, and she was convinced they would jump the fence and maul her.

Her main fear-based action was avoidance. If she saw a dog, she immediately crossed the street and turned the corner, even if the dog was on a leash two blocks away. She had changed her route to the library to avoid seeing the dog park but even the sounds of the dogs playing triggered anxiety. She was starting to be reluctant to go on hikes or long walks or to city parks or beaches for fear of seeing a dog. She was considering carrying pepper spray in her hand whenever she was outside (safety action).

In our first session, we discussed how anxiety works and went over the anxiety diagram together. By the end of the first session, she understood why her thinking and actions maintained her phobia and why they needed to change. Using the anxiety treatment diagram, we mapped out treatment plan. Before the next session, she was to list all her fears about dogs so we could work on them.

At the second session, Jessica reported that she'd casually mentioned at a family gathering that she was in therapy to overcome a fear of dogs and that she was puzzled about why she was so afraid. Her mother had exclaimed, "Don't you remember? When you were four years old, our neighbor's dog jumped on you and knocked you down. He was friendly and was licking your face, but you screamed and thought he was going to bite you. That neighbor moved away soon afterward and the family that moved in didn't have a dog. I didn't realize you were still scared." With that new information, we added the past event to our understanding of her phobia.

We reviewed her fears and together we came up with facts and counter statements. These included things like:

- Dogs have been living with humans for centuries and centuries.
- Dogs have been tamed and bred; they are not wolves.
- Dogs are called "man's best friend". People wouldn't have dogs for pets if they behaved like wolves.
- Even the dog that knocked me down when I was four was only being friendly. I was not bitten or attacked. And I am much taller and stronger now.

Next, we used VR to help her learn and practice diaphragmatic breathing and deepen her sense of relaxation. While she relaxed, we reviewed and reinforced the new information about dogs.

As homework, I had Jessica write down everything she could recall and everything her mother told her about the dog incident when she was four. First, she wrote it as if she were four years old again and it was happening. Then, she wrote down what she would tell her four-year-old self if she could go back in time with the new information we had covered in session. Jessica used her relaxation techniques as she read and re-read what she had written as a way of changing her narrative about the event and the lessons her brain had drawn from it.

We acknowledged that some dogs *are* poorly trained or unpredictable— but not the majority of dogs. I encouraged her to just observe any dogs she happened to see and answer some questions. Were they on a leash? Were they growling? Did the owner look frightened or tense?

At our third session, Jessica told me she no longer got upset when she thought about the past incident. She also said that she'd begun actually looking at dogs instead of quickly leaving the area. She still crossed the street, but now she stopped and observed the dog and owner.

She was actually shocked to see how relaxed and happy the dog owners were. "They're not even worried! Some of them are on their phones and barely pay any attention." She saw dog owners pull dogs away when the dog wanted to sniff something.

I shared information about how to approach a dog and signs that a dog is friendly or unfriendly. We also talked about what to do if a dog approached her and she didn't want to interact.

With her permission, we began in-session exposure. First, we looked at puppy videos on the computer. I had her rate her SUDS before, during, and after. She had a SUDS of 6 thinking about looking at puppies. Her SUDS dropped to 2 and then to 1 as we watched these videos together. While watching, I asked her what her fear would say ("The dog's going to attack. It's going to bite. Dogs are dangerous") then countered the fears by reviewing the facts and noticing what the videos actually showed.

Some VR products offer the option to show 2-D videos to a client wearing the VR headset. I had Jessica put on the VR headset and watch 2-D, non-immersive videos of adult dogs interacting with humans. Her initial SUDS of 4 dropped to 1. I then went from asking "What will your fears say? And what will you say back to them?" to voicing her fears saying things like, "That dog looks big and dangerous! It's just like a wolf. Dogs came from wolves. They are really wolves underneath. The dog's going to attack at any minute. All dogs are dangerous."

If she faltered or reported feeling more anxious, I reminded her to use her relaxation techniques and helped her review the facts. Her SUDS decreased and remained low.

We agreed that she would experiment with not crossing the street when she saw a dog. I also encouraged her to go to the dog park and observe how the dogs actually behaved. Did any dog jump the fence? When dogs chased each other and barked, were they attacking, or playing? Did what she observed support or refute her fears?

We agreed to meet in two weeks. Halfway through, she sent me a photo she'd taken near the dog park.

At our next session, we began VRET. We agreed to start with her virtually confronting a quiet dog that was muzzled and on a leash some distance away. She said that before treatment her anxiety would have been a 10, but that now she expected it would only be a 6 or 7. In fact, she was surprised to report that her SUDS was a 5. "My muscles aren't very tense. I'm more relaxed than I expected. I'm remembering everything I've learned and seen. Most dogs are friendly, and I know what to do."

When her SUDS dropped to a 2, I asked "What makes it a 2 and not a 4 or 5?" She replied, "I remind myself of what I'm learning." Then I asked, "What would bring it down to a 1or a 0?" She said she was still a little scared, but that when she forced herself to actually look at the dog, she became more comfortable. She agreed to deliberately look at the dog and tell me what she noticed until her SUDS was a 1.

We repeated the process, bringing the muzzled dog closer and closer. Her SUDS briefly went no higher than a 4 or 5 before dropping to a 1 even at the closest distance. However, she was telling herself that the muzzle kept her safe, indicating that there was some remaining fear.

We reviewed the signs of a friendly dog and resumed VR exposure using a dog without the muzzle, starting from the farthest distance.

I know this is leftover fear and I need to reprogram my brain. I know what to look for and I know what to do. This dog is on a leash. Its owner has a firm hold on the leash. The dog's tail is wagging. Its ears are up. It is not growling or baring its teeth, putting its ears back, or lunging. This is a friendly dog. There is no reason to be afraid.

She repeated these and similar statements with increasing confidence as, with her permission, I brought the unmuzzled dog closer and closer. Her highest anxiety level was a transient SUDS of 4, with most of her reports being between 2 and 0.

"I know now that I can face my fear and it goes down. I'm going to go to the dog park." I encouraged her to practice imagining asking to pet a dog and have a successful experience (a combination of imaginal exposure and imaginal rehearsal). If new fears arose, she was to write them down and question them in light of her new knowledge.

When we next met three weeks later, Jessica had been to the dog park at least once every week and was starting to make friends with some of the dog owners. The closer she got to the dogs, the more she realized how much taller she was than they were. She saw that even when a dog jumped on its owner, no one was knocked over or scared. She even—despite some trepidation and with the owner's permission—petted a small fluffy dog.

I expressed my delight at the positive changes, asking "What did you do that made those changes possible?" and asked her to tell me what she had learned. I highlighted her new knowledge and skills. She remarked that she was sharing what she'd learned about overcoming anxiety with her siblings.

Jessica eagerly resumed VRET and quickly felt comfortable with a virtual dog close to her while muzzled and then unmuzzled. I tested her comfort by again voicing the worst fears we'd identified. She had no problem refuting the fears and remaining calm.

I asked, "From 0 to 10, where 0 is not at all and 10 is absolutely, how much did you believe the fears when you first came to see me?" "Oh, a 10!" "And now, how much do you believe these fears in your gut?" "It's a 1. I know you need to have a little caution around strange dogs, but I don't think about them the same way at all." She no longer crossed the street. She was enjoying the city parks and had gone on a hike with friends.

A week after ending treatment, she called saying she'd been hiking with a friend when a golden retriever running free came up to them on the trail.

My friend knew how afraid I had been of dogs and asked me if I wanted her to get in front of me, but I said "no". I stood still and noticed that it was wagging its tail. Then the owner came up the trail. I asked if the dog was friendly and whether I could let it sniff my hand and pet it. And I did! Its hair was so silky. My friend was astonished, and I was really pleased.

Evidence Base

Côté and Bouchard (2005) reported on a series of 28 adults with spider phobia (arachnophobia) treated with VRET. Pre- and post-treatment measures included objective measures of arousal and information processing using Stroop tasks, a behavioral avoidance test, and a measure of participants' inter-beat intervals while looking at a live tarantula. Self-reports of decreased fear correlated with less behavioral avoidance.

> Analyses made on the pictorial Stroop task showed that information processing of spider-related stimuli changed after treatment, which also indicates therapeutic success. Psychophysiological data also showed a positive change after treatment, suggesting a decrease in anxiety. In sum, VRE led to significant therapeutic improvements on objective measures as well as on self-report instruments.
>
> (Côté & Bouchard, 2005)

Michaliszyn et al. (2010) randomly assigned subjects with spider phobias to exposure in VR or in vivo and reported that VR exposure effectively decreased fear (Michaliszyn et al., 2010).

Shiban, Pauli, and Mühlberger (2013) randomly assigned 30 spider-phobic subjects to be virtually exposed to spiders for four sessions, using either one VE setting or multiple virtual settings (Shiban et al., 2013). Self-reported anxiety, skin conductance levels, and behavioral avoidance significantly decreased in both groups but exposure in multiple contexts improved generalization to the real world behavior avoidance test. Similarly, VR exposure therapy for a specific phobia to dogs in children demonstrated a significant decrease in severity and symptom ratings post-treatment (Farrell et al., 2020).

If your system offers the option, augmented reality may be used with insect phobias. AR superimposes digital images onto the user's actual environment and may be viewed in VR, using special glasses, or on the display of phone or tablet. In other words, spiders or cockroaches could be seen crawling the actual desk or table in front of the client.

Botella et al. (2016) randomly assigned subjects with phobias of spiders or cockroaches to either in vivo or AR exposure (Botella et al., 2016). AR exposure was "well accepted" and subjects "significantly improved on all the outcome measures at post-treatment and follow-ups … [and reported that AR exposure was] … less aversive [than in vivo]".

References

Botella, C., Pérez-Ara, M. Á., Bretón-López, J., Quero, S., García-Palacios, A., & Baños, R. M. (2016). In vivo versus augmented reality exposure in the treatment of small animal phobia: A randomized controlled trial. *PLoS ONE*, 11(2). doi:10.1371/journal.pone.0148237.

CDC (n.d.). Exposure therapies for specific phobias. *Society of Clinical Psychology Division 12, American Psychological Association*. Retrieved September 3, 2021, from https://div12.org/treatment/exposure-therapies-for-specific-phobias.

Côté, S. & Bouchard, S. (2005). Documenting the efficacy of virtual reality exposure with psychophysiological and information processing measures. *Applied Psychophysiology and Biofeedback*, 30(3), 217–232. doi:10.1007/s10484-005-6379-x.

Farrell, L. J., Miyamoto, T., Donovan, C. L., Waters, A. M., Krisch, K. A., & Ollendick, T. H. (2020). Virtual reality one-session treatment of child-specific phobia of dogs: A controlled, multiple baseline case series. *Behavior Therapy*, 52(2), 478–491. doi:10.1016/j.beth.2020.06.003.

Manfield, P., Lovett, J., Engel, L., & Manfield, D. (2017). Use of the flash technique in EMDR therapy: Four case examples. *Journal of EMDR Practice and Research*, 11 (4), 195–205. doi:10.1891/1933-3196.11.4.195.

Maniscalco, K. & Edens, M. A. (2019). Bites, animal. StatPearls Publishing. www.ncbi.nlm.nih.gov/pubmed/28613602.

Michaliszyn, D., Marchand, A., Bouchard, S., Martel, M. O., & Poirier-Bisson, J. (2010). A randomized, controlled clinical trial of in virtuo and in vivo exposure for spider phobia. *Cyberpsychology, Behavior, and Social Networking*, 13(6), 689–695. doi:10.1089/cyber.2009.0277.

Shapiro, F. (2017). *Eye Movement Desensitization and Reprocessing (EMDR) Therapy: Basic Principles, Protocols, and Procedures*. Guilford Publications.

Shiban, Y., Pauli, P., & Mühlberger, A. (2013). Effect of multiple context exposure on renewal in spider phobia. *Behaviour Research and Therapy*, 51(2), 68–74. doi:10.1016/j.brat.2012.10.007.

Part III

Treating Other Anxiety Disorders

Chapters 13 through 17 focus on anxiety disorders other than specific phobias, including anxiety symptoms that commonly bring people to treatment, and give an overview of incorporating virtual reality (VR) when treating more complex anxiety disorders including:

- Panic disorder and agoraphobia
- Social anxiety disorder
- Stress, tension, and insomnia
- Posttraumatic stress disorder (PTSD)
- OCD, GAD, and illness anxiety disorder

Issues specific to each disorder are discussed briefly. Ways in which VR can assist treatment will be reviewed, followed in most chapters by one or more case examples illustrating virtual reality therapy (VRT). If you prefer to review key research findings first, start with the "Evidence Base" section at the end of each chapter.

DOI: 10.4324/9781003154068-15

13 Panic Disorder and Agoraphobia

Panic disorder and agoraphobia are discussed together in this chapter because they co-occur so frequently. Agoraphobia frequently—although not always—is motivated by fear of panic sensations.

In a way, panic disorder can be thought of as a phobia of panic symptoms and much agoraphobic avoidance stems from the fear of having a panic attack someplace where it would not be "safe" to panic.

Panic Disorder/Agoraphobia and the Anxiety Cycle

Anxiety Triggers

Genetics

Panic, other forms of anxiety, and mood disorders are common among blood relatives of clients presenting with panic disorder. It seems clear that genetics plays a role in a person's vulnerability to panic.

Chemical Triggers

Biochemical factors can also be important panic triggers. For example, several clients have had their first, or worst, panic attack in response to marijuana. Cannabis edibles seem particularly likely to trigger panic. With edibles, it can be hard to estimate the dose ingested and easy to take more than intended, because the response is delayed.

Stress and Self-Talk

Panic attacks are likely to occur when clients are stressed. If clients have unrealistic self-expectations, such as that they should be "in control" at all times or that they should never feel or show anxiety, then the experience of panic can be especially frightening.

DOI: 10.4324/9781003154068-16

Unhelpful Lessons from Past Events

Impossible demands, like the ones above, mean clients decide that the panic response implies that they are out of control or failing in some way, making them more fearfully wary of future panic symptoms and more stressed.

Additionally, experiencing panic symptoms during a certain activity, at a certain time, or in a certain place, may create a conditioned fear response linked to that activity, time, place, etc. and make future panic attacks more likely.

I might anthropomorphize the process and explain to clients:

> The Reacting Brain may have been initially triggered by stress, chemicals, or self-demands to pump out adrenaline. Then, when it saw you were frightened by what was happening in your body, it decided that everything associated with that experience—where you were, what you were doing, thinking, or feeling—was dangerous, otherwise you wouldn't have been frightened. Your Reacting Brain then becomes more determined to 'protect' you by releasing adrenaline when anything similar occurs.

Anxiety Sensations

Clients do not control their amygdala, which means they do not control whether adrenaline is released, and panic sensations created. Therefore, the emphasis in treatment is on accepting panic sensations, if and when they occur.

Common Fears

As mentioned earlier, I often conceptualize panic disorder as a phobia of panic sensations.

Client fears may focus on their body and they may misinterpret symptoms as medical emergencies. For example:

- "I feel short of breath. I'm suffocating."
- "I feel dizzy. I'm going to pass out."
- "I am shaky. I'm going to fall."
- "My heart is pounding; my chest is tight. I'm having a heart attack or a stroke."

Clients may also fear that since they did not choose to have SNS arousal, they are "out of control", that panic could worsen and never end, and/or that they could act in a dangerous manner or be unable to function.

Fear-Based Actions

Many clients with panic disorder want to have no anxiety (avoid) and respond to panic sensations by distracting themselves (mentally avoid/escape), trying to make the sensations stop (escape; fight the anxiety response), or trying to keep the sensations to some "safe" level (safety action). Responding to panic in these ways leads to anxious hypervigilant monitoring of thoughts and bodily sensations (look for danger).

Fear of experiencing panic can easily create agoraphobia. If panic is dangerous, clients may become afraid to be any place where they could not get help or leave.

Virtual Reality Therapy (VRT) for Panic and Agoraphobia

Treating Anxiety Triggers

Virtual reality (VR) can help clients learn to relax and practice stress management skills, but the thrust of treatment for panic disorder and agoraphobia is to reduce their fear of the sensations.

Treating Anxiety Sensations

VR's immersive qualities can deepen relaxation and help clients learn to manage anxiety. Use the virtual environments (VEs) where your client feels safest, most relaxed, and calm. Use the recorded instructions to teach or reinforce the anxiety management tools clients report work best for them.

Treating Fears

Using VR to teach and enhance clients' ability to manage anxiety is always done with the goal of accepting and tolerating panic attacks, not fearing the sensations. Clients don't have to *like* these sensations, just no longer fear them!

Only after you know clients' specific fears can you credibly explain why those the fears are either completely false or blown out of proportion. But intellectual knowledge is far less powerful than actual experience, which is where VR plays a key role in treating panic disorder and agoraphobia: exposure to stop fear-based actions.

Treating Fear-Based Actions: Panic Disorder

Interoceptive exposure exercises, which can be done following the instructions in the client workbook (McMahon, 2019) or a therapist manual (Craske & Barlow, 2006), are helpful because they create sensations similar to those that occur spontaneously during a panic attack.

VR and Interoceptive Exposure

With some VR products, you can add interoceptive exposure features to the virtual experience, for example, manipulating the visual appearance of the VE to mimic blurriness or tunnel vision and/or adding sounds of faster and louder heartbeats and/or breathing to mimic palpitations and hyperventilating.

You can also have clients do interoceptive exposure exercises immediately before or during VR exposure. Adding interoceptive exposure increases the therapeutic impact of virtual reality exposure therapy (VRET).

Although the frequency, intensity, and duration of panic attacks drop as a result of treatment, the goal of treatment is not necessarily that clients no longer *have* panic, but that they no longer *fear* panic, let it distress them, or have it interfere with their functioning.

Treating Fear-Based Actions: Agoraphobia

VR can be tremendously helpful for clients who struggle with agoraphobia. I wish I had had VR before 2010. Some of my agoraphobic clients could— just barely—make it into my office for our sessions but were too frightened to make the next step of pushing outside their "safety" zones.

Some clients with agoraphobia are too afraid to come to the office. Offering VRT via teletherapy makes treatment available to these clients. If clients get the necessary equipment and your VR system allows you to remotely control the clients' VR equipment, clients can begin treatment without leaving home.

Whether in the office or during teletherapy sessions, with VR you can transport clients to places and situations where they fear a panic attack would be dangerous (i.e., heights, airplanes, driving, isolated settings) or embarrassing (i.e., with other people in work, social, or public settings such as city streets, subways, etc.).

Depending on your VR product, you may be able to use Google Street View to transport clients to a specific geographic location they have been avoiding.

Treatment Challenges

If clients are too agoraphobic to come to your office, you and they will need a VR system that permits remote VR teletherapy.

Sometimes clients are so fearfully avoidant that they use mental avoidance or safety actions *during* VRET, which interferes with presence, immersion, and effective exposure. If your client's Subjective Units of Distress Scale (SUDS) levels do not rise during VRET, check that they are not taking some kind of fear-based action and review why and how they can participate in therapeutic exposure.

Figure 13.1 Public Setting VE Example

Case Examples

Angela

Angela's primary care provider referred her for panic disorder treatment as an alternative to prescribing benzodiazepines (which the MD preferred not to prescribe) or antidepressants (which Angela preferred not to take).

We identified Angela's anxiety triggers and discussed how her symptoms, fears, and actions mapped onto the anxiety cycle. This made sense to her and was both reassuring and validating. Since external stress seemed to be a possible trigger, Angela agreed to practice mindfulness meditation, diaphragmatic breathing, and stress management. She was not interested in using VR to learn these skills since she felt she grasped them quickly.

We replaced her fearful misconceptions about panic with facts and identified her fear-based actions: trying to fight the panic sensations and being anxiously hypervigilant to physical symptoms. The possibility of having a panic attack in a crowd scared her, although she did not avoid.

With Angela, I used VR to assist with interoceptive exposure, decrease her fear of crowds, check that treatment was working, and reduce the chance of relapse.

First, we did interoceptive exposure exercises together in session and created a hierarchy of exercises that she practiced at home. The following session, we began VR interoceptive exposure by placing her in a virtual location that felt safe to her (a deserted beach) and adding sounds of hyperventilation and rapid heartbeat and visual changes that mimicked visual changes from anxiety (pupil dilation, dizziness, and tunnel vision). We began with exposure to rapid heartbeat sounds since Angela reported that only bothered her a little. She reported her SUDS starting at 4 and dropping to 1. She quickly progressed through all the variables with rather mild anxiety that quickly dropped. By session's end her SUDS was a 1 even when I activated all interoceptive variables simultaneously.

Two weeks later, Angela returned, saying, "I just don't worry so much any more about whether I might panic. I kind of just think, 'oh well'." We agreed she was ready to face virtual crowds. We began in an open public area, adding more virtual people as she got comfortable, then moved to an office with several people, a window seat on an airplane with people seated next to her, and ended with a crowded elevator. Her SUDS got lower and lower, even when first entering a new VE, and they dropped faster and lower.

In our last VRET session, I challenged her to raise her fear as much as she could while I contributed by speaking her original fears ("I'm going to have a panic attack; it's going to be awful; this is a really bad place to panic" and so on). She basically responded, "So what?" and I pointed out that even when we were both *deliberately trying* to create fear, her anxiety only reached a 2. She said that anxiety at that level would be no problem and that she no longer worried about panic.

Kathy

Agoraphobia can take longer to overcome than panic disorder and the more extensive and entrenched the avoidance, the more courage and persistence it can require.

Kathy is a good example. The prospect of being alone or driving anywhere by herself brought on tears and frantic phone calls to her partner. Her partner was sympathetic but getting burned out and needed Kathy to become more independent.

I had the sense that she saw herself as vulnerable but exploring this led nowhere. She denied past traumas and I was unable to uncover any secondary gain from the agoraphobia. Kathy appeared to have insight, motivation, and understanding. She enjoyed our sessions and kept every appointment, although for financial reasons we only met monthly. We seemed to have a strong therapeutic alliance without negative transference or countertransference.

None of the common anxiety management techniques helped her. After several sessions, she could explain why panic was not dangerous and why tolerating panic—rather than avoiding—was necessary. On a few occasions she had endured panic symptoms without leaving, but progress was stalled. She left each session having created a plan with specific actions, only to return and report partial success at best with continuing fear and avoidance.

Her knowledge seemed abstract and intellectual rather than viscerally believed.

We started VR exposure at this point and the difference was dramatic. Sessions changed from engaged but mostly intellectual discussions to affect-laden experiences.

Kathy's greatest fear was "having a panic attack when I am alone with no one to help me". On some level, she continued to fear that panic would require emergency medical help.

We agreed to put her virtually in a public outdoor setting with other people around. Our plan was that I would voice her fears and she would counter them, hoping that doing this would help her strengthen and internalize her new knowledge. Almost immediately that plan had to change.

Kathy instantly became upset and tearful, with a SUDS of 10. It was clear she was having trouble reducing her fear, so I offered to switch roles: she would voice her fears and I would model talking back to them.

In a more emotionally present, vivid way than in any prior session, she talked about her fears of passing out, having a heart attack, or going crazy. Tearfully she voiced the need to call a safe person. Despite anxiety, she elected to remain in the virtual scenario.

Because she had had the best results in real life by actively challenging the fear, I modeled speaking in a confident, assertive voice, deliberately using words she had found helpful in real life, like saying to the fear, "What are we going to do? Pass out? I'm not going to pass out. Bring it on."

As we'd discussed in prior sessions, I externalized the fear ("Reacting Brain", "Fear"), addressed it in the second person ("you") and speaking for her in the first person ("I"): "I'm sick of you pushing me around. Fine, if you think we're going to pass out, make me pass out. I know you're scared but there is no danger. I'm sick of you. Come on! Do it. Bring it on! Make me pass out or have a heart attack right now."

I responded to each fear as she expressed it. When she would say, "We have to leave. I need to call my partner. Let's find somewhere to sit down," I replied, "I am not leaving. I don't have to call anyone. I don't have to sit down because I'm not going to pass out or go crazy or have a heart attack. This is just adrenaline. The doctors have told me I'm fine."

The effect was striking. The tears stopped. Her SUDS dropped from 8 to 2.

I asked if she wanted to change roles, and she did. I then repeated the same things she'd said earlier in VR with similar intonations of anxiety and distress. She held her own beautifully. She firmly refused to do any of the things the fear suggested. Her SUDS dropped further from a 2 to a 1.

As she removed the VR headset, she said, "I know what I need to do now." Her in vivo exposures between sessions became more deliberate, more frequent, and more effective. Her confidence rose, and her fear and avoidance dropped. By our last session, she was driving alone.

Evidence Base

Quero et al. (2014) found VR well-accepted by patients when used in the treatment of panic disorder and agoraphobia to provide interoceptive exposure and exposure to agoraphobic situations. Botella et al. (2007) reported that VRET for panic disorder with and without agoraphobia was as effective as in vivo exposure, that treatment gains were maintained at follow-up, and pointed out the cost-benefit advantages of VRET. Pelissolo et al. (2012) concluded: "Thus, VRET seems to be an effective treatment for PDA [panic disorder with agoraphobia] with short-term and long-term therapeutic results equivalent to those obtained with CBT." Botella et al. (2014) agreed that data support the efficacy of VRET for panic disorder and agoraphobia. Research also demonstrates mechanisms of cognitive change as a result of VRET (Breuninger et al., 2019).

References

Botella, C., García-Palacios, A., Villa, H., Baños, R. M., Quero, S., Alcañiz, M., & Riva, G. (2007). Virtual reality exposure in the treatment of panic disorder and agoraphobia: A controlled study. *Clinical Psychology & Psychotherapy*, 14(3), 164–175. doi:10.1002/cpp.524.

Botella, C., Garía-Palacios, A., Baños, R., & Quero, S. (2014). Panic disorder, agoraphobia, and driving phobia: Lessons learned from efficacy studies. In B. K. Wiederhold & S. Bouchard (Eds.), *Series in Anxiety and Related Disorders. Advances in Virtual Reality and Anxiety Disorders* (163–185). Springer Science + Business Media.

Breuninger, C., Tuschen-Caffier, B., & Svaldi, J. (2019). Dysfunctional cognition and self-efficacy as mediators of symptom change in exposure therapy for agoraphobia: Systematic review and meta-analysis. *Behaviour Research and Therapy*, 120, 103443. doi:10.1016/j.brat.2019.103443.

Craske, M. & Barlow, D. (2006). *Mastery of Your Anxiety and Panic: Therapist Guide* (4th ed.). Oxford University Press.

McMahon, E. (2019). *Overcoming Anxiety and Panic Interactive Guide*. Hands-on-Guide.

Pelissolo, A., Zaoui, M., Aguayo, G., Yao, S. N., Roche, S., Ecochard, R., Gueyffier, R., Pull, C., Berthoz, A., Jouvent, R., & Cottraux, J. (2012). Virtual reality exposure therapy versus cognitive behavior therapy for panic disorder with agoraphobia: a randomized comparison study. *Journal of CyberTherapy & Rehabilitation*, 5(1), 35–43.

Quero, S., Pérez-Ara, M. Á., Bretón-López, J., García-Palacios, A., Baños, R. M., & Botella, C. (2014). Acceptability of virtual reality interoceptive exposure for the treatment of panic disorder with agoraphobia. *British Journal of Guidance and Counselling*, 42(2), 123–137. doi:10.1080/03069885.2013.852159.

14 Social Anxiety Disorder

"It would be so embarrassing!"

Anxiety may occur in one, only a few, or most social settings. Clients may be fine with friends and family, but anxious when meeting new people. They may be comfortable with a few people, but anxious at parties or larger gatherings.

Some clients are only anxious when they have to speak or perform in public, take a test, or be formally evaluated. In fact, fear of public speaking is so common that Jerry Seinfeld made the classic joke that at a funeral most people would rather be in the casket than giving the eulogy.

Figure 14.1 Social Anxiety VE Example

DOI: 10.4324/9781003154068-17

Social Anxiety Disorder and the Anxiety Cycle

Anxiety Triggers

External Stress

Because social anxiety focuses on fears of being criticized or judged, try to gauge how supported or unsupported clients feel in their social and work situations. Are clients overly anxious, or are others, in fact, critical, rejecting, and judgmental?

Performers and athletes are often routinely subjected to harsh criticism. Not all workplaces are healthy. Not all friends and family are supportive. How is your client being treated?

Self-Demands

Perfectionistic self-demands have been an issue for every socially anxious client I have treated but may not be obvious. Perfectionism can underlie thoughts with surface plausibility: "I want to do a good job" or "I don't want to embarrass myself or let the team down."

Exploring such statements often uncovers unrealistic expectations along the lines of "I can't make a mistake," "I need to do this perfectly," or "If I were really a good presenter, every member of the audience would be totally riveted and no one would look at their phone, talk, or leave."

Self-Talk

Be alert for negative, distorted cognitions. Mind-reading and labeling are common. For example, "They think what I said was stupid. I look like an idiot. They think I'm incompetent."

Clients may selectively recall the negative ("I missed a note!") and discount the positive ("The audience only gave me a standing ovation because they're uncritical and polite").

Unhelpful Lessons from Past Events

When getting the history, be alert for past events that continue to influence a clients' thoughts and emotions. Did parents or authority figures expect perfection? What reactions to mistakes did clients experience or witness?

Clients often recount stories of music teachers who made them start over if they made a single mistake or coaches who routinely yelled, criticized, and humiliated. What assumptions about oneself, about others, and about the world would you reasonably expect clients to derive from such experiences?

Be alert to anxiogenic beliefs derived from past events. Common beliefs include:

- I have to be perfect.
- If I am anxious, I won't succeed.
- If others see my anxiety, they will judge me.
- Other people have no anxiety in social or performance settings.
- Other people perform perfectly and expect perfection from me.
- People have rigid, high standards and are judgmental and unforgiving.
- The world is a harsh place where people either succeed perfectly all the time or are humiliated failures.

Anxiety Sensations

These clients are usually most distressed by anxiety/panic sensations that may be visible and/or might impair physical performance, including blushing, sweating, trembling voice or hands, dry throat, tight chest, dizziness, difficulty concentrating, and not feeling present. GI symptoms can be particularly distressing.

Common Fears

Clients' fears may focus on certain sensations, for example, that GI symptoms will cause noticeable flatulence or the loss of bowel or bladder control. They may fear that anxiety might make them pass out, or that specific anxiety symptoms such as dry throat, tight chest, etc., could make them unable to speak, think, remember, or perform.

If clients make the dual assumptions that they must perform perfectly, *and* that others will leap on any sign of imperfection, then anxiety—especially visible anxiety—will trigger fear. If perfection is expected and imperfection is judged harshly, then every interaction feels like walking into a minefield.

Experiences or "mistakes" that others accept as normal or inconsequential such as forgetting a word, losing your place in a presentation, having a lull during a social conversation, showing anxiety, etc. are feared and must be avoided at all costs.

Fear-Based Actions

Naturally, these fears lead to fear-based actions that reduce anxiety in the moment but maintain and reinforce it over time. Students avoid speaking in class. Clients call in "sick" to escape meetings or sit in the back, saying nothing and avoiding eye contact.

Socially anxious clients hypervigilantly look for signs of being judged negatively such as, "That person looked at their cell phone because I'm boring and doing a terrible job of presenting," "Everyone sees I'm anxious and thinks I am incompetent," etc. They can easily misconstrue others' reactions. For example, "The person I'm speaking with looked down. They don't want to talk to me."

Preparing and practicing beforehand can be safety actions if they are excessive or if the goal is perfection. For example, "I wrote out every word of my presentation and said it aloud five times."

As with all anxiety issues, the more clients fight the anxiety thoughts ("Don't think that!"), emotions ("Don't feel anxious! Be calm! Be calm!"), or sensations ("Don't sweat! Don't blush!"), the more anxious and out of control they are likely to feel.

Two additional anxiety actions are near-universal in clients with social anxiety: self-judging and post-event processing.

Self-Judging

Self-judging clients focus on *evaluating* their performance *while* speaking, interacting or performing—rather than focusing on the task itself. On dates, clients criticize themselves if there is a brief lull in conversation or decide what they just said was "dumb". Speakers judge themselves because they said "uh", paused, or sounded or looked anxious. Performers and athletes focus on what they just "messed up" or "should have" done.

Post-Event Processing

Post-event processing is evaluating performance *after* the fact. This is not an objective, helpful review of what went well coupled with lessons for future improvement. It is a biased review highlighting the "evidence" of failure, rejection, and/or embarrassment. For example, "There was a horrible long pause. I couldn't remember what I was going to say. What a disaster."

Virtual Reality Therapy (VRT) for Social Anxiety

Social anxiety frequently occurs in situations where clients have to speak up within a group or speak to an audience (public speaking). Virtual reality (VR) enables clients to practice either situation repeatedly using different settings, with different size audiences, and with different types of audience reactions.

Treating Anxiety Triggers

Clients can practice using changed self-talk, self-expectations, and/or new lessons from past experiences while in virtual reality to strengthen their ability to access and believe such thoughts when stressed.

Treating Anxiety Sensations

Clients may complain of somatic reactions that seem legitimately embarrassing.

Figure 14.2 Public Speaking VE Example

For example:

- "I blush bright red."
- "My hands shake."
- "I sweat visibly."
- "I stutter."
- "My voice sounds trembly."
- "Sometimes I lose my train of thought."

Do not take these client reports at face value. Others may not hear their "trembly voice" or see the "bright red blush". Studies using objective measurements have found that socially anxious clients greatly overestimate their facial redness (Wild et al., 2008). Blushing, sweating, shaking, or the trembly voice of which clients are so painfully conscious may be minimal or even unnoticeable to others. Placing clients in an anxiety-producing virtual environment (VE) lets you judge how visible or intense their somatic symptoms really are and give corrective feedback.

If you confirm that clients' anxiety symptoms *are*, in fact, noticed by others, VR experiences can provide opportunities for clients to practice radical acceptance, distress tolerance, and cognitive restructuring to decatastrophize the experience and put it in perspective. Interventions from acceptance and commitment therapy may be helpful.

Treating Fears

You may wonder whether a client's critical self-judgments and negative post-event processing are reality-based and accurate. Is your client a poor speaker, a mediocre or underprepared performer? Does the client lack social skills?

In addition to asking clients what feedback they have received from unbiased observers and what, if any, real-world consequences ensued, observe your client as they perform or interact in VR. This will help you make your own judgment about referring for training in speaking or social skills as an adjunct or alternative to anxiety therapy.

Virtual experiences give clients opportunities to practice challenging their fears and assumptions about anxiety. Even when clients do visibly flush, tremble, sweat, or stutter, do not join them in catastrophizing. Interestingly, other people will take their cue from the client most of the time. If the client is matter of fact about their symptoms, others will usually be matter of fact as well. It can be very reassuring to realize that most people are just not that interested in us!

Treating Fear-Based Actions

The beauty of using VR in treating social anxiety is that you can bring "other people" into the session, control their reactions to the client, and observe your client's behavior.

Socially anxious clients may consider the gaps engendered by temporarily losing their train of thought or pausing during a presentation to be "endless". The "dreadful" pause in a conversation seems to last forever. Having clients experience such pauses while in VR gives you and your clients invaluable information about how long such pauses actually last in real time—as opposed to socially anxious time.

Clients experience VR as being real with immediacy and visceral impact. Some VEs are designed specifically for social anxiety, e.g., interacting with virtual others in a bar, pub, or café or speaking in a variety of venues and to different audiences.

VEs created for other fears may also be used with social anxiety. For instance, VEs of flying or driving may be used with anticipatory anxiety or post-event processing before or after a virtual party, date, talk, performance, competition, etc. You might have clients interact with the other people in the car or elevator or on the plane or the subway while you voice the others' replies.

While clients are in VR, you can model and prompt them to use new coping skills and new ways of thinking and behaving. As clients improve, you can voice their previous self-critical thoughts, monitor clients' self-reported distress using the Subjective Units of Distress Scale (SUDS), and track their ability to effectively counter these thoughts.

You might even have clients who are actors, singers, or musicians perform, either before a small virtual audience as if being judged in a competition or a large virtual audience in an auditorium.

Treatment Challenges

The challenge you are most likely to encounter is a relative paucity of VEs specifically for social anxiety. As of this writing, I know of no VEs for dating or performance anxiety (arts, music, sports, etc.) and only a limited number of VEs for test anxiety or school phobia.

Currently there is little diversity in the avatars or virtual others encountered in VR. Avatars are all able-bodied and cis-gendered and most are Caucasian.

Case Examples

Tom

Tom was an Asian businessman in his early 30s with social anxiety disorder. His parents had immigrated to the United States when he was seven years old. The transition in culture and languages made him feel like "an outsider". As the oldest son, he translated for his parents. As a teenager, he was embarrassed about his parents' accent, while simultaneously feeling guilty and ashamed of his embarrassment. He had been raised in a family and a cultural tradition that emphasized respect for authority as well as the importance of not losing face, offending others, or letting the family down.

He went to the most academically rigorous high school in the city, followed by a prestigious college, and then business school. He told me, "I perform fine in structured situations, like giving a presentation or critiquing a business plan, but in social settings I feel very anxious and awkward. I worry I will say the wrong thing."

Tom's English was superb, but he worried he might "use the wrong word" or that his (objectively slight) accent might lead others to think he was uneducated. He didn't want to "say the wrong thing" or embarrass himself or others. He had trouble using public restrooms for fear that the natural sounds or smells would be offensive.

He was avoiding business dinners and networking opportunities that were important for his career. And he found it hard to relax on a date. Women had told him that he seemed "shut off" or "cold" because he was too anxious to share any personal information.

He was motivated to change, although skeptical: "My parents don't believe in therapy." He was not afraid of anxiety itself, so we focused on changing self-demands and self-talk: "It's okay to be myself." "Dating is a mutual exploration between two people. No single dating experience defines me as a person or can say that I will never find a partner."

Tom also worked to counter unhelpful lessons from the past ("Not everyone is judging me"; "I don't have to be perfect") and to replace self-judging ("That was a dumb question") with a mindful focus on the present ("What do I want to know or ask about this person and their business?"). He began to focus on the goals of the interaction.

In VR, he became more adept at using changed thinking and acting on his values and goals. He practiced being more self-disclosing and saying what came to mind instead of self-censoring.

We started VR with speaking to small work groups where he was mostly comfortable. His anxiety level increased from 2 to 4 when he began sharing more personal information, before returning to 2. I then played the role of his critical inner voice doing post-event processing ("Why did you say that? You probably embarrassed them by sharing personal information. You should have waited and thought it over instead of being spontaneous.") and had him challenge and refute these statements.

We were both encouraged when his SUDS only rose to a 3, even in response to my most critical statements. At one point he had trouble responding and began feeling more anxious, so we switched roles. I modeled and prompted him, then we switched back. At that point, SUDS dropped to a 1.

Using VEs designed for small group public speaking or job interviews, I made participants' expressions and gestures more negative, i.e., frowning, head shaking in disagreement or disbelief. Tom did beautifully. His anxiety stayed low. Outside sessions, he began talking more casually with coworkers and feeling "more like a part of the group".

As he progressed, we moved to VEs where he was interacting informally. We used the VE designed for social interaction first to practice networking, and then to practice sharing personal information as if on a date with friends. By muting the recorded interactions, I could "speak" for the other people creating precisely the experiences Tom would find most helpful. He talked with his "date" while driving a virtual car.

Sharing personal information in a dating situation initially raised his anxiety to a 6. After about four repetitions, it dropped and remained between 2 and 3 which he said was quite tolerable.

Our final VR sessions used VEs designed for eating disorders and for OCD. In a virtual restaurant, he ordered from the menu and "ate" to elicit fears of embarrassing himself by spilling food or drink, getting food in caught in his teeth, or being asked a question while his mouth was full.

To reduce his discomfort using public restrooms in real life, I had him virtually enter and "use" a public restroom in VR. This felt sufficiently real that he said, "I don't know if I can do this. This is so embarrassing!" and reported SUDS levels of between 9 and 10.

I encouraged him to use diaphragmatic breathing and radical acceptance of both anxiety and the fact that everyone uses the restroom. As he used his skills, I continued to check his anxiety level. As soon as it dropped from 9 to 7, I emphasized and celebrated the drop, asking him, "What did you do that made that happen?" He became increasingly comfortable and confident, and ended the session with a SUDS of 3.

By the end of therapy, he'd been on several dates. He was more comfortable and felt that his dating experiences were more positive. He was letting himself say whatever he thought and felt more open and connected to others. He had been to a business dinner and a networking happy hour and allowed himself to eat and use the restroom.

At our last session he mentioned that his younger sister, who lived in another state, had flying anxiety and that he'd told her how much therapy had helped him and encouraged her to find a therapist who offered VRT.

Kimberly

Kimberley was a student in her mid-20s who sought help for public speaking anxiety. She had no history of trauma, no other issues, and no prior psychotherapy, although anxiety and mood disorders ran in her family. One relative had poorly controlled bipolar disorder and Kimberley remembers being terribly embarrassed by her relative's manic behavior.

Kimberly was self-conscious about her weight, which was in the high end of the normal BMI (body mass index) range, especially because her older sister was thinner and had been head cheerleader at their high school.

Kim was fair-skinned and blushed easily and visibly. Her older sister was flamboyant and "created drama" so Kimberly tried to "fly under the radar" and be unnoticed: "I don't like everyone looking at me."

Kimberley was motivated to overcome her fear of public speaking because she wanted to become a teacher and her college classes increasingly required class participation.

After preparing her with the skills to benefit from VR exposure, I had her start out by giving a brief prepared talk to a small group of friendly people, as if presenting to classmates in her study group. I gradually changed the classmates' responses from positive, to neutral, to bored, to actively negative and critical.

Kimberley's anxiety level showed a transient increase with each change, but using her skills brought the anxiety down. The highest anxiety ever got was a SUDS of 6 dropping to a low of 1. At times I could see that she was blushing, but she did not let that stop her.

We had her speak to increasingly larger virtual groups while I made the audience increasing negative and hostile, confirming at each step that Kimberley's anxiety was under control.

At our fifth session, I had her give an impromptu speech on "How I Overcame Public Speaking Anxiety", prompting her to share with the audience everything she had learned and the tools that worked for her. With her permission, I controlled and voiced the responses of her virtual audience, moving from enthusiastically positive and supportive to increasingly challenging until she could respond calmly even to outrageous statements like:

> Well, I don't think you're over your public speaking anxiety! I mean I can see you're blushing. What's that about? It seems to me you're just a hot mess. You'll never be able to speak to a group or in public or in front of a classroom. Nobody who blushes can ever be a teacher.

Needless to say, I only made such statements after having evidence that she could successfully counter them. As I watched, her posture became even more erect. Her tone of voice became more confident. She replied to the obnoxious audience member, "I'm sorry you feel that way. I do blush, but it's not a big deal. I love teaching and look forward to having my own classroom."

Outside sessions, she was speaking up more in class and study groups and getting positive feedback from her teachers and peers. Her new internal response to blushing was, "If my face is red, who cares?" and when a friend commented, "Your face is really red," she replied, "Yeah, it lets me know I care about what I'm talking about." I congratulated her on an absolutely brilliant response.

We scheduled a follow-up session in a month just in case she wanted to check in. A week prior, she called to cancel, saying she was doing "really well".

Evidence Base

There are relatively few studies on using virtual reality exposure therapy (VRET) with social anxiety disorder. Anderson et al. (2005) reported that it reduced public speaking anxiety (Anderson et al., 2005). Similarly, a randomized controlled trial of VRET for social anxiety disorder found evidence of efficacy (Anderson et al., 2013) and Kampmann, Emmelkamp, and Morina's (2016) meta-analysis of technology-assisted treatment of social anxiety disorder included three VRET trials and reported that "Patients undergoing ... VRET showed significantly less SAD symptoms at post-assessment than passive control conditions ($g=0.82$)". In a three-arm randomized trial, VRET was more effective compared to the CBT condition, and was more practical for therapist to deploy (Bouchard et al., 2017).

References

Anderson, P. L., Price, M., Edwards, S. M., Obasaju, M. A., Schmertz, S. K., Zimand, E., & Calamaras, M. R. (2013). Virtual reality exposure therapy for social anxiety disorder: A randomized controlled trial. *Journal of Consulting and Clinical Psychology*, 81(5), 751–760. doi:10.1037/a0033559.

Anderson, P. L., Zimand, E., Hodges, L. F., & Rothbaum, B. O. (2005). Cognitive behavioral therapy for public-speaking anxiety using virtual reality for exposure. *Depression and Anxiety*, 22(3), 156–158. doi:10.1002/da.20090.

Bouchard, S., Dumoulin, S., Robillard, G., Guitard, T., Klinger, E., Forget, H., Loranger, C., & Roucaut, F. X. (2017). Virtual reality compared with in vivo exposure in the treatment of social anxiety disorder: A three-arm randomised controlled trial. *British Journal of Psychiatry*, 210(4), 276–283. doi:10.1192/bjp.bp.116.184234.

Kampmann, I. L., Emmelkamp, P. M. G., & Morina, N. (2016). Meta-analysis of technology-assisted interventions for social anxiety disorder. *Journal of Anxiety Disorders*, 42, 71–84. doi:10.1016/j.janxdis.2016.06.007.

Wild, J., Clark, D. M., Ehlers, A., & McManus, F. (2008). Perception of arousal in social anxiety: Effects of false feedback during a social interaction. *Journal of Behavior Therapy and Experimental Psychiatry*, 39(2), 102–116. doi:10.1016/j.jbtep.2006.11.003.

15 Stress, Tension, Insomnia

Stress, tension, or insomnia may be a client's primary complaint or may be distressing symptoms accompanying other anxiety diagnoses. These complaints may be especially prevalent if you work in behavioral medicine, primary care, pain programs, rehabilitation, or with the elderly or medically ill.

Symptoms and contributing factors for these three complaints are so tightly linked that if a client only mentions one or two, be sure to ask then about the others.

This chapter discusses how virtual reality (VR) can help with these issues. It covers applying the anxiety cycle model described in Chapter 2, various VR therapy (VRT) interventions, and treatment challenges, concluding with three case examples.

Stress, Tension, Insomnia, and the Anxiety Cycle

When discussing these complaints, you can describe the anxiety diagram as a "stress" cycle.

Triggers

Genetics

Genetic factors and upbringing influence personality and the degree of stress a client experiences in different situations. Situations requiring lots of sustained interaction with many people can be energizing and pleasing for an extrovert but stressful, tension-inducing, and exhausting for an introvert.

Chemical/Physical Triggers

Alcohol and other drugs can worsen stress and contribute to insomnia. Several commonly prescribed medications can cause insomnia as can medical issues including sleep apnea, lung disease, bladder issues, gastric reflux, nasal tumors, restless legs syndrome, and others. Poor quality sleep (interrupted, light, or

DOI: 10.4324/9781003154068-18

restless sleep) or insufficient sleep increases stress and fatigue while lowering mood, creating a vicious cycle.

External Stress

Clients often minimize the impact—or even fail to recognize the presence—of chronic external stressors until physical symptoms occur. Stresses such as frequent jet lag, working long hours, working night shifts or varying shifts, insufficient exercise, excessive screen time, watching news just before bed, poor sleep hygiene, or noise can all contribute to stress, tension, and insomnia.

Self-Talk/Self-Demands

Patterns of self-talk such as all-or-nothing thinking, labeling, catastrophizing, and other thinking distortions can create or increase stress. Once sleep problems occur, negative cognitions about sleep ("I can't function if I can't sleep"; "This is awful"; "I will be a wreck"; "I have to sleep!") can exacerbate insomnia and tension.

Self-criticism or impossible self-demands—such as needing to please everyone or do everything anyone asks—make every task, decision, action, or interaction another stressful opportunity for failure.

Unhelpful Lessons from Past Events

Past experiences can foster resilience, optimism, and calm—or create stress and tension. An adult who was neglected, abused, or a parentified child may have learned lessons like, "My needs don't matter", "Don't ask for what you want because you won't get it", "Put others first", and similar rules about living in the world.

Stress/Tension Sensations

In addition to some or all of the symptoms associated with panic attacks, physical symptoms of stress and tension can include increases or decreases in appetite and/or energy. Clients may complain of a sense of urgency or pressure accompanied by muscle tension which may be acute or chronic. Clients may report that they find themselves grinding or gritting their teeth (bruxing) or unconsciously tensing their jaw, neck, shoulders, chest, or other body parts which may result in headaches, jaw, neck, or shoulder pain, etc. Stressed clients may be holding their breath, overbreathing, or breathing in a tense, shallow way that can create more somatic symptoms.

Nocturnal panic symptoms (panic symptoms that occur while sleeping) and resultant worry about panicking can create stress. Any source of stress and tension contributes to insomnia. Clients may find it hard to relax enough to go to sleep or stay asleep.

Common Fears

Stress-inducing thoughts often focus on problems and feared outcomes, rather than solutions ("I can't relax! What if I don't get to sleep?"). A repetitive, ruminative focus on endless tasks creates stress, tension, anxiety, and adds to insomnia ("What if I can't get it all done?").

Stress-Inducing Actions

A common but unhelpful action in response to stress, tension, or insomnia is "Try Harder!" This approach never works for insomnia—in fact, it makes insomnia worse and more distressing.

Even when the "Try Harder" approach works for stress and tension, it is only adaptive in situations with an achievable goal and a time-limited, relatively short deadline. Otherwise, clients push themselves—or are pushed by others—to work at a short-term crisis pace on an ongoing basis. This is like trying to run at the pace of a 50-yard sprint for an entire 26-mile marathon.

Virtual Reality Therapy (VRT) for Stress, Tension, Insomnia

Stress

VR instructions and environments can help clients learn and practice techniques for countering stress such as mindfulness and relaxation. Clients who like the VR instructions and want to practice at home can use their phone to record these instructions during a session.

Clients may reduce their stress by changing or avoiding stressful situations, leaving stressful situations, or accepting situations which cannot be changed. VR can help with any of these options.

Clients for whom the appropriate response to a stressful situation is to set limits using effective, assertive communication techniques can practice their assertiveness skills in VR to gain comfort, confidence, and facility with this manner of communicating. Practicing assertiveness using virtual environments for public speaking anxiety has the benefit of being realistic, emotionally impactful—and safe. You get to observe your clients' communication skills and give feedback.

Because you can control the other people's reactions within the VE, you can make practice easy at first (positive, accepting, supportive reactions from others) and move to more and more challenging situations (negative, challenging reactions). With your help, clients can problem-solve foreseeable issues in advance and repeatedly practice interpersonal communication skills until they are sufficiently skilled and comfortable.

Some clients' best stress management response is to leave a stressful situation. Stress symptoms may be the body's message that a current situation is untenable and unhealthy.

When leaving a stressful job, it is tempting—but usually professionally unwise—to vent about stressful aspects of the workplace. Clients may appreciate the opportunity to safely vent to a virtual boss in VR and then, after processing the experience, return to their virtual workplace and rehearse more effective ways of resigning. They can also practice interview skills for job hunting in VR.

Finally, if there is nothing about the situation your clients can change and they cannot—or choose not to—leave, VR can help them learn anxiety management tools such as mindful acceptance.

Tension

VR can help relieve pain caused by tension, such as headaches or neck, jaw, or shoulder pain. Virtually traveling to another place helps redirect clients' attention away from their body. Immersion and distraction in VR can offer temporary pain relief and help break a tension-pain-tension cycle (Mallari et al., 2019).

VR products with recorded instructions for progressive muscle relaxation (PMR) may be uniquely effective in releasing tension. Once learned, clients can practice PMR during activities that trigger tension. For example, if driving is associated with neck, shoulder, arm, hand, or jaw tensing, clients can practice relaxing while virtually driving. Clients who find themselves tense riding public transportation, carpooling to work, attending work meetings, or being in bed at night and ruminating can practice in the relevant VEs.

If tension is linked to a specific geographic location, such as visiting a difficult relative or a medical center, you may be able to teleport the client to that location in VR and then practice new responses and create new associations.

After experiencing relief in VR, clients may be motivated to practice at home. If clients have compatible equipment, and depending on the available options, they may be able to re-enter VEs used in session, repeat recorded VR experiences from a session, or use self-help VR apps.

Insomnia

Encourage clients experiencing poor sleep or frequent fatigue to be evaluated by their healthcare provider to rule out medical causes. Getting less than seven to nine hours of sleep a night (or getting restless, interrupted, or nonrestorative sleep) is known to result in decreased mood and increased stress and anxiety.

Cognitive behavioral therapy for insomnia (CBT-i), the recommended treatment for insomnia, encourages clients to physically relax and to change their thinking and mental focus. By now you know that VR can be extremely effective in teaching relaxation and mindfulness. Within a virtual world, clients may go to a Zen meditation garden, beach, meadow, forest, mountain, waterfall, wooded glen with a stream, under the sea, or any number of realistic or fantastic environments (like floating in space).

VEs of a bedroom or a darkened house may be useful in therapy. As clients learn to challenge and replace unhelpful thoughts about sleep, they can practice the new ways of thinking while lying in bed or sitting in a darkened house, either at bedtime or having awakened in the middle of the night.

Treatment Challenges

Emotionally Shut Down

Some clients react to anxiety or stress by intellectualizing and emotionally distancing so as to minimize distress. VR may provide a calm environment where these clients can safely experience their emotions. The immersive quality of VR can also help break through defensive intellectualization and help clients become more in touch with their emotional responses.

Clients with No Good Options

Some clients struggle with stress, tension, and insomnia because they have no way to reduce their external stressors. Clients may be unwilling or unable to leave a stressful situation and need to accept their situation. For example, clients with chronic or untreatable diseases, who are family caregivers, or who lack the resources to move away from a dangerous neighborhood, etc.

Because VR is engaging and impactful, it can make it easier for clients who are feeling overwhelmed to learn new skills. In addition to using VR to support coping skills, virtual experiences can also provide a needed escape from burdens and sorrows.

Clients may be able to visit beautiful sites anywhere in the world. VEs of pleasant experiences, quiet meditation gardens, nature scenes, and so on may offer a temporary respite. The endless vista of a beautiful beach with gentle ocean waves may trigger religious or spiritual experiences of awe, wonder, and oneness.

Case Examples

George: Tension

George contacted me because "my nurse practitioner Helen said I should see you. My neck and shoulders are always tight and I'm starting to have pain".

George's job was stressful, but he loved it. He was a high-energy guy who ran triathlons during the summer and skied or snowboarded in winter. He enjoyed a fast-paced life but agreed that he needed to learn to relax as well.

The nature scene VEs that other clients found conducive to relaxation and mindfulness, George found "boring". He preferred progressively tensing and relaxing different muscle groups (PMR) while following the recorded instructions and watching an avatar perform the exercises. This combined physical activity with the immersive visual and auditory stimulation of a virtual world.

Through his experiences in VR, George learned to notice muscle tension before it escalated into pain and became more adept at monitoring his tension levels and reducing them. He said that VR was an important steppingstone in learning how to do this.

Lisa: Stress

Lisa sat on the edge of her seat, so visibly stressed that I found *myself* getting stressed just watching and listening to her. She and her partner were parents of a boy with special needs. They had no family nearby to help and often felt overwhelmed.

On top of that, Lisa was a freelance worker, so her income fluctuated unpredictably. Her present contract was stable, but stressful, and paid far less than it should. Her boss, Thea, was described as "sarcastic and demanding". Lisa's coworkers advised her that the best approach with Thea was to be firm and straightforward because "Thea likes things out on the table" but Lisa had trouble standing up for herself in general, especially with authority figures.

Lisa's lack of assertiveness not only made dealing with Thea increasingly stressful, it also limited her income. Lisa routinely bid for contracts at a low price without negotiating.

Lisa's partner was increasingly frustrated and told her, "I don't know what you want me to do. I know you're stressed, but you don't do anything to change the situation. When I give you advice, you never follow it. I'm getting fed up." That conversation prompted some serious soul-searching on Lisa's part. "I have to change. I have to deal better with stress."

Our first sessions focused on understanding the sources of her stress. Her immigrant parents had taught her to "Work hard. Don't complain. Be self-reliant. Don't ask for help." As a high school athlete, she was told, "Suck it up. Don't whine. Be strong. Be a team player." She came to understand that, while these lessons had some benefits, they did not serve her well when she needed to advocate for herself or obtain services for her son.

As Lisa got more comfortable with the idea of being assertive, I had her practice scenarios in VR. Since meeting with her son's teacher and principal felt intimidating, we used a VE developed for test anxiety to practice waiting in the school hallway, reminding herself that she had a right to speak up and a duty to support her son. A VE of a small office meeting was used to simulate her meeting with school staff about her son's needs.

The virtual office environment was also used to practice making appropriate requests and setting limits with coworkers. She worked up to politely, but firmly, responding to a female avatar dressed in professional clothes until she could remain appropriate assertive even when the "virtual boss" was frowning. Eventually she practiced interviewing for contracts and negotiating appropriate compensation.

As she transferred her skills from VR to real life, her relationship with Thea improved and she felt closer and more relaxed with coworkers. When the time came to renew her contract, she successfully negotiated for better compensation. The additional income allowed her and her partner to afford childcare so they could go out on date nights, which further improved their relationship.

By the end of therapy, Lisa's entire posture had changed. She sat back in the chair in my office. The tiny muscles in her face had relaxed. Her vocal pace was slower. She looked younger and more confident. And we both felt less stressed.

Don: Insomnia

Don was referred by his physician as an alternative to trying another prescription sleep medication. Don had tried trazodone, zolpidem, mirtazapine, clonazepam, as well as melatonin and herbal teas. "Each one worked for a week or two, then stopped working. I'd rather not rely on medicines to sleep and my doctor agrees, so here I am."

A thorough work-up had uncovered no medical reason for Don's insomnia which had begun during a stressful time at work following business trips to multiple time zones that left him jet-lagged and threw off his sleep cycle. "I just haven't been able to get back on track. The longer this goes on, the worse I feel. I'm tired and grouchy. I'm snapping at my wife and kids and I think my employees have started to avoid me." He agreed to increase his exercise, get more natural light, decrease alcohol, establish a sleep routine, and track his sleep.

Don asked if VR might possibly help as well: "I had the best sleep of my life" on family camping trips in the woods. We agreed to put him in a virtual mountain forest near running water and set his phone to record the sounds of the forest stream. While he saw and heard that soothing natural environment, I added suggestions that he could relax and allow an easy, natural flow of happy childhood memories.

He opened next week's session by saying, "That was amazing. Not only am I sleeping better, but I started having all these memories that I'm sharing with my kids about camping with their grandparents. I'd forgotten how great those trips were."

We agreed to pair relaxation training with immersion in other nature VEs. He recorded instructions for diaphragmatic breathing while virtually floating under the sea and I added suggestions that when trying to sleep he could imagine his body drifting and gently supported and that he could treat any distracting thoughts like the fish that swim into view and out of sight without any effort or interaction on his part.

He also practiced relaxing on a virtual beach at sunset and in other nature VEs. He enjoyed his VR experiences and recalled them when he wanted to sleep.

His sleep records revealed the impact of exercise and alcohol on his sleep, clarifying that his trouble sleeping on business trips was not only due to jet lag. Using the hotel gym, cutting down on alcohol, and using the techniques learned in VR helped him sleep better during and after trips.

I have a couch in my office, so in our last session, I had him lie down in reality while he was "lying down" in a virtual bed in a darkened virtual room. In this VE, he practiced bringing on upsetting thoughts that he was not sleeping and then physically relaxing and letting go of those thoughts while recalling memories of being in nature.

He told me, "Even when my sleep cycle is off a bit because of traveling, it doesn't start a cycle of insomnia because I know what to do. I don't stress about it."

References

Mallari, B., Spaeth, E. K., Goh, H., & Boyd, B. S. (2019). Virtual reality as an analgesic for acute and chronic pain in adults: A systematic review and meta-analysis. *Journal of Pain Research*, 12, 2053–2085. doi:10.2147/JPR.S200498.

16 Posttraumatic Stress Disorder (PTSD)

"It's still a bad memory, but I'm not so frightened by it now."

This chapter provides an overview of the uses for virtual reality (VR) in posttraumatic stress disorder (PTSD) treatment that is intended for readers experienced in treating this condition, *not* as training in PTSD treatment. Readers interested in learning to treat PTSD should obtain training and/or supervision in evidence-based treatments, consult best practice guidelines, and read the relevant research including publications by PTSD experts such as Drs. Debra Beidel, Edna Foa, Tamara McClintock Greenberg, Judith Herman, Albert "Skip" Rizzo, Barbara Rothbaum, Bessel Van der Kolk, etc. Pharmacological interventions can also help support PTSD treatment.

PTSD and the Anxiety Cycle

Triggers

Genetics

Genetics may increase someone's vulnerability to developing PTSD after trauma.

Chemicals

Substance misuse is commonly comorbid with PTSD and can worsen symptoms and interfere with treatment.

Self-Talk/Self-Demands

Self-talk that creates guilt or shame may contribute to PTSD following trauma.

DOI: 10.4324/9781003154068-19

Unhelpful Lessons from Past Events

Clearly, the most relevant anxiety trigger for PTSD is past traumatic events. Experiencing or witnessing life-threatening or horrifying experiences is the cause of PTSD.

War is one of the best-known PTSD causes, but many others exist. PTSD can result from physical or sexual abuse, other violent incidents (shootings, bombings, crashes, assaults, etc.), natural disasters (floods, hurricanes, fires, tornadoes, etc.), or similar events.

Sensations

Disturbances of arousal and reactivity are common in PTSD. Changes often include a mix of hyperarousal, hypoarousal (or psychic numbing), and emotional blunting (persistent inability to experience positive emotions).

PTSD-related cues may be internal (memories, thoughts, feelings) or external (people, places, objects, scents, sounds, activities, situations). Physiological hyperarousal in response to these cues can be particularly intense or prolonged. Clients may experience intense fear states that include panic and flashbacks, feeling or acting as if the trauma is recurring again in the present. Feelings may be so extreme as to block out the client's awareness of present surroundings. In this state, the sensations associated with the trauma often feel very real. This is related to the PTSD symptom of reexperiencing, which has neurobiological underpinnings.

For example: James served two tours of duty in the jungles of Vietnam. Years later, he continued to struggle with PTSD symptoms. The sounds of a helicopter overhead caused a panic attack. When he smelled rice cooking, suddenly all he could see was dense, green jungle foliage.

Common Fears and Thoughts

A basic fear is that the trauma is occurring again or will re-occur. PTSD is characterized by intrusive, distressing memories yet may also include inability to recall important aspects of the traumatic events.

Traumatic experiences can create persistent distorted thinking. Trauma may shatter clients' views of themselves as strong, moral people, of others as friendly, and of the world as being safe or just. Religious beliefs may be questioned. Trauma survivors may struggle to find forgiveness or self-forgiveness. Nightmares and intrusive recollections are common. Trauma survivors frequently blame themselves for traumatic events.

Fear-Based Actions

Clients may need to reconstruct a worldview that incorporates the reality of their traumas, but this requires coming to terms with their experiences.

Recalling or reexperiencing the trauma can be so painful that clients strenuously try to avoid or escape from internal and external stimuli associated with the traumatic events.

Flashbacks and the intensity of terror can feel overwhelming and lead to involuntary avoidance (emotional numbing and/or dissociation) as well as deliberate avoidance. Avoidant coping is felt to play a pivotal role in PTSD symptom maintenance (Weiss et al., 2019).

Clients may become hypervigilant and develop safety actions that interfere with psychological healing.

It is vital to understand and empathize with the intensity of the distress while explaining that avoidance, escape, and hypervigilance maintain the disorder.

Virtual Reality Therapy (VRT) for PTSD

Clients with war-related PTSD or complex PTSD deserve to see therapists who specialize in these areas. If you have that expertise, VR can be a useful tool.

Treating Anxiety Triggers

Whether or not your client is safe influences treatment focus and goals. Whenever possible, you want your client to *be* safe—as well as *feel* safe.

Figure 16.1 Combat PTSD VE Example

Increasing client safety may be a top priority if your client is currently endangered (i.e., living with an abusive partner, in a dangerous neighborhood, a member of a group targeted for violence, etc.) or engaging in risky, life-endangering behaviors. Trying to reduce fear when the client is still in avoidable danger is at best unlikely to work and at worst may be counterproductive or even potentially dangerous.

Treatment for substance misuse may be essential. VR can help clients virtually practice and strengthen refusal skills as part of substance abuse therapy.

For example, I sometimes have anxiety treatment clients who have experienced life-threatening traumatic situations. I recall one client who told me, "My panic attacks happen when I get on the bus to go to work." As we continued to speak, he revealed that he had been robbed at gunpoint three times in the past six months. I told him he did not need treatment for anxiety as much as he needed to get a new job as soon as possible.

Treating Anxiety Sensations

As with other disorders, VR can help teach and reinforce coping skills for PTSD. The immersive nature of VR may help clients with PTSD feel safe, making self-calming and grounding easier while improving distress tolerance. Using relaxation skills and visiting relaxing virtual environments (VEs) may help clients get to sleep at night or return to sleep if awakened by nightmares. Time in enjoyable VEs can reward clients for the hard work of exposure.

Treating Common Fears

The importance of evaluating present safety was mentioned above. Some PTSD fears can be countered with facts: clients are safe; the trauma is passed. But this, by itself, is rarely sufficient.

Trauma can shake (or destroy) religious beliefs and basic beliefs about oneself, other people, the world, one's worth, and the existence of justice or safety. Clients struggle not only with fears but with blame, guilt, shame, sadness, and other negative emotions.

Treating PTSD requires addressing these moral/existential issues. As clients find beliefs and ways of thinking that permit healing during the course of treatment, VR can provide settings in which to practice fact-based reassurance, forgiveness and compassion, other new healing narratives, and supportive self-talk.

Treating Fear-Based Actions

A 2019 review of clinical practice guidelines for PTSD found that all five guidelines strongly recommended trauma-focused therapies such as prolonged exposure (PE), cognitive processing therapy (CPT), or trauma-focused cognitive behavioral therapy (TF-CBT), and four strongly recommended EMDR

(Hamblen et al., 2019). VR can be incorporated with any of these treatment approaches.

If you use EMDR, certain VR products can provide appropriate visual and auditory stimuli.

VEs are available for the 9/11 World Trade Center disaster, specific war zones (Vietnam, Iraq, and Afghanistan), sexual assault, car crashes, and criminal violence.

In addition to VEs specifically designed for PTSD, other VEs can provide trauma-relevant exposure. For example, being the driver or passenger in a virtual car may be relevant for PTSD stemming from an automobile accident, abduction, or carjacking. A virtual house or virtual bedroom may be relevant to PTSD from intimate partner abuse or other abuse, molestation, or assaults that took place in the home. Virtual medical settings may be relevant for clients who had to be medically evaluated or treated following an assault.

VEs for agoraphobia, claustrophobia, or heights may be relevant if the client was assaulted in a public place, on a metro or train, or abducted from a public place. These VEs can also help the client prepare to re-enter public spaces such as streets, elevators, etc.

Clients may be more anxious in a crowd or alone. Your VR system may give you control over the number of virtual people in a VE with the client.

Clients may revisit trauma sites through 3-D photographs of specific locations using Google Street View.

When your client is ready to face trauma-related stimuli in VR, create a formal or informal hierarchy and begin gradual exposure. Actively support and encourage the client. Closely monitor their physical, cognitive, and emotional responses by asking, "What is happening in your body?", "What is your fear saying?", "What is your anxiety level from 0 to 10?"

Actively prompt clients to use their preferred skills for coping with physiological arousal and countering fearful thinking. Subjective Units of Distress Scale (SUDS) levels should begin to decrease as they use these skills.

If the client's reported anxiety level does not drop, consider whether some element of treatment may be missing. Missing elements might include any of the following:

- Needing more preparatory therapy in order to tolerate exposure, i.e., addressing dissociation, emotional numbing, etc.
- Not understanding trauma's effects and its treatment.
- Not having learned effective anxiety management tools or not using them appropriately.
- Not uncovering all the client's fears or distressing thoughts.
- Not effectively and credibly countering those fears and thoughts.

When clients report being able to cope in situations that used to trigger posttraumatic stress symptoms, VR can be used to test and strengthen positive treatment results and decrease chances of relapse.

Treatment Challenges

VEs are not available for some types of trauma that result in PTSD. For example, there are no VEs of flooding or tornadoes. VEs for victims of criminal violence have been researched but are not commercially available (Cárdenas-López et al., 2014).

Treatment goals, duration, and/or intensity may need to be adapted for clients who were repeatedly traumatized and may have complex PTSD, will continue to be traumatized, or are currently in danger.

Some clients may continue to be regularly exposed to trauma due to their work. Examples include military personnel in combat, police officers, prison guards, fire fighters, emergency medical technicians (EMTs), paramedics, healthcare professionals routinely treating emergent or traumatic injuries, and so on.

Case Examples

Linda: PTSD Post-Automobile Accident

As I mentioned, I do not specialize in war-related or complex PTSD, but I occasionally see clients with simple PTSD. Linda is one example.

Linda remembers it was raining that evening. She was annoyed that she hadn't brought her umbrella and worried the groceries would get wet when she brought them in from the car. She was a few blocks from home at the stop sign on the highway exit ramp, and thinking about what she'd make for dinner, when an SUV plowed into her from behind, pushing her car into the busy intersection. The driver was texting and hadn't seen her.

Linda was so frightened by this experience that she started having trouble driving, even on city streets. She constantly checked her rearview mirror, felt panicky, and avoided freeways completely, which added an hour to her commute.

She had frequent nightmares, startled easily, was irritable with her children and coworkers, had trouble relaxing and enjoying herself, and reported other symptoms meeting the diagnostic criteria for PTSD.

There was no family history of anxiety. Linda had never had a problem with anxiety prior to the accident and reported no other anxiety triggers.

She was frightened whenever she saw a car coming up behind her. She was even more cautious and fearful when she had passengers in her car because she felt responsible for their safety. When she was a passenger herself, she was so focused on watching out for other cars that she could barely carry on a conversation.

In addition to the usual interventions for PTSD, I had Linda spend a few minutes in VR nature scenes that she found "calming" and "safe". These brief respites made it easier for her to talk about her accident.

I had her learn and practice progressive muscle relaxation (PMR) because she was protectively hunching over the steering wheel and tense while driving. She revisited relaxing VEs at home, while following the PMR instructions. After two weeks, she was sleeping better and less irritable.

We discussed how the accident had shaken her sense of safety and her trust in other drivers. To prepare for virtual driving, we created an informal hierarchy starting with driving alone on city streets and working up to driving with passengers on a dark, rainy highway.

Driving alone on city streets with little traffic in VR triggered a SUDS of 2 that quickly dropped to 1. Adding more cars, then adding passengers caused a transient increase in anxiety.

Stopping at a traffic light or being in a traffic jam with cars all around triggered a SUDS of 7. She tensed, started repeatedly checking the car mirrors, and felt like she was about to be rear-ended. Vivid memories of the accident intruded, although she was able to stay present.

I encouraged Linda to practice diaphragmatic breathing and relaxation and to stay focused on the present reality where traffic was actually moving and stopping appropriately in VR. Her car was not being hit.

I also reminded her to say aloud the facts and statements she found most helpful and calming: "I drive a safe car. Most drivers are safe drivers. The other drivers just want to get to wherever they are going. Pay attention to what is happening now, not what happened then." And similar statements that we had created together. Her SUDS rather quickly decreased to 2 or a 3.

At our next session, I had her repeat these virtual driving experiences and pointed out that her anxiety level peaked at a 4 this time—about half what it was last time—and rather quickly dropped to a 2. I congratulated her and had her talk about what she was doing that worked.

With her permission, I then had Linda start driving a virtual highway. We began with her driving from a city street onto the entrance ramp and then merging with highway traffic. Her SUDS shot up to 8. I reminded her to use all her skills, prompted her to use the self-statements that worked best for her and played the PMR instructions. She began to visibly relax. After 20 minutes, her anxiety had dropped to 4.

We took a break. When she returned to driving on the highway, her anxiety briefly hit 5, but quickly decreased to 4, then 3, then 2.5, until it was 2. We ended the session with a few minutes in her preferred relaxing VE and set homework. In addition to continuing to practice PMR in VR at home, she agreed to alternate writing about the accident with writing about a future time when she would be driving on the highway and successfully handling anxiety.

Linda walked into my office for the next session and elatedly reported that she had driven to work on the highway for the first time since the accident. "I was anxious, but I remembered everything you told me, and I did it." We reviewed what she was doing that was working and confirmed that other PTSD symptoms were continuing to remit.

She said she was actually looking forward to virtual driving. This time, she drove the entrance ramp onto the highway with minimal anxiety, so we spent most of the session having her drive on the highway with cars behind her and then taking the exit ramp. She practiced only intermittently checking the mirrors in her virtual car and coping with the anxiety triggered by decreasing her hypervigilance.

This time her anxiety spikes were lower and decreased more quickly. She also was becoming more confident in her ability to cope with symptoms when they did occur.

In our final session, I had her driving with passengers on a dark rainy night. Her SUDS stayed between 1 and 3, at which point I challenged her to "Try to make yourself afraid. What will your fear tell you?" and checked her anxiety, asking her for a SUDS level after a few minutes.

Her anxiety stayed low, mostly at 2. The frightening thoughts and memories no longer had the same power over her. And when they recurred, she had tools for coping.

By the end of therapy, her nightmares had stopped, she was happier and less irritable, and had resumed driving the freeways. She told me, "I will always be more aware of the car behind me, especially when I am stopped, but I feel like me again."

Evidence Base

Research findings are somewhat mixed, but generally find that virtual reality exposure therapy (VRET) is as effective as standard exposure therapies for PTSD from combat and other causes (Beck et al., 2007; Beidel et al., 2019; Cárdenas-López et al., 2014; Carl et al., 2019; Kothgassner et al., 2019; Loucks et al., 2019; Maples-Keller et al., 2017; McLay et al., 2017; Reger et al., 2016; Rizzo & Shilling, 2017).

References

Beck, J. G., Palyo, S. A., Winer, E. H., Schwagler, B. E., & Ang, E. J. (2007). Virtual Reality Exposure Therapy for PTSD symptoms after a road accident: An uncontrolled case series. *Behavior Therapy*, 38(1), 39–48. doi:10.1016/j.beth.2006.04.001.

Beidel, D. C., Frueh, B. C., Neer, S. M., Bowers, C. A., Trachik, B., Uhde, T. W., & Grubaugh, A. (2019). Trauma management therapy with virtual-reality augmented exposure therapy for combat-related PTSD: A randomized controlled trial. *Journal of Anxiety Disorders*, 61, 64–74. doi:10.1016/j.janxdis.2017.08.005.

Cárdenas-López, G., De La Rosa, A., Durán-Baca, X., & Bouchard, S. (2015). Virtual reality PTSD treatment program for civil victims of criminal violence. In P. Cipresso & S. Serino (Eds.), *Virtual Reality: Technologies, Medical Applications and Challenges* (269–290). Nova Science Publishers.

Carl, E., Stein, A. T., Levihn-Coon, A., Pogue, J. R., Rothbaum, B., Emmelkamp, P., Asmundson, G. J. G., Carlbring, P., & Powers, M. B. (2019). Virtual reality exposure therapy for anxiety and related disorders: A meta-analysis of randomized controlled trials. *Journal of Anxiety Disorders*, 61, 27–36. doi:10.1016/j.janxdis.2018.08.003.

Hamblen, J. L., Norman, S. B., Sonis, J. H., Phelps, A. J., Bisson, J. I., Nunes, V. D., Megnin-Viggars, O., Forbes, D., Riggs, D. S., & Schnurr, P. P. (2019). A guide to guidelines for the treatment of posttraumatic stress disorder in adults: An update. *Psychotherapy*, 56(3), 359–373. doi:10.1037/pst0000231.

Kothgassner, O. D., Goreis, A., Kafka, J. X., Van Eickels, R. L., Plener, P. L., & Felnhofer, A. (2019). Virtual reality exposure therapy for posttraumatic stress disorder (PTSD): A meta-analysis. *European Journal of Psychotraumatology*, 10(1), 1654782. doi:10.1080/20008198.2019.1654782.

Loucks, L., Yasinski, C., Norrholm, S. D., Maples-Keller, J., Post, L., Zwiebach, L., Fiorillo, D., Goodlin, M., Jovanovic, T., Rizzo, A. A., & Rothbaum, B. O. (2019). You can do that?!: Feasibility of virtual reality exposure therapy in the treatment of PTSD due to military sexual trauma. *Journal of Anxiety Disorders*, 61, 55–63. doi:10.1016/j.janxdis.2018.06.004.

Maples-Keller, J. L., Bunnell, B. E., Kim, S.-J., & Rothbaum, B. O. (2017). The use of virtual reality technology in the treatment of anxiety and other psychiatric disorders. *Harvard Review of Psychiatry*, 25(3), 103–113. doi:10.1097/HRP.0000000000000138.

McLay, R. N., Baird, A., Webb-Murphy, J., Deal, W., Tran, L., Anson, H., Klam, W., & Johnston, S. (2017). A randomized, head-to-head study of virtual reality exposure therapy for posttraumatic stress disorder. *Cyberpsychology, Behavior, and Social Networking*, 20(4), 218–224. doi:10.1089/cyber.2016.0554.

Reger, G. M., Koenen-Woods, P., Zetocha, K., Smolenski, D. J., Holloway, K. M., Rothbaum, B. O., Difede, J. A., Rizzo, A. A., Edwards-Stewart, A., Skopp, N. A., Mishkind, M., Reger, M. A., & Gahm, G. A. (2016). Randomized controlled trial of prolonged exposure using imaginal exposure vs. virtual reality exposure in active duty soldiers with deployment-related posttraumatic stress disorder (PTSD). *Journal of Consulting and Clinical Psychology*, 84(11), 946–959. doi:10.1037/ccp0000134.

Rizzo, A. & Shilling, R. (2017). Clinical virtual reality tools to advance the prevention, assessment, and treatment of PTSD. *European Journal of Psychotraumatology*, 8(5). doi:10.1080/20008198.2017.1414560.

Weiss, N. H., Risi, M. M., Sullivan, T. P., Armeli, S., & Tennen, H. (2019). Posttraumatic stress disorder symptom severity attenuates bi-directional associations between negative affect and avoidant coping: A daily diary study. *Journal of Affective Disorders*, 259, 73–81. doi:10.1016/j.jad.2019.08.015.

17 GAD, OCD, and Illness Anxiety Disorder

"VR helped me think about things differently."

This chapter explains the uses of virtual reality (VR) in treating generalized anxiety disorder (GAD), obsessive-compulsive disorder (OCD), and illness anxiety disorder (sometimes called health anxiety and previously known as hypochondriasis). These disorders are all characterized by intrusive ruminations that result in compulsive mental or physical behaviors.

Issues specific to each disorder are briefly discussed. Cases illustrate clinical applications of VR. Although medication can assist treatment for some clients, pharmacological interventions are not covered, since the focus is on virtual reality therapy (VRT).

GAD, OCD, Illness Anxiety Disorder, and the Anxiety Cycle

Anxiety Triggers

Genetics

Clients with anxiety disorders often report a family history of anxiety, suggesting that genetics plays a role in heightening vulnerability to anxiety. Understanding that genetics may be a factor helps provide clients with an explanation for their symptoms and can be used to emphasize the importance of learning effective coping tools.

External Stress

External stress does not usually play a primary role with these disorders. However, any stress may increase anxiety or a sense of vulnerability. Illness can increase fears related to disease or death.

DOI: 10.4324/9781003154068-20

Self-Talk / Self-Demands

Underlying assumptions may include the following:

- The world (or my mind or body) is unpredictable and easily dangerous.
- I am vulnerable and/or I can't cope with illness, distress, etc.
- I can't rely on others (or myself).
- Worry is protective and either prevents or reliably predicts danger.
- Guaranteed safety is possible and necessary.
- Absolute certainty is possible and necessary.
- The absence of guaranteed safety or certainty means that there *is* danger.
- If a bad outcome is *conceivable*, it is *likely*.
- I must remain hypervigilant and make plans for all possible dangers.

Unhelpful Lessons from Past Events

In addition to learning from relatives with similar concerns, specific past events may contribute to clients' fears and actions. Past trauma or lack of safety or predictability may contribute to intrusive, ruminative worry.

OCD clients with religious obsessions or scrupulosity often report a strict religious background and are acting on an overly rigid understanding of religious rituals, prohibitions, or exhortations.

Past events may contribute to fears of illness or the underlying beliefs that create and sustain such fears. For example, the client's parent or other important figure may have been ill, died, or been overly fearful of illness. Sometimes illness anxiety disorder starts after the client experiences an unexpected illness.

Anxiety Sensations

All three disorders create distressing anxiety resulting in partial or full sympathetic nervous system arousal.

Common Fears

GAD, OCD, and illness anxiety can be conceptualized as phobias of uncertainty, imperfection, and risks that move progressively from broader to narrower foci of fearful attention.

Clients with GAD experience intrusive, distressing, difficult-to-control worry about nearly everything. GAD is sometimes referred to as the "what if…?" disease. Clients seek certain, guaranteed safety. There is a sense that if something could conceivably go awry, it is not only possible, but likely and would be catastrophic.

Rather than worrying about everything, clients with OCD focus their obsessional worry on one or more specific physical or mental stimuli. For example, dirt, germs, harmful or blasphemous thoughts, harmful or recklessly irresponsible behavior resulting in harm, etc. Uncertainty of safety, less than perfect memories of completing safety actions, or a lack of perfection (i.e., perfect cleanliness, perfect hygiene, perfect thoughts, perfect behavior, etc.) are seen as signaling danger.

Illness anxiety clients focus their worries on health and somatic sensations and fear that every physical sensation or change is a sign of serious illness. While not having somatic delusions, they are anxiously preoccupied with possibly having or developing a serious illness. Normal, benign physical sensations or changes are interpreted as signs of serious illness and the severity or consequences of any actual medical conditions are blown out of proportion. These clients may hold under-lying beliefs that they are physically fragile and/or assumptions that any physical change or deviation from an ideal is a warning of severe, imminent illness.

Fear-Based Actions

Fears described above create self-doubt and worry, resulting in hypervigi-lance and repeated safety actions. These clients attempt the impossible goal of guaranteed safety by trying to foresee and avoid or prevent risk or harm, seeking assurance as to the absence of risk or harm, or compulsively plan-ning how they might cope with or survive feared dangers.

Escape/Avoid

If possible, these clients will leave situations that trigger their anxiety. However, intrusive rumination is central to these disorders and it is hard to escape one's thoughts. Since thoughts of threat and danger cannot be avoi-ded, these clients try to avoid presumed dangers, remain hypervigilant to them, and take safety actions to prevent or cope.

Look for Danger/Take Safety Actions

As noted above, clients with GAD may repeatedly seek reassurance and believe that worrying is protective.

Clients with OCD respond to fears (obsessions) with safety actions (com-pulsions) such as repeated checking, cleaning, touching, mental safety rituals, etc. A classic example is responding to an obsessional fear of germs or illness with compulsive excessive hand-washing and cleaning. With "pure obses-sional" OCD, the compulsive safety action is a mental action such as mentally repeating certain numbers, words, prayers, etc. Both obsessional and compul-sive types of compulsions can coexist, as in the Javier case example below.

Clients with illness anxiety may compulsively seek reassurance or fearfully avoid medical care, afraid of having their fears confirmed. They often make repeated medical appointments, demand multiple medical tests, and hypervigi-lantly check their bodies for signs of illness and the internet for information on diseases.

Fighting Anxiety

Clients with any of these disorders may try to fight their anxiety—i.e., try to not have worries or "dangerous" thoughts—which of course does not work and contributes to constant anxious hypervigilance.

VRT for GAD, OCD, and Illness Anxiety

Treating Anxiety Triggers

Genetics

Clients cannot change their genetic inheritance, but it is encouraging that the adult brain is more malleable than was previously assumed. Intriguingly, PET scans show overactivation of certain brain areas in OCD and this overactivation normalizes when OCD is effectively treated—either pharmacologically or with exposure and response prevention (ERP).

External Stress

Coping skills for anxiety taught and practiced in VR can help reduce the impact of stress. Clients can practice actions to reduce stress while in related virtual environments (VEs).

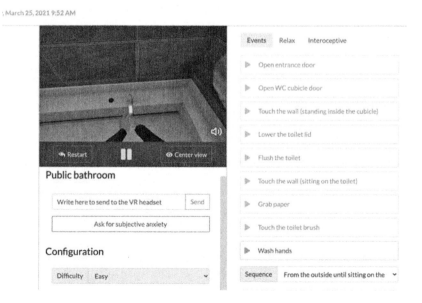

Figure 17.1 Washing Hands VE Example

Self-Talk/Self-Demands and Unhelpful Past Lessons

Treatment may include replacing unhelpful self-talk, unrealistic self-demands, and conscious or unconscious lessons that contribute to fear, worry, and rumination. Interventions may include insight, creating a different narrative, gathering evidence supporting alternative positive core beliefs, identifying values and committing to act on them, positive psychology interventions, and others. VR may provide a venue where clients can rehearse new cognitions and insights to foster generalization and transfer to real world situations.

Treating Anxiety Sensations

Pleasant, rewarding virtual experiences may strengthen the treatment alliance, decrease missed or cancelled appointments, and reward clients' involvement in treatment.

Because VR is engaging and immersive, clients may more easily learn and practice diaphragmatic breathing, progressive muscle relaxation, and mindfulness. Entering VR can be engaging enough to temporarily disrupt anxious ruminations and hypervigilance or mental compulsions. VEs provide opportunities for deliberately refocusing attention away from concerns or somatic sensations.

Using VR for relaxation may provide relaxation training, uncover fears (especially deeper, meta-level fears), *and* provide exposure. For example, relaxing may trigger more worry uncovering fears of "letting down my guard" or "not being prepared".

Treating Common Fears

It can be hard to resist providing reassuring facts when your client is distressed, and reassurance provides (temporary) relief. The pitfall is that refuting fears one at a time is an endless, fruitless task that actually feeds their anxiety cycle. Being reassured about one specific worry or symptom simply allows another one (or several!) more to pop up, like playing a game of "Whack-a-Mole." Part of your job is not to get sucked into discussing or disputing individual worries as they arise—one after another, and another, and another, ad infinitum.

Clients' reactions to various VEs may uncover previously unverbalized worries or obsessions. VR can also give clients opportunities to reduce their belief in intrusive worries/obsessions. Practicing a changed response to fears in your presence fosters success because you can encourage, support, and reinforce your client.

You can challenge clients to "bring on" worries or obsessions while in VEs and measure the client's anxiety on the Subjective Units of Distress Scale (SUDS) while also testing for changes in the client beliefs about specific worries/obsessions/fears, the value and accuracy of worrying/reassuring/compulsive behaviors, and their own ability to implement changes.

Check anxiety by asking: "On a 0 to 10 scale, where 0 is not at all and 10 is absolutely, how anxious does that worry/OCD thought/information about illness make you?"

To check beliefs, you might ask:

- "On a 0 to 10 scale, where 0 is not at all and 10 is absolutely, how much do you believe what the worry/thought/OCD/fear/Reacting Brain is saying?"
- "On a 0 to 10 scale, where 0 is not at all and 10 is absolutely, how much do you believe that such thoughts are accurate, reliable, appropriately protective, and justified based on the facts?"
- "On a 0 to 10 scale, where 0 is not at all and 10 is absolutely, how much do you believe you will be able to respond differently?"

Ideally, the client reports *low* numbers in response to questions about anxiety, belief in specific worries, and belief in the helpfulness and accuracy of worrying, and *high* numbers in response to the question about confidence in applying new skills and knowledge. Such numbers can validate treatment effectiveness, reassure the client, and help you both decide to terminate treatment.

Even when your client reports low numbers when you're hoping for high (and vice versa), it is still a win-win. You get an accurate sense of where the client currently is in treatment and can move forward with interventions accordingly. Plus, it gives a baseline against which to measure progress.

Treating Fear-Based Actions

Even when clients have insight that their repetitive fears are out of proportion, insight alone rarely reduces the occurrence of distressing worries or obsessions. As the treatment cycle diagram emphasizes, it is important that the client *accept* the fact that life never offers guaranteed safety or certainty, *act* on this fact, and *take the "risk"* of stopping the fear-based actions.

Since these clients are so frightened by the possible consequences, VR may be the only acceptable exposure option, at least at first. VR is a uniquely flexible way to provide tailored exposure. Clients can face anxiogenic stimuli virtually, at a tolerable pace, and in a way that feels sufficiently safe. You can take the client to avoided places or activities by placing your client in a specific VE or by virtually teleporting the client to real world settings.

Seeing how clients respond in VR gives you a window onto their progress. Ideally, clients will move from endlessly disputing or believing and acting on each new worry, obsession, or fear to gaining the insight that these thoughts are not reality-based and having the courage to change their actions based upon this insight.

Worries that plague GAD clients are so multi-focused and ever-changing that creating VEs specifically for GAD might seem like an impossible and endless task. The "good" news is that because clients with GAD worry about so very many things, almost any VE may be helpful.

VEs created to provide exposure for fear of needles or MRI machines can be used with clients who fear illness whether those fears are caused by GAD, OCD, or health anxiety. At least one VR product has VEs where clients view prerecorded television programs discussing various risks that may be relevant for any of the three disorders. Many VEs can be repurposed for disorder-specific exposure. For example, driving or being a passenger in a virtual car may be used in the context of driving to or from a medical test or appointment and worrying about the results or driving to visit a sick or dying friend.

Exposure and Response Prevention for OCD

Exposure and response prevention (ERP) is an evidence-based treatment for OCD (Law & Boisseau, 2019). ERP is consistent with the anxiety treatment model used in this book: deliberately facing fear (exposure) while acting on the facts and avoiding fear-based actions (response prevention).

I have seen ERP work and I have also seen how anxiety-provoking and challenging ERP can be for clients. Some ERP therapeutic tasks with clients can be done in your office, like touching doorknobs or wastebaskets and not washing your hands, but these options are limited. VR provides many other options.

Some VEs developed specifically for OCD treatment can be used for ERP. For example, VEs of entering a public restroom, entering the toilet stall, sitting on the toilet, touching the stall wall, and washing hands afterward.

Here are other examples of VEs that might be used for ERP in OCD treatment.

VEs for Fear of Germs/Washing and Cleaning

Obviously, the public restroom VE is relevant, but so are VEs where clients are in public, especially if they are in close contact with virtual others. For example, on a subway, in a car with passengers, at work, on a plane, or in social settings.

VEs involving food and drink can elicit fears of germs or contamination, as can VEs with insects or animals. A work setting might be used to address obsessive fears that either the client or coworkers have not sufficiently cleaned shared mugs, plates, silverware, or common areas.

VEs of medical settings can be seen as teeming with germs and risk, i.e., "What if the healthcare provider didn't adequately wash and is spreading dangerous germs?" or "What if someone with a contagious disease sat where I am sitting or is near me?"

VEs for Hyperresponsibility/Checking

Obsessive fears focused on feeling overly responsible can include thoughts such as:

- "I left appliances on or plugged in. There will be a fire and I'll be responsible for people dying."
- "I left the gas stove on. There will be a gas explosion and it will be my fault."
- "I left the door unlocked. There will be a robbery and family members will be harmed because of my carelessness."
- "Maybe I hit someone while driving. I need to check and monitor reports of hit-and-run accidents."

Driving VEs can be used for the above and similar fears such as not closing the garage door or not confirming that a pet was safely inside the house, by having the client virtually drive away, resisting the urge to return and check or by making the client a passenger in the car and "unable" to go back.

You might virtually transport clients to distant locations to confront being unable to check or place them on the street outside their home to resist the compulsive need to go back inside and check "just one more time, just in case".

VEs for Fear of Thoughts or Mental Images

Clients with OCD may experience frightening, intrusive thoughts or images of performing some harmful or inappropriate behavior. They may worry about impulsively being violent toward others or themselves, blurting out obscenities or insults, saying "the wrong thing," and so forth. Some clients have thoughts of sexual acts that horrify, rather than titillate, them.

Any VE where clients are in the company of others may be relevant for these fears, especially situations in which acting on such thoughts would seem particularly inappropriate or dangerous. VEs for needle phobia may evoke fears of grabbing the syringe and harming oneself or others. Social, work, and elevator settings may be used for obsessive fears about speech or behavior. Height VEs may be used for thoughts such as "What if I jumped? If I think about jumping or imagine it, that means I might do it." Or "What if I push someone off?"

Even VEs of being inside a house may be potentially useful. These VEs may be labeled as designed for worry exposure for GAD, fear of the dark or of storms, or anticipatory anxiety that accompanies flying phobia. But they could potentially be used for exposure to thoughts of harm with an attention to possible "weapons" at hand, i.e., throwing lamps, breaking a window and using jagged glass, etc.

VEs for Compulsive Ordering

Currently there are no VEs specifically relevant for ordering compulsions and fear of disorder or asymmetry. However, the VEs mentioned above may be used to trigger fears that the client has left home or work without ordering or that others have messed up things that had been ordered.

In the future when cameras that create 3-D VR photos and videos become affordable and easy to use, perhaps clients will take VR photos or videos of temporarily un-ordered belongings and bring them to sessions for personalized exposure.

Treatment Challenges

COVID-19

The pandemic has made fears of being exposed to, or potentially exposing others to, potentially fatal illnesses more credible. This is especially true for COVID-19 because people can be asymptomatic and still spread the disease and disease effects can range from no or few transient symptoms to serious, lingering symptoms, hospitalization, or death. Mixed messages about the prevalence and seriousness of the virus exacerbated confusion and uncertainty. These factors all clearly increased GAD, OCD, and illness anxiety fears while protective societal measures such as mask wearing, social distancing, and sheltering in place tended to entrench avoidance behaviors generally.

Risk Aversion

Clients are often more willing to take what feels like a purely personal risk (such as confronting a phobia, risking embarrassment, or feeling panicky) than they are to take actions which they believe may put others at risk or violate their religious beliefs.

Case Examples

George: GAD

George was a pleasant-looking man in his late 30s. He sat on the edge of his seat in my office and leaned forward anxiously. I noticed an underlying tension in his face and just about his first words to me were, "I'm a worrier. I've worried all my life. My kids say I'm driving them crazy, but I think they aren't careful enough." His wife and two teenage daughters had urged him to seek treatment. They were concerned about the distress George felt from constant over-worrying and were tired of endlessly reassuring him and altering their own behavior.

VR helped George learn diaphragmatic breathing and progressive muscle relaxation (PMR). The first time he listened to the recorded instructions for PMR while in a relaxing VE, he said in wonder, "I almost fell asleep. I haven't been that relaxed in years!"

With his permission, I had used his phone to record the PMR instructions and he practiced them at home, recalling the experience of being in the relaxing virtual world, which heightened his ability to relax. Had we been doing teletherapy, George would have had VR equipment at home, allowing him to re-enter the relaxing VE while listening to reinforce the power of the PMR instructions.

We then moved on from changing his physical response to worry to changing his emotional and cognitive response.

We used many different VEs for practice. For example, while virtually driving on a dark, rainy road, George practiced responding to worries that he might cause an accident, be the victim of an accident, or that his wife or daughters might be in an accident. On the virtual beach, he practiced coping with worry about a tsunami. Waiting for a virtual subway was an opportunity to handle thoughts that someone would fall, jump, or be pushed in front of an oncoming train. In virtual heights situations or elevators, he could practice dealing with worries about shoddy construction, insufficient protections, inadequate safety inspections, earthquakes, or terrorist attacks. And so on.

George's SUDS in response to worry thoughts dropped from 8 or 9 down into the 1 to 3 range. He grew more comfortable taking the "risk" of telling himself, "Things will probably be okay. If something does happen, I will deal with it then. I have coped with things in the past, I will cope with whatever may happen," and his belief in these statements increased from close to 0 at the start of treatment to close to 9 by the end.

To help cement these positive changes and prevent relapse, he returned to VEs which had initially triggered a lot of worry. I verbalized his prior worries associated with the VEs and he countered those worries. During this process, I frequently checked his SUDS level. If you use biofeedback, this is an excellent time to check biofeedback measures as well.

Finally, while he was in VR, I asked him to deliberately think about his previously distressing worries and try to increase his anxiety level. I kept close track of his SUDS, ready to intervene if his anxiety level rose too high or he wasn't able to decrease it. We were both thrilled when he said that he no longer got very anxious, even when he was trying to. He told me, "I just thought, 'That's ridiculous.' I told it, 'You're just my worry voice. You always say the same thing and you don't know the future. I'm not listening to you anymore.' And you know what, I didn't get anxious."

Javier: OCD

Javier presented complaining of intrusive, distressing obsessional thoughts of his loved ones dying and feared his thoughts might cause them harm: "What if I think of my wife or son dying and they do die?" He worried about bringing home germs from public places and infecting his loved ones with a fatal illness. As a result, he found it hard to go out in public and would often avoid or leave events. He was cancelling business trips and refusing to travel on vacation. He also washed his hands excessively and urged family members to do so as well. When apart from family, he called or texted family members multiple times daily, repeatedly seeking reassurance that they were all right. His anxiety sky-rocketed if he did not immediately hear back, especially if he had just thought about them dying.

He reported "obsessively" repeating a special prayer. This was actually a mental compulsive safety action intended to protect his family and undo any possible harm caused by his thoughts.

I discussed OCD and its treatment and showed him photographs of PET brain scans to bolster his confidence that the treatment process would be successful, even if he found it uncomfortable.

We used VR to help him gain the ability to voluntarily relax his muscles, shift his breathing, and develop a mindful awareness of his environment. The immersive nature of VR helped shift his mental attention away from mental obsessions and compulsions to learning and applying these skills. Spending time in VEs at the start and end of each session made treatment more acceptable.

Using anxiety tolerance skills—both in session and at home—became a way of responding to the distress of terrifying obsessional thoughts with acceptance and detachment, rather than through fighting the distress, engaging in compulsive reassurance-seeking, or praying.

In sessions, he agreed to enter a series of VEs associated with obsessional thinking based on a hierarchy. His first VE was being alone in a virtual public elevator. He deliberately evoked the thought that he was picking up germs (exposure), but used breathing, muscle relaxation, and mindful awareness to tolerate the fact that he was deliberately choosing to not call or text (response prevention). When his anxiety in that situation decreased, we included having him deliberately think of the possibility that loved ones were ill or could die, and not responding with compulsive prayer. This was scary and took several sessions.

Over time, Javier tolerated virtually entering public settings he viewed as increasingly "germ-laden" such as increasingly smaller and crowded elevators, cars with an increasing number of fellow passengers, the subway, a plane, and a public restroom.

He worked up to driving a virtual car and imagining that he had just left a "germ-laden" public place or that he would be traveling and unable to reach his family. In the final sessions, he took a virtual cab to the airport, boarded and flew with strangers on a business trip, and used a public restroom while imagining that he did not repeat protective prayers, text, or call every few minutes.

By the end of treatment, he stated that obsessional fears still occurred, especially when he was stressed or family members were ill, but that he no longer cancelled business trips. He was not compulsively praying in response to fearful thoughts and had decreased the frequency of calling or texting family members to once a day.

Anne: Illness Anxiety Disorder

Anne was referred for treatment by her primary care provider because:

> No matter what I do, she's back the next week or month convinced she has a disease. She keeps wanting the same tests repeated and more tests ordered. The fact that all these tests are normal, and she is actually healthy doesn't seem to make a difference. Honestly, I'm at my wits' end. I hope you can help.

Anne was dubious but did wistfully say, "I'd like to worry less about my health."

It was hard for Anne to imagine redirecting her attention away from a hypervigilant focus on her body and not taking actions like calling her physician or Googling illnesses, but she was motivated, and her family was supportive of her desire to change.

Similar to VRT for OCD, VR was used to help Anne calm down at the start and end of sessions. The goal of treatment was to help her change her reactions to observed physical sensations.

At first it was easier to change her thoughts or imagine changing her reactions when she was in peaceful, relaxing VEs that felt "safe" to her, such as the beach.

We worked first on changing her self-talk when she read or heard about an illness or noticed a physical sensation. We then used VR so she could practice and reinforce these new responses. She ranked a hierarchy of virtual situations from less to more likely to trigger fears of illness and where such fears would feel less or more frightening. She moved from practicing new skills and thinking in virtual nature scenes and isolated public places and worked up to practicing them within crowds.

As her SUDS decreased and her ability to counter health worries increased, she practiced while in virtual hospital or clinic waiting rooms and while virtually getting blood drawn. After she was repeatedly successful, I used VR to strengthen her skills and help prevent relapse by voicing her illness fears while she was in these VEs. I might say, "That person looks like they might be sick. I better check how I'm feeling. I bet something awful is wrong with me that the doctors have missed. I need to do an internet search of possible illnesses." She would practice talking back, "That person is probably fine. Even if they are sick, it doesn't mean that I am sick or going to get sick. What is actually happening right now?" She would tell herself, "Focus on reality. Do slow breathing, relax your muscles, and be mindful. You're probably fine. If there's a problem, you can deal with it then. Your job is to live your life and enjoy it."

Anne commented that practicing new responses in VR helped. "It made it more real. Like I was really doing it, not just talking about doing it. And practicing in different places helped too. Last week, I went for my pap smear and didn't even look up signs of cervical cancer beforehand!"

Evidence Base

It seems logical that VR can be used with OCD, GAD, and illness anxiety, but research is sparse. GAD patients in two pilot studies reported decreased anxiety when VR was used for relaxation and exposure (Gorini & Riva, 2008; Repetto et al., 2013) and virtual reality exposure therapy (VRET) successfully reduced excessive fear of COVID-19 in three patients described as meeting diagnostic criteria for GAD (Zhang et al., 2020). Kim et al. (2008, 2009) documented that VEs elicit anxiety and checking behavior in OCD patients suggesting that VR may help diagnose and treat OCD. No published research was available on VRT for illness anxiety.

References

Gorini, A. & Riva, G. (2008). The potential of virtual reality as anxiety management tool: A randomized controlled study in a sample of patients affected by generalized anxiety disorder. *Trials*, 9(25). doi:10.1186/1745-6215-9-25.

Kim, K., Kim, C.-H., Cha, K. R., Park, J., Han, K., Kim, Y. K., Kim, J.-J., Kim, I. Y., & Kim, S. I. (2008). Anxiety provocation and measurement using virtual reality in patients with obsessive-compulsive disorder. *CyberPsychology & Behavior*, 11(6), 637–641. doi:10.1089/cpb.2008.0003.

Kim, K., Kim, C. H., Kim, S. Y., Roh, D., & Kim, S. I. (2009). Virtual reality for obsessive-compulsive disorder: Past and the future. *Psychiatry Investigation*, 6(3), 115–121. doi:10.4306/pi.2009.6.3.115.

Law, C. & Boisseau, C. L. (2019). Exposure and response prevention in the treatment of obsessive-compulsive disorder: Current perspectives. *Psychology Research and Behavior Management*, 12, 1167–1174. doi:10.2147/PRBM.S211117.

Repetto, C., Gaggioli, A., Pallavicini, F., Cipresso, P., Raspelli, S., & Riva, G. (2013). Virtual reality and mobile phones in the treatment of generalized anxiety disorders: A phase-2 clinical trial. *Personal and Ubiquitous Computing*, 17(2), 253–260. doi:10.1007/s00779-011-0467-0.

Zhang, W., Paudel, D., Shi, R., Liang, J., Liu, J., Zeng, X., Zhou, Y., & Zhang, B. (2020). Virtual reality exposure therapy (VRET) for anxiety due to fear of covid-19 infection: A case series. *Neuropsychiatric Disease and Treatment*, 16, 2669–2675. doi:10.2147/NDT.S276203.

Part IV

Other Issues

This section covers three other issues related to virtual reality therapy (VRT):

- Using virtual reality (VR) with therapeutic approaches other than cognitive behavioral therapy (CBT).
- Frequently asked questions regarding clinical issues, VR products, troubleshooting, and practical concerns.
- Future directions for VR therapy.

DOI: 10.4324/9781003154068-21

18 Virtual Reality and Non-CBT Therapies

Virtual reality (VR) is a flexible, powerful, atheoretical tool that can be used with many therapeutic approaches. The uses of VR described above are mainly in the context of cognitive-behavioral therapy (CBT), which is my primary approach. This chapter explores how VR can be used with a variety of other treatment approaches (listed alphabetically). I encourage you to imagine how VR can be integrated in your practice.

Acceptance and Commitment Therapy (ACT)

Virtual reality therapy (VRT) is complementary and consistent with ACT. Virtual experiences can facilitate training in skills such as diaphragmatic breathing, muscle relaxation, or mindfulness that can foster acceptance of distress.

Clients can practice acceptance while entering distress-evoking virtual environments (VEs). After clarifying their values and goals, clients can virtually practice acting on their commitment to do what is needed and helpful, even when it is uncomfortable or challenging.

Art and Music Therapy

Several websites and apps offer clients the ability to create virtual artwork or music. Cost and features vary but even the less expensive VR art-making tools allow clients to experiment with brushstrokes, scale, and animation. Digital art therapy avoids spills and mess, needs no time-consuming preparation or clean-up, and allows clients to create impossible things. Having fewer reality constraints can free the imagination. Virtual art can be instantly modified or deleted.

Applications of VR for music therapy are less developed but are being explored and researched. Australian researchers are developing an online VR platform to help quadriplegics improve breathing, voice, mood, and social connectedness by participating remotely in group singing. Neurologic Music Therapy (NMT) incorporates VR to help retrain motor function in stroke patients with upper limb hemiparesis. Baka et al. reported that this

DOI: 10.4324/9781003154068-22

approach "helped patients to improve their kinetic performance, in a faster, more efficient and motivating manner" (Baka et al., 2018).

Dialectical Behavior Therapy (DBT)

The range of available VEs provides many settings in which clients can practice one-mindfully focusing on the present. Practicing DBT skills in realistic virtual settings may improve transfer and generalization to real life. Client cooperation in entering VR can be highlighted and reinforced as an example of willingness. Some VR products incorporate mindfulness instructions to reinforce mindfulness skills. Pleasurable VEs provide positive experiences and may strengthen the use of imagery or relaxation to improve the moment.

VR provides safe practice environments where emotions can be triggered, and virtual interactions experienced, without the risk of damaging actual interpersonal relationships. Interacting with avatars allows clients to practice observing and describing nonjudgmentally. You can speak for virtual others while clients practice interpersonal effectiveness skills, e.g., GIVE, DEAR MAN, and FAST.

Aspects of virtual experiences can be controlled by the therapist to minimize excessive distress. If intense reactions *are* triggered, the VR can be paused or stopped while reactions are processed and the client practices distress tolerance skills such as self-soothing, paying attention to the five senses, radical acceptance, etc.

Eye Movement Desensitization and Reprocessing (EMDR)

Some VR products include visual or auditory stimuli specifically designed for use *during* EMDR. All VR products offers immediate, vivid way for clients to practice new ways of reacting following EMDR. You and your clients can confirm that desensitization and reprocessing have occurred.

Practicing in VR strengthens changes and increases clients' confidence. Pleasant VR experiences can reinforce client engagement and effort, decrease distress, or end sessions with a positive affective experience.

Hypnosis/Hypnotherapy

Some VR products can create entrancing, changing patterns of colors that may facilitate clients entering a hypnotic state. Visual and auditory stimuli in VR may engage client attention, perhaps enhancing their receptivity to hypnotic suggestions. Hypnosis for pain control can be combined with the distraction and absorption of VR.

Clients may respond more deeply to suggestions for relaxation while viewing relaxing VEs. Hypnotic suggestions for responding differently to stressful situations may be given—and their efficacy tested—while clients are experiencing stress-inducing VEs.

Mindfulness and Mindfulness-Based Therapies

VR can be a powerful way to bring the client "into the moment". Almost any VE can be used to practice mindful awareness and many VR products include mindfulness instructions. In VR, clients can practice mindfulness under increasingly challenging situations, helping to prepare clients for using mindfulness in real life.

Narrative Therapy

Pleasant VR experiences can reinforce clients for attending and doing the work of therapy. Positive VR experiences can trigger positive mood which is associated with cognitive flexibility and creative problem-solving. Clients can experiment with applying new narratives within VR. They can test out the effects of their changed story, practice viewing situations in a new way, and prepare to carry their revised story into real world situations and interactions.

Positive Psychology

Dr. Barbara Fredrickson and others have explored the benefits of positive emotions (Fredrickson, 2009). As mentioned above, people demonstrate more cognitive flexibility and creativity when in a good mood. They find more creative solutions to problems and are more open and open-minded.

VR can facilitate a range of positive emotions. Clients may be intrigued by VR and hopeful that VRT can help. VEs can foster serenity and peace or induce feelings of awe. You may be able to teleport clients to some of the most beautiful, awe-inspiring places on earth. Learning new skills and overcoming fears and problems in VR creates pride and increased confidence.

Psychodynamic Therapy

Psychodynamic psychotherapy strives to increase clients' self-knowledge and freedom of action. As a result of corrective emotional experiences and insights gained in therapy, clients cope more effectively with situations and relationships encountered outside therapy.

VR can bring outside situations into the office to give clients opportunities to apply insights and measure progress. Clients may be more in touch with their emotions when processing affect that was just evoked in a virtual encounter, compared with discussing an experience that happened in the past.

Some clients are reluctant to talk about difficult topics because this elicits intense emotions. VR can help these clients learn anxiety management or provide calming spaces in which they feel safe enough to allow emotions to surface.

Other clients talk at length *about* emotions but use intellectualization as a defense against *experiencing* affect or emotionally engaging with the material. When relevant VEs are available, entering VR may help these clients become more immersed and present, resulting in a more lived emotional experience.

Relaxation Therapy

VR is beautifully complementary to relaxation therapy. Most clients have several VEs they find pleasant and relaxing. Entering these VEs helps clients initially achieve a relaxed state. Repeatedly entering favorite VEs may help clients relax more quickly and deeply.

Some VR products also include relaxation instructions. Having clients listen to these instructions while in a pleasant VE creates a more memorable, immersive experience. Clients may record the VR instructions and listen to them for home practice.

Having clients practice relaxation while virtually confronting stress-inducing situations prepares them to use relaxation when stressed in real life.

Schema Therapy

Schema therapy (or schema-focused therapy) integrates techniques from cognitive-behavioral therapy, psychodynamic theory, attachment theory, and emotion-focused therapies. It uses insight into lifelong patterns, affective change techniques, and the therapeutic relationship.

In VR, clients can practice changing their long-standing—but dysfunctional—patterns of thinking, feeling, and behaving. Mindfulness and other affect management skills can be taught and practiced in VR. Pleasant or relaxing VEs can help clients self-soothe. Positive experiences in VR strengthen the therapeutic alliance.

Solution-Focused Therapy

As the name implies, solution-focused therapy (also known as solution-focused brief therapy) focuses on helping clients find and implement solutions. One well-known intervention is "The Miracle Question", quickly summarized here as "What if you woke up and a miracle had happened, and your problem was all gone? How would you know? What would you do differently?" (Franklin et al., 2012).

When you have a VE that is relevant to a client's problem, placing the client within that VE allows the client to not simply imagine and describe what they would do differently if there was a miracle, but to actually show you and practice their new actions in VR. In the virtual world, clients can try out new ways of reacting or interacting while you support, observe, and prompt as needed.

References

Baka, E., Kentros, M., Papagiannakis, G., & Magnenat-Thalmann, N. (2018). Virtual reality rehabilitation based on neurologic music therapy: A qualitative preliminary clinical study. *Lecture Notes in Computer Science (Including Subseries Lecture Notes in Artificial Intelligence and Lecture Notes in Bioinformatics)*, 10925 LNCS, 113–127. doi:10.1007/978-3-319-91152-6_9.

Franklin, C., Trepper, T. S., Gingerich, W. J., & McCollum, E. E. (Eds.). (2012). *Solution-Focused Brief Therapy: A Handbook of Evidence-Based Practice* (pp. xx, 426–xx, 42. Oxford University Press.

Fredrickson, B. (2009). *Positivity: Top-Notch Research Reveals the 3-to-1 Ratio That Will Change Your Life*. Crown Publishers/Random House.

19 Frequently Asked Questions

This chapter answers questions therapists have raised about virtual reality (VR) during workshops or consultations. Questions are organized into clinical, VR product, troubleshooting, and practical sections.

Clinical Questions

What Are the Risks?

Virtual reality headsets are used by millions of people each day without harmful effects. There are some low likelihood risks to consider depending on your client population and VR system.

Medical Contraindications

Seizures can sometimes be triggered by photic (visual) stimuli such as flashing or flickering lights. If a client has epilepsy or other seizure disorders, eye problems, a pacemaker, hearing aids, or other medical devices that could potentially be affected by magnets or electronics in a VR headset, or any medical issue that might be aggravated by VR, I recommend getting a signed release of information and contacting the client's healthcare provider to confirm that VR is not medically contraindicated.

Nausea

Queasiness triggered by VR, sometimes called cybersickness, was more common in the past before current technologies for motion tracking and graphics. Some people seem more prone to this reaction (Mittelstaedt, 2020; Saredakis et al., 2020).

Because nausea can occur, mention it as a possible side effect when obtaining informed consent for using VR and ask clients to tell you if they feel queasy.

In my experience, nausea is more likely when clients are moving in VR but not physically. Clients' visual inputs indicate movement while their

DOI: 10.4324/9781003154068-23

proprioceptive body feedback indicates they are stationary. For example, when a client is physically seated but the client's virtual self is walking.

You can minimize this contradictory feedback by having a client's body position match the avatar's body position. For example, if a client is walking or standing in VR, have the client physically stand up (even if there is not space for them to walk); if the client is seated in VR, have the client seated.

Teleporting from place to place can avoid these contradictions between visual and proprioceptive stimuli. When clients are teleported from one location to another, the screen briefly goes black and when it lights up again, clients are in their new location. If your VR product does not offer teleporting, have clients who are prone to nausea close their eyes before being moved and open them after arriving.

Tripping or Falling

Clients in VR see and react to the *virtual* environment visually surrounding them, *not the physical environment actually surrounding them*. If clients physically move while in VR, watch that they do not trip over or walk into anything.

If the VR headset is connected with wires (tethered), be sure the client does not get tangled in the wire or trip over it.

If your VR system has clients stand on a raised vibrating platform, ensure that they don't fall off the platform. Consider creating a protective barrier by placing the platform against a wall, in a corner, and/or backing chairs against it.

Sensitization

Sensitization occurs when clients have frightening experiences that outpace or overwhelm their coping abilities and may result in their becoming more afraid. Since clients respond to virtual reality as if it was real, you want to avoid virtual experiences that could overwhelm and sensitize clients, leaving them more fearful rather than less.

The goal of virtual reality exposure therapy (VRET) is to have clients cope *successfully* with a frightening experience, so they feel less afraid. This process is sometimes called desensitization or habituation.

To reduce the risk of sensitization, I recommend:

- Understanding the client's anxiety cycle and reducing anxiety triggers, as clinically appropriate.
- Verifying that clients have effective anxiety tolerance skills before starting exposure.
- Experiencing each VE yourself, before using with any clients.
- Describing VE options to your client in advance, so they know what to expect.

- Tailoring exposure experiences for each client.
- Monitoring client responses during exposure and adjusting or stopping as needed.

Will VR Decrease Treatment Alliance?

If you have never used VR, you may be concerned that clients will feel disconnected because of the lack of eye contact, or that you will be distracted by the technology and less attuned to your clients. Two studies have examined this question.

Ngai and colleagues specifically designed a study to test the hypothesis that clients receiving VR exposure therapy would have lower levels of working alliance (Ngai et al., 2015). Clients received eight sessions of group exposure or individual VRET and completed a standardized self-report measure of working alliance after each session. Hierarchical linear modeling showed "high levels of working alliance" and "no differences in working alliance".

Wrzesien et al. studied the "quality of collaboration" between client and therapist during one intensive cognitive behavioral therapy (CBT) exposure session, comparing augmented reality exposure therapy (ARET) to in vivo exposure (Wrzesien et al., 2012). The authors reported "a greater level of distraction was observed for therapists in ARET", but therapists in both groups received "high collaboration scores" and treatment was equally successful in reducing phobic avoidance. These findings are congruent with overall research on VRET and consistent with my clinical experience.

Obviously, as you add VR to your therapeutic toolkit, you will continue your usual actions to foster and maintain a positive therapeutic alliance. Positive VR experiences can also strengthen that therapeutic alliance.

These suggestions may help you increase treatment alliance:

- For in-office work, locate your therapist workstation where you can smoothly switch between looking at your screen and looking at the client. This will make it easier for you to stay attuned to your client's reactions and needs.
- Actively monitor, coach, support, and reinforce clients while they are in VR. This may be especially important during VRET when clients face challenging virtual situations.
- Take time to familiarize yourself with the content and therapist controls for any VE or VR product before using it in session, especially if the product is new to you, you have not used it recently, or the vendor has updated the controls.

Is VR Suitable for Clients of All Ages?

I have used virtual reality therapy (VRT) with clients ranging in age from mid-teens to mid-eighties.

Research by Grenier et al. shows that VR can compensate for age-related decline in the ability to create vivid images in older anxiety clients (Grenier et al., 2015).

Using VR to reduce anxiety and pain in children undergoing medical or dental procedures has been widely researched. There is less research on VR for anxiety treatment with children, but VR does show potential in pediatric psychology, and for treating fears and phobias in autistic children and adults (Maskey, Rodgers, Grahame et al., 2019; Maskey, Rodgers, Ingham et al., 2019; Parsons et al., 2017).

What About Diversity?

VRT is used clinically worldwide. Research has found VRT to be effective with clients varying in age, gender, race, socioeconomic background, country, and presenting problem. Researchers around the world continue to actively study and expand VR's clinical applications.

On the other hand, currently the avatars (virtual representations of the client and/or other people) in many VEs are predominantly young adult, cisgender, able-bodied, and usually Caucasian. Some VR products do offer more diversity.

Hopefully, we will gain more ability to modify avatars to make clients' virtual image congruent with their physical selves and for virtual others to more accurately reflect real world diversity. VR is being used as a tool for diversity training, but these VEs may not be available or suitable for therapy.

Can Trainees Use VRT with Clients?

As a supervisor, you decide whether and when a supervisee can use VR with clients the same way you decide whether and when a supervisee can use any other clinical tool or intervention. Can the supervised trainee offer safe, effective treatment?

Trainee therapists need to become familiar with the VEs, variables, and controls. The time required will vary with the number and complexity of the VEs, but VR therapist controls are fairly self-explanatory.

You might want to review the supervisees' treatment plan and be sure they understand how to minimize and handle possible VR risks and side effects. I suggest confirming that trainees using VR for exposure are able to:

- Explain anxiety and its treatment and present the rationale for VRET.
- Evaluate whether clients are likely to benefit from VRET and prepared for exposure.
- Create an exposure hierarchy.
- Effectively support client coping during exposure and handle any distress.

Do I Need Specialized Informed Consent?

I do *not* have a separate VRT informed consent form in my private practice. However, I advise you to check whether your practice setting might require an added layer of consent.

My advice is to include general information about VRT risks and benefits in your standard consent form, where you explain your approach to therapy, common risks, and benefits of treatment. You will also discuss client-specific risks during treatment, as appropriate.

What About Charting While Clients Are in VR?

I take notes during sessions, including while clients are in VR, as the basis for charting each session. Charts and other records for my practice are stored in an online electronic health record (EHR) system.

Note-taking helps me capture important comments, information, and insights. During VRET, I note the clients' Subjective Units of Distress Scale (SUDS) levels, fears expressed, and what helps.

Some VR systems can record VEs, events, and variables. You may print this out and give a copy to the client or add it to the client's chart. Some VR systems let you record client SUDS, biofeedback data, and/or write your notes within the VR system during the session.

Before entering patient identifying information and other protected health information (PHI) into your VR system, be certain your system complies with applicable data privacy regulations. The current US regulation is HIPAA (Health Insurance Portability and Accountability Act of 1996).

You might be able to do charting or other tasks while a client listens to recorded instructions that they have heard before or relaxes in a VE that is familiar to the client, but you should have a clinical rationale for having clients in VR and should be present and monitoring client response. I would never put clients in VR just so I could chart, nor would I send them into another room for VR but charge for my time as if I were present with them and actively conducting therapy.

Where Can I Get More Training?

Sources of additional training range from self-study to formal supervision. Here are some options:

- Read articles in reputable peer-reviewed journals about clinical uses of VR.
- Attend accredited continuing education workshops, either online or in person, such as those available through the American Psychological Association (www.apa.org/education/ce) or PESI (www.pesi.com/).

- Obtain consultation or supervision from professionals experienced in VRT.
- Consider the educational courses or materials offered by vendors of VR products you use.

Always evaluate the source and quality of training materials or courses and whether they are appropriate for your practice.

VR Product Questions

See also VR Equipment and Content Types in Appendix A.

Will VR Be Useful for My Practice?

However valuable VR is generally, the real question is how often will you use it with *your* clients? These questions may clarify how often, and with whom, you could utilize VR.

How many of your clients:

- Report anxiety, worry, or panic or have an anxiety disorder?
- Are anxious about places, situations, or activities they could confront in VR?
- Might more easily talk about difficult issues while in a safe, relaxing virtual place?
- Would feel that a pleasant VR experience makes therapy more enjoyable?
- Complain of stress, tension, pain, or insomnia?
- Have trouble relaxing?
- Would benefit from mindfulness, diaphragmatic breathing, or progressive muscle relaxation?

How Do I Choose VR Products?

Different practice settings have different needs for VR products. Here are some questions to consider:

- Which anxiety disorders and symptoms are you most likely to treat using VR?
- For what purposes would you use VR in these treatments?
- Which VEs and control options will be most useful with your clients? Always consider the actual content of the various VEs because a VE designed and labeled for one purpose can often be used for other purposes.
- Is language a factor for your clients? Some VR products allow you to change signage, instructions, and pre-recorded avatar statements from English to Spanish and/or French.

- Do you want to be able to use VR for teletherapy as well as in-person sessions? If so, make sure the product supports teletherapy.
- If the VR system requires Internet access, do you have strong reliable Wi-Fi service in your office?
- If you work in a clinic, hospital, or other setting where network access may be restricted, will you be allowed to connect VR headsets or other devices to the office network and access Internet websites for VR product vendors? If not, look for VR products that do not require Internet access.

Companies making VR for use in psychotherapy vary in how VR content is created, the available virtual environments (VEs) and variables, client and therapist equipment requirements, and their cost and pricing models, i.e., purchase vs subscription. All these variables may influence your choice.

Where Can I Find More VR Content?

You are most likely to use VR content created for therapeutic use and provided by your VR products. However, additional VR content can be found in many places online and may be useful in therapy.

Online content is available in multiple formats to provide compatibility with different types of headsets. Some headset vendors offer content through their own app store. Smartphone headsets probably have the most content options.

For example:

- Google Street View provides 360-degree photos and videos of different locations that can be viewed through the Street View app on a smartphone.
- YouTube and other online video services offer channels for virtual reality 3-D videos, 180 or 360-degree videos, videos with 3-D stereoscopic effects, etc.

Be selective about using such content in therapy and *always* preview it.

CAVEAT: YouTube videos are neither designed for therapeutic use nor screened for possible harm. In fact, the goal of many videos is to provoke an intense reaction. This may be fine for thrill-seekers without anxiety or a trauma history, but such videos could be countertherapeutic for clients. I warn clients of this if they want to search for VR content to use for exposure on their own.

What About Using Consumer VR Apps?

VR products designed for use by therapists provide curated VR content. Consumer VR apps offer a wider variety of content designed for (and marketed to) the general public for independent use.

Advantages

- Apps are affordable.
- They may provide instructional materials and/or VEs for self-exposure or relaxation.
- Clients may use them during in-person or teletherapy sessions or for homework between sessions to support treatment gains.
- Some apps are based on solid research and contain most or all elements of evidence-based interventions.

Disadvantages

- You do not see what the client sees.
- You have no ability to control or individualize experiences for your client.
- You need to evaluate whether the content is suitable for your client and likely to be helpful.
- Apps vary in ease of use, quality of content, and may or may not have quality research supporting the claims made. When there is good quality research re: the app's usefulness, consider whether your client matches the characteristics of the subjects in the research study, and whether you will use the app in a way that is comparable to how it was used in the study.
- Consumer reviews are more likely to reflect ease of use rather than evidence-based interventions or effectiveness.
- Consumer apps may be updated automatically without providing notice about changes in features, appearance, or user instructions.

When Evaluating Consumer VR Apps

Two resources for evaluating consumer VR apps and other mental health apps are the American Psychiatric Association's App Evaluation Model (The App Evaluation Model, n.d.) and the One Mind PsyberGuide (Mental Health App Guide | One Mind PsyberGuide, n.d.) website.

When considering recommending an app, consider asking these questions:

- What is the privacy policy? Who owns the data and what happens to it?
- What is the content, i.e., what information does it present, which coping skills does it teach, what VEs does it have for exposure or relaxation? Does it offer augmented reality (AR) features?
- Is it consistent with your practice? Have you tried it?
- What does the app claim to do? If something sounds too good to be true, it probably is.

- Was the app developed with input from experienced, reputable clinicians and researchers?
- Is it consistent with evidence-based best practice, and if it says it offers research-supported interventions, how *many* of the recommended treatment components are *actually* included?
- Is there effectiveness research, i.e., evidence that it does what it claims to do, and research on side effects, unintended consequences, or negative reactions? Are there foreseeable risks?
- What are the hardware requirements? Is it easy to use?

Troubleshooting

Don't panic if you run into technical issues with VR, even during a session. Most clients are remarkably forgiving. Here are general suggestions for common issues. See also specific instructions from your vendors and contact the vendor for technical support, if needed.

Smartphone in the Headset Gets Hot

Some VR systems use a smartphone within a headset. The phone *will* get hot, but this is not necessarily a problem. I have had clients use this type of VR headset for most of a 60-minute session without issues. Some phones stay cooler than others and the type of headset may make a difference. Removing the phone from the headset while it is not being used helps it cool down.

Headset Lenses Fog Up

Fogged lenses can be caused by heat from the electronics and/or from client body heat and perspiration. Some clients flush and visibly perspire while virtually confronting fears. And some people are warmer than others—as anyone who has disagreed about a thermostat setting knows.

If lenses fog up or get smudged, wipe them with a lens cleaner cloth. If that does not work, try using an alcohol wipe or lens cleaner fluid along with the cloth. If lenses *still* fog up, take a brief break to let both the client and the equipment cool down.

VE Is Too Dark or Bright

Most headsets provide some type of brightness adjustment. For a smartphone-based headset this control may be within the Settings app on the phone.

Clients Can't Hear Me

If a VE is too loud, or the client's headphones or earbuds block your voice, lower the speaker volume on the smartphone or headset.

For headsets that hold smartphones, if the phone is connected to head-phones built into the headset, try disconnecting the headphones and playing the VE audio over the phone's speaker.

VR Headset Not Working

If there are headset issues, the VE may not appear, VE images may stutter, be distorted or freeze, the screen may go black, or the user may see a mes-sage such as "waiting" or "loading". Problems may appear when you start using a headset or during use.

Headset issues are typically caused by problems with power, Internet connections, or software. Hardware problems with the headset or VR server outages can happen but are less common.

Different troubleshooting procedures are provided for smartphone or wireless headsets and wired or tethered headsets that attach directly to a computer.

Smartphone or Wireless Headset

Here are some general troubleshooting suggestions if you cannot start a headset or one stops working:

- Is the headset or smartphone on? Check the battery indicator and the ability to see or access other apps or functions on the device.
- Is the smartphone or headset running the correct app and is the app working? Consider restarting the app.
- Is display brightness setting too low?
- If your system includes handheld controllers or other devices, check controller connection status and battery levels.
- Is your Wi-Fi Internet connection working? If other devices on the same Wi-Fi network cannot connect to Google.com or other websites, you may have a network problem.
- Is the headset or phone connected to Wi-Fi? Check device settings for the correct Wi-Fi network name, a secure connection, and good signal strength.
- Try restarting the smartphone or headset, following the vendor's instructions. This may involve powering down the device and turning it back on.
- Contact tech support for your VR product.

Wired or Tethered Headset

Wired or tethered headsets connect to a computer that runs special software to support headset functions. If there are multiple wires connecting the headset to the computer, these wires may have to be plugged in in a specific sequence. There may also be a startup sequence for setting up a headset and physical space limits. See the vendor instructions for details.

General troubleshooting suggestions if a tethered headset will not start or stops working:

- Is the computer on and working? Make sure it is not in power-saving mode, screen saver, or sleep mode.
- If your system includes handheld controllers or other devices, check their connection status and battery levels. There may be lights on the controllers or a status display in the computer app or the headset.
- If an Internet connection to the computer is required, check to see that it is working by opening a website in a browser.
- Is the computer running the correct software for supporting the headset? Check the software for any error messages, prompts for user input or actions, update messages, or software freeze/crash.
- Is the headset turned on and powered? Check headset indicator lights or status display in the computer.
- Check all the cables connecting the headset to the computer to make sure they are plugged in correctly. If there is a cable issue, follow the vendor's instructions for disconnecting and connecting the headset, this may include plugging in cables in a specific sequence and a headset startup procedure.
- Try exiting and restarting the VR app within the computer.
- Power down and restart the computer, then restart the VR app within the computer.
- Contact tech support for your VR product.

Practical Questions

Is VR Hard to Learn?

VR products vary in complexity, ease of use, and setup requirements. Software may be pre- installed, or you may have to download and set up software for the smartphone, headset, or computer. This process is usually straightforward and may take from a few minutes to an hour.

Therapist controls are generally self-explanatory and should quickly become familiar. Depending on your learning style, you may want to read the therapist manuals, which may be provided online, or simply play with the system until you feel comfortable. Some companies offer webinars or individual training.

Your biggest investment of time will be going through the relevant VEs to learn the details and understand how you might use the controls to individualize clients' virtual experiences. You *will* want to know what clients will see and hear, and the effects of changing different variables. You can begin by exploring the VEs you are most likely to use at first and expand your knowledge over time. You don't have to master all the VEs before using VR clinically.

Prioritize. While it is good to have at least a cursory knowledge of all the VEs so you can choose among them, you do not need to be familiar with the details of every VE before starting to use VR.

Persevere. It may take a little time to become comfortable with the VR controls. Hang in there. It is worth it.

Is There Tech Support?

Vendors of VR therapy products do offer tech support, although hours may be limited. Support may be available via chat, email, or phone. Consumer VR apps vary in terms of their support options.

Be patient. The technology is improving, but as with any tech device, problems can occur.

Stay calm when there are glitches. Clients tend to take their cue from you.

Pre-Session Preparation

If your VR equipment needs to be charged, you may wish to keep it plugged in or recharge it at the start of each workday, so it is ready for use. Clients may also have to charge their home equipment prior to teletherapy sessions. Check battery levels in handheld controllers or other battery powered devices.

Software Updates

VR software and the supporting components (smartphone, headset, computer, etc.) will probably have software updates to correct errors. Updates may also add new features or change existing features.

In general, you want to stay current with all the latest updates and fixes for your system. You also want to avoid having sessions interrupted to install updates or being surprised by changes in the way something works.

Since each system is different, ask each vendor for your VR therapy products if you need to do anything to install software updates and how to avoid interruptions or surprises. Some vendors may provide advance notice of software upgrades.

Equipment Protection

Some VR equipment is desirable enough to be stolen. You may want to lock up VR equipment when it is not being used or anchor equipment to furniture using security cables.

If VR equipment is shared among therapists, decide where it will be stored securely when not in use, how therapists can reserve it for their use, and how to keep it charged.

Can Clients with Glasses Use VR?

Newer VR headsets fit over glasses, although there are exceptions. Clients can adjust the focus on all but the most basic headsets. Even when the focus is not ideal, it is typically good enough for therapy. Glasses with corrections for reading and distance viewing (bifocal or progressive lenses) may only show VR content clearly through the distance portion of the lenses.

Are VR Headsets Uncomfortable?

Headsets are generally comfortable and well-tolerated. Certain headsets are somewhat heavy and might exacerbate neck issues. Clients on the autism spectrum may dislike the sensory input of wearing a headset.

If clients *do* experience discomfort from the headset, you might try:

- Adjusting the straps to improve comfort.
- Having clients use a neck support pillow or sit back or recline in a position where their head is supported. Having the client's physical position mirror their avatar's position in VR is less important than avoiding pain.
- If the headset permits, clients can hold the headset up to their eyes, transferring weight from the head and neck to the arms. Take breaks as needed to rest the arms.

If none of the above work and the VR product is compatible with a smartphone, the client might try using an inexpensive cardboard headset. These headsets provide poor visual clarity but are the lightest option.

Are VR Headsets Unhygienic?

VR headsets sit above the nose on the face and the straps touch the client's head and hair. Disposable face covers can provide a barrier between the headset and the face. Some therapists disinfect headsets after each client with antibiotic wipes (such as alcohol wipes) or UV light devices.

If you work with physically ill or immune-compromised clients, follow your facility's guidelines for disinfecting equipment used with patients.

Charging and Billing for VR

There are no special billing codes for using VR in the US. The billing codes are the same as for regular psychotherapy sessions.

Some therapists absorb the cost of VR equipment as part of providing high quality care and attracting clients. Others raise their fees across the board to cover these expenses.

The option of charging more for VRT sessions raises questions:

- Is a higher fee charged, regardless of the amount of session time actually spent in VR?
- Is a higher fee charged if clients get queasy or do not respond to VR?
- Will a higher charge become a barrier to your suggesting VRT, or for clients agreeing to it?

References

Grenier, S., Forget, H., Bouchard, S., Isere, S., Belleville, S., Potvin, O., Rioux, M. È., Talbot, M., Pachana, N. A., & Oude Voshaar, R. C. (2015). Using virtual reality to improve the efficacy of cognitive-behavioral therapy (CBT) in the treatment of late-life anxiety: Preliminary recommendations for future research. *International Psychogeriatrics*, 27(7), 1217–1225). doi:10.1017/S1041610214002300.

Maskey, M., Rodgers, J., Grahame, V., Glod, M., Honey, E., Kinnear, J., Labus, M., Milne, J., Minos, D., McConachie, H., & Parr, J. R. (2019). A randomised controlled feasibility trial of immersive virtual reality treatment with cognitive behaviour therapy for specific phobias in young people with autism spectrum disorder. *Journal of Autism and Developmental Disorders*, 49(5), 1912–1927. doi:10.1007/s10803-018-3861-x.

Maskey, M., Rodgers, J., Ingham, B., Freeston, M., Evans, G., Labus, M., & Parr, J. R. (2019). Using virtual reality environments to augment cognitive behavioral therapy for fears and phobias in autistic adults. *Autism in Adulthood*, 1(2), 134–145. doi:10.1089/aut.2018.0019.

Mental Health App Guide | One Mind PsyberGuide (n.d.). Retrieved March 11, 2021, from https://onemindpsyberguide.org/apps.

Mittelstaedt, J. M. (2020). Individual predictors of the susceptibility for motion-related sickness: A systematic review. *Journal of Vestibular Research: Equilibrium and Orientation*, 30(3), 165–193. doi:10.3233/VES-200702.

Ngai, I., Tully, E. C., & Anderson, P. L. (2015). The course of the working alliance during virtual reality and exposure group therapy for social anxiety disorder. *Behavioural and Cognitive Psychotherapy*, 43(2), 167–181. doi:10.1017/S135246581300088X.

Parsons, T. D., Riva, G., Parsons, S., Mantovani, F., Newbutt, N., Lin, L., Venturini, E., & Hall, T. (2017). Virtual reality in pediatric psychology. *Pediatrics*, 140 (November), S86–S91. doi:10.1542/peds.2016-1758I.

Saredakis, D., Szpak, A., Birckhead, B., Keage, H. A. D., Rizzo, A., & Loetscher, T. (2020). Factors associated with virtual reality sickness in head-mounted displays: A systematic review and meta-analysis. *Frontiers in Human Neuroscience*, 14(96). doi:10.3389/fnhum.2020.00096.

The App Evaluation Model (n.d.). Retrieved March 11, 2021, from www.psychiatry.org/psychiatrists/practice/mental-health-apps/the-app-evaluation-model.

Wrzesien, M., Burkhardt, J.-M., Botella, C., & Alcañiz, M. (2012). Evaluation of the quality of collaboration between the client and the therapist in phobia treatments. *Interacting with Computers*, 24(6), 461–471. doi:10.1016/j.intcom.2012.09.001.

20 Future Directions

Gazing into my crystal ball, here are my predictions for virtual reality (VR) and therapy.

Increasing Demand for Virtual Reality Therapy

Potential clients are already learning about the benefits of virtual reality therapy (VRT) and seeking out therapists who utilize this technology. Consumer demand will continue to increase as media coverage highlights additional uses for VR in therapy and treatment options for additional mental health conditions.

Advances in VR Equipment

The pace of technological progress has been breathtaking. Computers are smaller, faster, and more powerful. Internet access is easier, faster, and more reliable. Computer graphics continue to improve. Improvements in computer processing speed and other changes have reduced the incidence of cybersickness.

VR headsets may gain more ability to track client actions and quantify how a client responds within a virtual environment (VE). For example, VR headsets currently used by researchers can collect synchronized measures of user gaze, pupil dilation, EEG signals, and other biological reactions to stimuli. Headset data may be combined with measurements from wearable biosensor devices to create new biofeedback options.

Augmented reality (AR) technology that combines camera input with computer imaging is a related VR technology that may be more widely used for therapeutic applications in the future. Some current VR headsets include cameras that could support AR applications. Future generation AR headsets and glasses may have multiple therapeutic uses.

Increased Affordability and Availability

VR client and therapist equipment should continue to become more easily available and affordable. The cost of VR products designed for use in

DOI: 10.4324/9781003154068-24

therapy is likely to decrease as a result of technological advances, economies of scale for larger markets, and the economic effects of competition.

For teletherapy or homework, clients will be more likely to already have home VR equipment which may be compatible with the VR systems or products used in therapy. More clinics, hospitals, and other settings where psychotherapy is performed will have VR equipment for a variety of uses.

More and Better Therapeutic Tools

When I first started using VR in 2010, there were only a few basic VEs available for treating a limited number of issues: PTSD, substance abuse, relaxation training, and fears of flying, heights, public speaking, and thunderstorms. The range of available VR content has increased dramatically since then.

VE's are currently available for more than 20 different specific phobias. VR content is also available for a range of other anxiety disorders, pain relief, eating disorders, substance use, ADHD, body image disorders, etc. VR also supports training for many relevant specific skills, and other clinical uses.

In addition to new VEs, options have been added to some existing VEs to enable more control over aspects of the client's virtual experience. These options provide better exposure control and more ability to individualize each VR experience for your client.

Cameras for taking VR compatible 3-D photos and recording 3-D videos are widely available as inexpensive, easy-to-use, consumer products. Thousands of users are creating and sharing VR content online.

Computer-generated imagery (CGI) virtual environments are becoming easier to create with new technology. In the coming years, you, or your client, may be able to create custom VR content uniquely suited to each therapeutic situation.

Epilogue

My goal in writing this book was to introduce therapists to VR as a flexible tool with many clinical applications and to encourage its adoption and use. I wanted to demonstrate that VR is compatible with a wide range of anxiety conditions and therapeutic approaches. Finally, I wanted to emphasize that VR is a *tool*, not a treatment.

I invite you to share what was helpful for you and your clients.

If you like the book and can recommend it, please post online reviews and share on social media so others may benefit.

I am equally interested in hearing suggestions on making the book more helpful. If you have suggestions or dislike any aspect of the book, please let me know so it can be improved in future editions.

Thank you for your time, attention, and interest in VR.

Warmest best wishes, Elizabeth.

Email me at elizabeth@elizabeth-mcmahon.com.

DOI: 10.4324/9781003154068-25

Appendix A: VR Equipment and Content Types

This appendix provides a concise guide to virtual reality (VR) equipment and virtual environment (VE) content types.

You will need a VR therapy product, the VR equipment required for this product including a compatible VR headset and therapist workstation, and optionally an Internet connection via Wi-Fi for the VR equipment. VR therapy products vary in the specific equipment they require, what equipment is included as part of their product offering (if any), and if this equipment needs to connect to the Internet via Wi-Fi. Connecting to the Internet can be an issue in some organizations. Check with your organization's IT department.

Some VR therapy product packages include all the necessary equipment, some include a VR headset but not the therapist workstation, and some do not include any equipment. If you already own VR equipment, you may be able to use it with compatible therapy products.

For more information about specific VR products, contact the product vendors. At the time of this writing, companies offering VR software specifically for psychotherapy include BehaVR, Inc., C2Care, In Virtuo, Psious, and Virtually Better, Inc. Start with a single VR therapy product and consider adding other products if you need additional virtual environments or client training materials.

You may wish to consult with other mental health professionals who use VR or be able to refer clients as appropriate. One resource may be Dr. Howard Gurr's website Virtual Reality Therapists International (www.vrtherapistsinternational.com). The Society for Virtual Reality Therapy (www.svrt.org) is another resource for therapists and consumers.

VR Equipment

Basic equipment for VR therapy includes a VR headset (see Figure 1.1) and a therapist workstation (see Figure 1.2). These are described in more detail below.

During in-office therapy sessions, the client wears the VR headset, and the therapist selects and controls what the client sees in VR by using the controls on the therapist workstation. You are both in the same room and this works with all types of headsets and workstations.

During teletherapy, the client wears a VR headset, and the therapist selects and controls their experience using the therapist workstation. The difference is that client and therapist are in different locations and the communication between the headset and therapist workstation goes over the Internet. Some VR products and headsets can be used for teletherapy but not all. Check with the product vendor.

VR Headsets

A virtual reality headset is what the client puts on their head to enter a virtual environment (VE). These headsets include computer driven displays and lenses that provide three-dimensional images. Images are adjusted as the user moves their head or moves physically to provide an immersive experience. Coordinated sounds add to the experience. Optional features include gaze tracking, handheld controllers, simulated auto or airplane controls, etc.

There are three basic types of VR headsets:

- Smartphone-based headsets or holders where you insert a smartphone and use the phone's display and processor to provide VR images.
- Wireless headsets that are self-contained.
- Wired or tethered headsets that connect to a specially equipped computer using one or more cables.

Smartphone-based headsets are often the least expensive option. Clients may be able to use one of these with their own smartphone. Therapists who are routinely using VR with clients will want a dedicated smartphone for this purpose. A smartphone specifically for VR can be an inexpensive Android phone and does not need cellular telephone service or a SIM card.

Wired or tethered headsets are generally not suitable for teletherapy because the headset and computer must be in the same location.

Therapist Workstations

The therapist workstation provides the ability to select, control, and monitor what the client is experiencing in VR. The workstation may support other functions including the ability to record session events or take notes.

Some VR products will work with most personal computers (Apple Mac or Microsoft Windows) and tablet devices (Apple iPad or Microsoft Surface) that support a Web browser and Internet access as the therapist workstation. You may be able to use your existing computer or tablet to control these products. Check with the product vendor.

Tethered or wired headsets typically require a special "gaming computer" with specific graphics hardware features to support headset functions. These headsets will not work with typical office computers. Check with the product vendor for details. Laptop-style gaming computers have batteries but must be connected to power while being used for VR. These gaming computers may be usable for other functions when they are not being used for VR.

Some vendors use specialized tablet devices as the therapist workstation for their VR therapy products. This combination of VR headset and tablet may not require Internet access. These products are not suitable for tele-therapy because the headset and tablet communicate using short-range wireless technology such as Bluetooth.

Augmented Reality (AR)

Augmented reality (AR) is a related technology that combines computer-generated images with images of the actual environment. For example, a client can look at their desk through an AR-enabled smartphone and see virtual insects crawling over their desk.

Very few VR therapy products currently support AR. More therapy-specific AR content may become available in the future as AR features are added to VR headsets and headsets designed specifically for AR become more practical.

VR Content Types

Virtual environments can include three types of content: CGI images, 3-D videos, and 3-D photographs (including stills from 3-D video). The content type or source influences the amount of detail and how realistic the environment seems, how closely a virtual environment resembles real life. Environments that are primarily CGI provide the ability to control or change aspects of the client's experience, and the flexibility to move around within a virtual space. Pre-recorded videos do not provide as much flexibility for change or movement and photographs are static.

Virtual environments include combinations of content types. For example, CGI effects may be used to modify a 3-D video so that you can change the weather or time of day, or CGI avatars may be superimposed on a 3-D filmed or photographed background. Pre-recorded 3-D videos may be entirely CGI content, which has the disadvantages of video without the control typically provided by CGI.

Each content type has pros and cons for use in virtual reality therapy (VRT) as explained below.

CGI Pros and Cons

In a CGI VE, the entire world and every object the client sees is created by software. People in virtual environments are computer-generated representations called avatars. The client may or may not be able to see their own avatar.

Figure A.1 CGI VE Example

Pros of CGI VEs:

- Clients are immersed within a three-dimensional VE that surrounds them, and they may be able to move around within this environment and interact with virtual people or objects.
- CGI maximizes your ability to customize the VE and the client's experience within the VE to be optimally beneficial for clients.
- You may be able to control many variables such as the client's location within the environment, time of day, weather, the number of other people (avatars), what avatars look like, where they are located and how they interact with the client, driving or flying conditions, elevator or room size, etc.

Cons of CGI VEs:

- CGI objects, scenery, and people can be cartoon-like in appearance.
- Navigating within a virtual space can be unrealistic, allowing a client to walk through walls, sink into the floor, etc.
- Objects and locations are generic: clients drive on generic roads, stand in generic elevators, fly on generic airplanes, and speak in generic rooms.
- If you pause the VE to process the experience with your client, the VE *may* stop displaying so the client is no longer immersed within the virtual world.

3-D Video Pros and Cons

In 3-D videos the client sees specific real people, places, and actions.

Pros of 3-D videos:

- Like CGI VEs, VR videos are three-dimensional and immersive.
- Locations, people, and activities filmed are actual places, people, and actions.
- Details of the images are true to life and realistic and so may be more convincing and experienced by clients as more real than CGI.
- When a VR video is paused, the VE may remain visible, allowing you to pause the action but keep your clients in the virtual world while you help them process the experience.
- For some clients, specific locations are relevant and helpful, e.g., virtually driving over the Golden Gate Bridge may be particularly helpful for clients in the San Francisco Bay area who fear driving, bridges, and/or heights.

Cons of 3-D videos:

- Actions and movements are limited to what was filmed in real life. You can start, stop, or rewind the video but you can't change what happens.
- Your ability to change VE variables such as time of day, weather, audience reaction, or avatars' clothing style is limited to any variations that were filmed or can be superimposed onto the recorded video using CGI.

Figure A.2 3D Video VE Example

- CGI special effects or controls superimposed onto 3-D video can look unreal and be unconvincing. For example, manipulating a driving video recorded on a sunny day to make it appear to be raining or dark.

3-D Photos Pros and Cons

A 3-D photo has a similar appearance to a 3-D video but without motion. Pros of 3-D photos:

- VR photos are 3-D and immersive.
- Details are true to life because photos are of specific, real settings.
- VR photos generally don't trigger nausea since clients aren't moving around within the VE.
- For clients who are unusually fearful, avoidant, or distress intolerant, VR photos may provide the lowest level of VR exposure.
- Some VR products can use Google Street View to put clients into 3-D photos of specific locations so clients can return to scenes associated with traumatic—or positive—experiences. Clients can practice skills while immersed in actual places.

Cons of 3-D photos:

- You have no ability to control or change anything.
- Clients remain in one location and cannot interact with avatars or move around within the VE.

Appendix B: Virtual Reality Therapy Checklist

This list summarizes suggested actions for structuring and supporting successful anxiety treatment, including virtual reality (VR), to make it easier to incorporate them into your practice.

From the First Contact

- Establish and maintain a positive therapeutic alliance. Clients should trust your expertise and that you are working in their best interests.
- Listen for each client's anxiety triggers.
- Also listen for clients' somatic sensations, fears, and fear-motivated actions.
- Explain how each client's experience fits the anxiety cycle so the client feels understood, has an explanation for their experiences and for treatment interventions, and has hope that treatment will help. Use motivational interviewing techniques as needed.

Before Using Virtual Reality with a Client

- Before using any virtual environment (VE) with a client, experience the VE yourself and become familiar with the VE content, variables, options, and therapist controls.
- Explain to clients what they will see and hear within a VE, before starting the VE or before changing VE variables.
- Offer your client a choice of VEs.
- Get clients' agreement before placing them into a VE or changing variables.

During VR

- Position the client so their physical body position mirrors their avatar's body position in VR, if possible. For example, if the client is standing in VR, have the client stand in real life.

Before VR Exposure Therapy (VRET)

- Ensure that clients have learned at least one effective anxiety tolerance skill.
- Work with clients to articulate, explore, and counter their fears.
- Create a formal or informal exposure hierarchy so exposure can be graduated and appropriate.

During VRET

- Be actively involved, especially early in the process of exposure and/or if clients report high or rising anxiety levels on the Subjective Units of Distress Scale (SUDS). Clients facing feared virtual situations should not feel unsupported or alone.
- Remember to use your usual therapeutic skills.
- Frequently ask clients to report their anxiety level (using the 0–10 SUDS scale), their thoughts and fears, and their physical reactions.

Support Progress

- Periodically after getting a SUDS rating, ask "What makes your SUDS a [number they gave] as opposed to a [higher number]?" This helps identify what clients are doing that reduces their anxiety. It can also uncover unhelpful responses such as distraction, reassurance, or mental safety actions that will undermine their success.
- Highlight skill use and praise progress. Have them articulate what works ("Wow, you brought your anxiety down by a third in only two minutes! What did you do that made that possible?") and repeat their statements.
- Ask questions such as, "What does your Reacting Brain [or childlike brain, scared child, etc.] need to hear from you?" or "What does the fear say? What can you say back to it?"
- If clients become too fearful, stop VR and process what's happening. You might change to a relaxing VE before and/or after processing.
- As clients become less anxious, you can voice their fears while they counter them. For example, "Now I'm going to be your fear brain, and you're going to be your smart, adult, rational Thinking Brain and talk back to me, okay?"
- If clients cannot counter their fears, coach them, or stop and return to exploring and countering their fears.
- If anxiety drops but does not reach 0–1 level, ask the client if the current anxiety level would be acceptable to them—not interfering or too distressing.

Relapse Prevention

- Ask clients to deliberately try to increase their anxiety by thinking or stating their fears (or having you state them) and then bring their SUDS down.
- Highlight how much lower their highest SUDS is now, compared to previously.
- Ask questions like: "Is there anything that's likely to come up that you would have trouble coping with?" If yes, practice coping with those issues in VR.

Index

Printed in Great Britain
by Amazon